Checkbook's 2022 Guide to Health Plans for Federal Employees

43rd Edition

By Walton Francis and the Editors of Consumers' Checkbook

Contents

Chapter 1

Introduction, Basics, and Changes for 2022

What the Guide Does

Checkbook's Guide to Health Plans for Federal Employees gives you vital shopping information that you cannot get from any other source. It tells you how much money you can save by changing—or by staying in—your health insurance plan. It summarizes thousands of facts about the plans to simplify your choice. The *Guide* comes in both print and online versions. They are almost identical, but the print version is more convenient for many, and the online version allows more depth and details. The online version is particularly useful for Federal agencies that subscribe for all their employees, giving the employees invaluable money-saving advice while saving the agencies money as well, since they pay most of the premium cost. We show employees how to save thousands of dollars in unnecessary costs. Federal agencies also save, over a thousand dollars on average, for every employee who switches to a lower-cost plan using our advice. In both versions:

- Our ratings cover **all** of about 280 health insurance plans available to Federal employees and retirees, including about 20 national plans, and about 260 health maintenance organizations (HMOs) and other local options, including two dozen Consumer-Driven and High Deductible plan options. We also compare several dozen plans that pay most of your Medicare premium if you join their Medicare Advantage plan, and several dozen more that provide enriched benefits for doing so.
- Wherever you live, we rate all the plans where you live or commute.
- Our **ratings** of plan costs take into account premiums, catastrophic limits, and estimates of likely out-of-pocket costs for medical expenses of every kind.
- We compare plans for **insurance value** in dealing with unforeseen medical expenses, not just for the routine costs you can predict.
- We **compare** limits on out-of-pocket costs based on the actual coverage allowed by each plan, not just what the plan seems to say before you read the fine print.
- We rate plans for **each coverage group**—employees in different pay systems, annuitants with or without Medicare, former spouses, families of various sizes, children at age 26, part-time employees, and former employees.
- We rate plans according to how well each covers **low, average, or high medical expenses**, analyzing coverage of all major types of cost.
- We adjust our estimates for the **tax advantages** that reduce the after-tax premium cost to most employees (but not retirees) by about one fourth.
- We provide information on **coinsurance, copays and other cost sharing**, so you can quickly determine whether a plan pays well for a benefit you need.
- We provide **accurate estimates of potential exposure to catastrophic expense** by adjusting plans' claimed limits on out-of-pocket expenses, so they don't omit important categories of cost.
- We give you data on **coverage features** of each plan, including skilled nursing, dental, and hearing aid coverage.

- We address **plan quality** and provide data on **enrollee satisfaction** with each plan's service. We provide in-depth results from an annual survey in which plan members rate their plans on ease of getting needed care, customer service, claims processing, and other factors.
- We **rate dental and vision** plans as well. We provide dollar estimates of likely dental costs, taking into account both premiums and out-of-pocket expense. We compare dental coverage in all plans, not just standalone plans.
- We provide up-to-date **information on changes in the FEHB program**, including Medicare coordination changes, new laws and regulations, and more.
- We provide detailed **consumer advice** on which plan options work best in different situations, on plan advantages you may not have thought about, and on mistakes to avoid.

As a result, the *Guide* gives you a solid basis for selecting the best health or dental plan for you and your family. Hundreds of thousands of employees and annuitants have followed our advice over the years, and many of them have saved thousands of dollars a year by finding better coverage for lower premiums. **There is no other source of plan comparisons or Open Season advice that provides even half of these features.**

The Setting

Every Federal employee and annuitant can choose from twenty plans or more. Choices include well-known national plans, such as three Blue Cross/Blue Shield options; local plans available in many areas, such as the Aetna, Humana, UnitedHealthcare and Kaiser plans; and plans sponsored by unions and employee associations, such as the American Postal Workers Union (APWU) and the Government Employees Health Association (GEHA). You are free to join most union and association plans, regardless of your employing agency and whether you are an employee or annuitant. At most you must pay annual dues, which are generally near $30. However, a few plans restrict enrollment. For example, two plans are open only to those involved in foreign affairs, intelligence, or defense—a pool, however, that is very large and covers many agencies.

You can switch plans for the coming year during the annual Open Season, scheduled from November 8 through December 13, 2021. You are also free to switch among plans at certain other times—for instance, if you marry. You are allowed to switch from plan to plan regardless of preexisting conditions, even if you are in the hospital when the new plan enrollment year begins.

> ### *Getting "Free" Health Insurance*
>
> Some Consumer-Driven and High Deductible plans provide you a savings account larger than your actual premium cost after taxes. You can end the year with more money than you started if your medical costs are low.

Hundreds of thousands of employees and annuitants are still enrolled in plans that are much more expensive than average, and that give them no needed extra benefits. In Open Season almost all of these persons will be able to reduce premium costs greatly while maintaining or even improving benefits.

As always, this year's *Guide* reflects changes as plan options have been added or dropped, benefits modified, and premiums gone up in some plans and down in others. For newly hired employees, and those who can change plans after Open Season, the information in the *Guide* applies throughout the year.

The Savings

Whether your family's circumstances are "average" or unusual, some HMOs, some national plans such as Blue Cross Basic and GEHA Standard option, and a number of High-Deductible and Consumer Driven plans offer big savings compared to other plans. To help decide which is best, we estimate likely, and not so likely, costs to you under each plan, and compare coverage features of the plans and several aspects of customer service. In addition to dollar costs, customer service is an important element of plan choice, particularly for HMOs. We present customer survey data on plan satisfaction, data on which plans are least likely to have claims disputes, and data on accreditation.

Our tables rate each plan on total expenses—including premium and out-of-pocket costs. The tables show what each plan will cost you in an "average" year and in years when your medical costs are much higher or lower than average. As our tables show, **likely savings available to most employees and annuitants range from hundreds to thousands of dollars a year**.

You should not pick a plan on the basis of its premium, benefit coverage, or catastrophic expense guarantee alone. We help you avoid these traps by including all of these complex factors in our ratings.

The information we give you is especially important if you expect a major change in your medical or financial situation. If you plan to have a baby next year, or face heavy dental bills, the plan that was best for you last year may not be best this year. Also, if you will retire, divorce, leave Federal employment, or join Medicare, you should review your choices very carefully.

Even if your plan satisfies you, why not consider switching to another? Those who switch in Open Season save hundreds of millions of dollars every year for themselves and their employing agencies, through migration to lower-cost plans that offer better value. You, too, can share in these savings.

Consider the following examples. If you are a single employee in the Washington, DC area, our estimates show that you are likely to save well over $1,000 next year by joining the Kaiser HMO Standard Option instead of the Blue Cross Standard Option, the most popular plan. If you are unwilling to make such a drastic departure from fee-for-service medicine, you can save about $1,000 by enrolling in the Blue Cross Basic plan rather than the Standard Option. We rate a half dozen Consumer-Driven (CD) and High Deductible (HD) options as equal to or better than even Blue Cross Basic for most enrollees. All of these estimates include your premium cost, your savings from tax preferences, and your likelihood of a range of expenses up to and including a catastrophically expensive illness.

Protect Your Retirement

It is not expensive to enroll in the FEHBP for the five years before retirement. Several plans have annual self only premiums below $1,500. These plans cost under $1,000 after tax savings. Some plans give you savings accounts higher than the tax advantaged premium cost.

Perhaps you are a retired couple with Medicare parts A and B. The majority of such retirees select the Blue Cross Standard option. But we rate the MBHP High Deductible plan, the Aetna Direct plan, the Blue Cross FEP Blue Focus option, the Blue Cross Basic option, the CareFirst High Deductible plan, and the Aetna Advantage plan as likely to save you $4,000 or even more next year. Why? Most of these plans, like Blue Cross Standard Option, allow you to pay nothing for hospital and physician charges when you have Medicare parts A and B. In some of them their prescription drug coverage is not quite as good, but their premiums are far lower. So, you start the year with major savings in hand. The Consumer-Driven plans have "Personal Care Accounts" that you can spend on dental costs and drugs that Medicare doesn't cover to offset the cost of the Medicare premium. Blue Cross Basic and a handful of other plans in most areas now provide a partial Part B premium rebate. Our ratings show that you can save even more if you enroll in one of several plans that will pay most or all of your Part B Premium and give you a free Medicare Advantage plan in which you pay nothing for doctor and hospital bills, no matter how high. In the Consumer-Driven plans, and most High Deductible plans, you have the potential for large savings in future years if you build up your account. Our comparisons show that even the most popular plans may not be the best buys.

Using the Guide

We prepared the *Guide* because we know that choosing the right plan can be difficult, even if you have time to read hundreds of pages in plan brochures. The coverage details are hard to understand and trying to compare multiple benefit details simultaneously is very difficult. As a result, it is often hard to determine which plan is best for you. Many employees depend on advice from their friends or stick with a "name brand" or the plan sponsored by their own union. However, that choice can waste hundreds or thousands of dollars.

The Office of Personnel Management (OPM), which administers the program, sets standards for plan benefits and for information in plan brochures, and also presents summary plan comparison information on its Web site. The complexity of comparing plans is substantial. We have studied and restudied each plan and have checked many details with plan officials. But we have undoubtedly missed a few limitations or special coverages. So, before making a final choice, you should compare the brochures of several plans.

We structure the *Guide*'s advice and information as follows:

- You are reading the "Introduction, Basics, and Changes for 2022."
- "Comparing Plan Costs" explains how and why some choices can save so much money.
- "Cost Comparisons and Advice for Employees and Former Employees" explains and provides our cost ratings for each plan, organized separately by eligibility group.
- "Cost Comparisons and Advice for Annuitants" provides cost ratings for each plan that take into account higher medical costs for the elderly, and compare the effects of enrolling in Medicare Part A alone, or enrolling in both Parts A and B.
- "Cost Sharing" provides basic information on plan benefits for hospital, medical, and prescription drug expenses.
- "Coverage Features" addresses features such as skilled nursing and mental health coverage.
- "Dental, Vision, and Hearing" compares standalone plans with each other and with the dental, vision, and hearing aid coverage in the health insurance plans.
- "Plan Types and Flexibility" explains the various types of plans and how they affect your ability to use the provider of your choice and to achieve additional savings.
- "Quality and Service" describes several measures of quality of plan service and presents quality ratings for all plans.
- "Premiums and Taxes" explains how premiums and out of pocket spending can be tax advantaged and how much employees can save.
- "Key Tips and Final Plan Selection" reminds you of factors vital to you and gives advice on making a final decision among plans.
- "Our Methods and Data Sources" explains the information we use to create our ratings.

> ### *Be Sure to Elect a Survivor Annuity for Your Spouse*
>
> If you die and your spouse receives no Federal pension, your spouse will lose FEHBP coverage forever. If you die while enrolled as self-only, your spouse will also lose coverage.

We rate health plans by their likely cost to you for both premiums and cost sharing, taking into account your pay system, employment or retirement status, family size, age, health status, location, and other factors. For example, we present information on premium cost to employees using the "premium conversion" tax-advantaged basis automatically available to employees, but not available to retirees. Online *Guide* users reach the table applicable to them by answering questions regarding family size, age, retirement status, health status, zip code, pay system, and several other factors. They see a summary ratings table for their area and then have the option to choose whether to look at tables providing detailed cost comparisons, cost sharing, coverage features, plan flexibility, or plan quality for plans in their area. Readers of the print *Guide* turn to applicable cost comparison and other tables within each of the book chapters. Information on the cost, coverage, and features for local plans in all States is available online simply by entering your zip code, and in the print *Guide* is provided in summary in a table at the end of the "Key Tips and Final Plan Selection" chapter.

The information contained in our print and online versions is almost identical. Both versions allow users to compare plans based on their pay system, age, family size, and health status. Many people prefer to use paper copies. However, the online *Guide* makes the customization, selection, and presentation of comparative information exceptionally fast and convenient, and you can print out plan comparisons customized to your needs. In the Washington, D.C. area, you can use the online version to see which plan networks include your doctors. Not everyone uses the Internet, so we publish both versions and let individual purchasers decide which they want. In addition, many Federal Departments and agencies provide free access to the online version for all their employees. You can check to see if your agency provides free access, at *Guidetohealthplans.org*.

General FEHB Program Procedures

The Federal Employees Health Benefits (FEHB) program is an unconventional government program. Instead of giving you one "take it or leave it" choice, the government authorizes plans to compete for your premium dollar. It pays most of the premium cost—up to 75 percent for annuitants and most employees—and even more for employees of some other agencies, such as the FDIC and SEC. Taking into account tax savings, the government pays between 70 and 80 percent of premium costs for most plans for employees (but not retirees). Nationally, about 280 plan options are offered, with almost all employees and retirees eligible to join 20 or more. You decide which plan you want to join. If you are not satisfied, you can switch in the next Open Season.

The FEHB program enrolls about 8 million persons. Enrollees spend over $60 billion a year through their health plans. About five percent of enrollees switch among plans in most Open Seasons. Until the Medicare Advantage program, which was modeled on the FEHB program and now voluntarily enrolls over 40 percent of all Medicare beneficiaries, it was the largest "managed competition" system for harnessing consumer choices to contain health insurance costs. Studies have shown that it outperforms both Original Medicare and private employer plans in coverage, cost control, and consumer satisfaction.

OPM sets minimum financial, administrative, and benefit terms and conditions for every plan participating in the program. Insurance companies and OPM agree each year on contracts setting forth both benefits and costs. A few key points about FEHB plans are:

- All employees and annuitants can enroll in whatever plan they choose, or not enroll at all.
- Everyone can change plans once per year in Open Season. You also may switch plans or options in circumstances such as marriage, birth of a child, or geographic transfer. If you belong to an HMO and move out of its service area, you may enroll in a new plan.
- A family or self plus one enrollment covers only immediate family members: your spouse and children. Coverage for children now lasts until they reach age 26, unless they are severely handicapped. In that case they may be eligible at any age.
- **Plans cannot exclude coverage for any preexisting conditions or illnesses your family may have when you switch plans**. You may switch to gain the best coverage for your condition and use the new plan without penalty.
- Plans must publish brochures in a common format that provides a clear explanation of their benefits and your cost for covered services, how you access plan services, how you get approvals, and your rights in disputes.
- Each plan must pay for the medical and related costs as explained in its brochure—no more and no less. If a brochure says that a particular category of service is limited or excluded, believe it.
- Plan brochures may word the same benefits differently. Sometimes the wording used is not clear to a layperson. However, **you can often figure out what specific benefit language really means by comparing two or three brochures to see how they differ**.

Check Your Brochure!

Do not stay in the same plan without reading at least "How We Change" for next year or join a new plan without checking any benefits of particular importance to your health care.

Getting Information

Our website at *Guidetohealthplans.org* includes a great deal of useful information including not only uniquely informative plan comparisons, but a great deal of advice including Questions and Answers addressing more than one hundred problems. OPM has a website with plan brochures and a great deal of other useful information at *www.opm.gov/insure*. You can access this site at most libraries if you do not use the Internet in your home or office. Unlike many government websites, OPM's are user friendly and easy to navigate. You can also visit plan websites directly. This is especially useful if you want to check how a particular plan covers your medicines.

You change plans by filling out OPM's form SF 2809 or an online equivalent. Personnel offices have copies and will give you form SF 2809 if you decide to change your enrollment. In many agencies, an online service such as "Employee Express" can be used to change plans. Annuitants are mailed only abbreviated information and should use the Internet to get more details. A special OPM procedure provides an easy way for annuitants to order paper copies of plan brochures.

If you have a problem getting information from these normal channels, you can call OPM for help. There is an automated phone system, called "Open Season Express" at 800-332-9798 to help annuitants get brochures, change plans, or get other help. In addition, the retirement information office number is 1-888-767-6738. This office can answer many questions and help you with enrolling in a Medicare-participating HMO. We caution, however, that these numbers are often overburdened with calls—don't wait until the last minute.

Of course, Checkbook provides information on contacting each plan directly, including its telephone number and website, along with information on enrollment limitations. On our website you can download plan brochures and access the provider list and drug formulary for each plan.

Enrollment Limitations

Many plans are open to all employees. However, HMOs require that you live in their service area, and a few plans require that you work for a particular agency or join a specific union. Most of the union plans allow any Federal employee to join. This generally means that you can enroll in the plan no matter what agency you work for, but you may have to pay a small amount for annual dues and become an "associate" member of the union. Some plans are restricted to particular agencies or categories of employees. For example, the Foreign Service and Compass Rose plans enroll employees who serve in foreign affairs, defense, or intelligence functions (both plans interpret these limitations broadly, but they differ in details as explained in their brochures).

Use and Trust Plan Brochures

You can download PDF copies of plan brochures at the Checkbook, OPM, and plan websites, and either use them online or print copies. Plan brochures are necessary to determine what benefits each plan covers or does not cover. In some cases, a plan does not mention a service at all in its brochure but has assured us that its claims manual (which is not available to employees) says the service is covered. You cannot fully rely on this, however, since OPM has stated that the brochure "is the only official description of the benefits provided by each plan. Do not rely on statements not contained in the brochure. Study the brochures carefully." We agree and endorse OPM efforts to assure that brochures are consistently and clearly written. Indeed, compared to most public and private insurance, the FEHB brochures are models of clarity. They are particularly well organized to facilitate comparisons of particular topics, such as surgery or maternity.

Unfortunately, health plan brochures have mushroomed in length. In 1990 the average national plan had a brochure 29 pages in length; by ten years later the average grew to 77 pages. For local plans, brochures grew over the same period from 16 to 65 pages, on average. Some of the increase represents increased clarity through "plain English," some is due to increased complexity in plan benefits, and some is due to unnecessary detail. Nonetheless, downloading brochures is easily accomplished, and vital to final plan selection. Once you have an electronic version, you can easily use "find" to search the brochure for any topic of concern to you.

Why Premiums Differ

The General Schedule (GS) employee and retiree share of the annual premium varies widely among plans. In national plans it ranges from about $1,200 to over $4,000 for individuals, and from about $3,000 to about $10,000 for self plus one or larger families. What explains these vast premium differences?

First, plans vary in the kinds of enrollees they attract. Some plans attract families who expect higher expenses. Some have a disproportionate share of high-cost annuitants who joined when premiums

Contacting National and D.C. Area Plans

Plan code(s)	Plan name	Plan phone	Website	Enrollment limitations
Z2R*	Aetna Advantage (Med Adv)	888-267-2637	aetnaretireeplans.com	None
22, F5, N6, Z24	Aetna HealthFund & Advantage	888-238-6240	aetnafeds.com	None
JN, QQ	Aetna Open Access & Saver	800-537-9384	aetnafeds.com	None
47	APWU	800-222-2798	apwuhp.com	Pay dues
47R*	APWU-Hi (Medicare Advantage)	855-383-8793	uhcretiree.com/apwuuhp	Pay dues
42	Compass Rose	888-438-9135	compassrosebenefits.com	Intel/Foreign Aff/DOD
42R*	Compass Rose (Medicare Adv)	888-438-9135	compassrosebenefits.com	Intel/Foreign Aff/DOD
10, 11, 13	Blue Cross	800-411-BLUE	fepblue.org	None
2G, B6	Carefirst	888-789-9065	carefirst.com/fedhmo	None
40	Foreign Service	202-833-4910	afspa.org/fsbp	Intel/Foreign Aff/DOD
25, 31, 34	GEHA	800-821-6136	geha.com	None
E3	Kaiser Mid-Atlantic	877-574-3337	kp.org/feds	None
E3R*	Kaiser Mid-Atlantic (Med Adv)	877-547-4909	kp.org/feds	None
JP	MD-IPA	877-835-9861	uhcfeds.com	None
JPR*	MD-IPA (Retiree Advantage)	844-481-8821	uhcfeds.com/medicare-plans	None
41, 45	MHBP	800-410-7778	mhbp.com	Pay dues
48	MHBP HDHP	800-694-9901	mhbp.com	Pay dues
45R*	MHBP (Medicare Advantage)	888-267-2639	aetnaretireeplans.com	None
32, KM	NALC	888-636-6252	nalchbp.org	Pay dues
38	Rural Carrier	800-638-8432	rcbphealth.com	Rural carrier
38R*	Rural Carrier (Medicare Adv)	888-267-2637	aetnaretireeplans.com	Rural carrier
44	SAMBA	800-638-6589	sambaplans.com	None
AS, L9, LR, V4, Y5, Y8	United	877-835-9861	uhcfeds.com	None
LRR*, L9R*, ASR*, Y81R*	United (Retiree Advantage)	844-481-8821	uhcfeds.com	None

* This Medicare Advantage plan has special enrollment procedures.

were lower and do not realize that their plan is no longer a good buy. Unfortunately, Federal agencies all too often neglect to encourage sensible Open Season choices, and employees and retirees are all too often dilatory about looking for savings. Despite repeated urging over the years, the Congress has failed to address this problem, which could easily be accomplished by a technique called "risk adjustment" and long used by Medicare. Plans that face higher costs have to cover those costs through higher premiums. Premiums in such plans far exceed the fair value of their benefits.

Second, plans differ in the generosity of benefits they offer. Variations include coverage of different expenses; coinsurance, the percentage of each expense you pay; and deductibles, the amount you have to pay before the plan will reimburse any expenses for a service. Plans with higher cost sharing can charge lower premiums. This is one reason the new Consumer-driven plans have such low premiums.

Third, plans vary in how well they manage costs. A well-run HMO can reduce hospital costs by 25 percent or more compared to traditional insurance through case management. Fee-for-service plans review utilization and use panels of preferred providers. "Disease management" techniques are powerful tools to contain costs.

Fourth, cost sharing creates incentives for doctors and patients to be less wasteful. High deductibles discourage unnecessary visits, while 100 percent reimbursement of psychiatric or laboratory and imaging costs encourages overuse of these "free" services. High Deductible and Consumer-Driven plans' premiums benefit somewhat from slightly younger and healthier enrollees, but mainly from their incentives to reduce unnecessary care. Also, the time and trouble to file claims for expenses slightly above the deductible discourages some enrollees from applying for them.

Fifth, variations in the proportion of enrollees with Medicare Parts A and B has a big effect on plan premiums, since Medicare is "primary" (pays first) for retirees and covers over four-fifths of hospital and doctor costs. Most HMO benefits are so good that retired enrollees often do not sign up for Part B, which puts these plans at a major disadvantage in keeping premiums low.

Sixth, the formula for sharing premium costs magnifies the differences in what you pay. For GS employees and annuitants, the government pays 75 percent of the overall cost of each plan, up to a maximum amount. This varies each year according to a complex formula. The maximum contribution in 2022 for GS employees and annuitants is about $6,400 for self only, $13,600 for self plus one, and $14,900 for families. There are separate formulas for most postal employees, and for employees of the SEC, FDIC, and several other agencies, higher government shares. A few types of enrollees, such as former employees, get no government contribution and must pay the full premium.

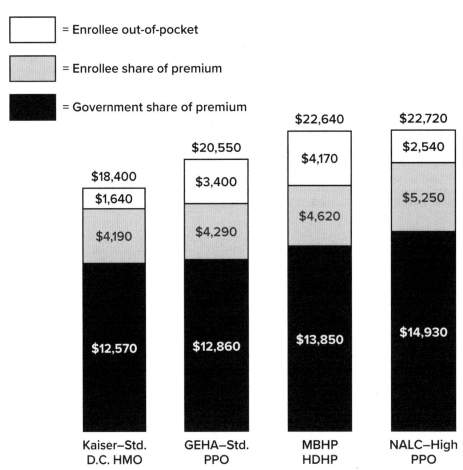

Comparison of Total Cost, Enrollee Cost, and Government Share Under Four Family Plans in 2022 (GS Premiums, Before Tax Savings)

□ = Enrollee out-of-pocket

▨ = Enrollee share of premium

■ = Government share of premium

	Kaiser–Std. D.C. HMO	GEHA–Std. PPO	MBHP HDHP	NALC–High PPO
Total	$18,400	$20,550	$22,640	$22,720
Enrollee out-of-pocket	$1,640	$3,400	$4,170	$2,540
Enrollee share of premium	$4,190	$4,290	$4,620	$5,250
Government share of premium	$12,570	$12,860	$13,850	$14,930

Employees pay the entire premium amount above the government's share. This employee share is far higher for the more expensive plans because the government contribution is capped by an all-plan average. For example, the total premium cost of the APWU High option for self-only is about $9,000. The government pays the maximum contribution of about $6,400 for GS employees and you pay the extra $2,600. In contrast, under the APWU Consumer-driven option and some other plans, you pay about $1,800 after the government contribution, a premium saving of about one-third.

You pay modestly for insurance from a well-run plan, but you pay more for a plan's inefficiencies, its unusually generous benefits, or its disproportionate share of high-cost enrollees.

The chart "Comparison of Total Cost, Enrollee Cost, and Government Share" shows how the employee's premium, the total premium (employee and government share), and the employee's out-of-pocket costs compare for a family of four under several family plans. All these factors contribute to premium differences and explain why some plans are such bargains. Of course, some of the differences are offset by what you may have to spend out-of-pocket if you pick a plan with less comprehensive benefits. That is why our ratings tables include both the cost of insurance and the cost of medical bills that are not covered. It would be foolish to select a plan just because it has the lowest premium. It would be equally foolish to pick a plan just because it seems to have the best benefits if you wind up paying more in premiums than those extra benefits are worth to you.

For 2022, most plans' premiums are about the same as this year and a few are lower, but premiums in several plans have risen dramatically. Many plans have changed benefits. As is true every year, opportunities for big savings by switching plans are significant.

Changes for 2022

In recent years, there have been significant program-wide changes to the FEHB program. The recent change that has been probably been the most important to Federal employees was coverage of adult children until age 26. Another recent change of great importance to Native American tribal employees was to extend to them eligibility to enroll in FEHB plans as if they were federal employees.

For this year there are several major changes. First, a bad surprise can happen to the unwary consumer who uses a provider that isn't in the preferred provider network of the consumer's health plan. Some plans cover out-of-network care at an increased enrollee share, but some don't cover that care at all. And the sky can be the limit for the charges that the enrollee may face when going out of network, often after an accident and with no control over who will provide care. Last year Congress acted on a bipartisan basis to pass the "No Surprises Act". This new law bans almost all surprise billing and takes effect for almost all insurance, including all FEHBP plans, on January 1, 2022. Second, in recent years the FEDVIP dental and insurance program has been expanded to cover military families and military retirees. In 2022, OPM plans to expand FEDVIP eligibility further, to many part-time and temporary employees. Third, as part of the effort to keep the Postal Service solvent, postal employees will now pay the same premiums as most General Schedule employees. Postal workers were always FEHB members, but until 2022 most were given better premium rates.

Finally, starting several years ago OPM has asked plans to adopt cost-saving coordination with Medicare, a reform that saves money for the program because Medicare usually pays first, which reduces FEHB premiums, and also offers savings for annuitants because their out-of-pocket costs are reduced. Most national plans already had such "wraparound" benefits. Dozens of local plans have now added them. Most annuitants with both Parts A and B of Medicare now can enroll in a wide range of all plan types—PPO, HDHP, CDHP, and HMO—that provide these savings. OPM now also allows plans to reimburse enrollees for part of the cost of Medicare Part B premiums, and use of this technique is growing fast. But the biggest change is that plans are now allowed to offer special "Medicare Advantage" plans to their enrollees as part of their FEHB enrollment. Medicare Advantage is an insurance program modelled after the FEHBP but with added improvements, and now attracts over one-fourth of Medicare enrollees. This new feature started small, but there are now over seventy plans offering this option. Most of them provide free or greatly reduced cost sharing, and many also reimburse most or even all of the Part B premium. These changes have greatly changed the calculus for the "to B or not to B" decision upon turning age 65, and now make Medicare Part B enrollment a far better buy than in years past.

Chapter 2

Comparing Plan Costs

We compare health plans based on their likely cost to you, taking into account plan benefits and premiums, together with your pay system, employment or retirement status, family size, age, health status, location, and other factors. A key element of our ratings are estimates of likely out-of-pocket costs under each plan, based on actuarial estimates of the size and likelihood of low, average, and high spending for families of different sizes and ages. Our ratings also reflect varying premium levels and tax situations faced by different eligibility groups. Full time employees pay lower premiums than annuitants because of tax advantages, and far lower premiums than those who must pay the entire premium. Postal union members and Federal Deposit Insurance Corporation (FDIC) and Securities and Exchange Commission (SEC) employees pay less because the government pays a higher share than for GS employees and annuitants. Neither annuitants nor those who pay full premiums obtain "Premium Conversion" tax advantages. These premium cost differences can reach thousands of dollars a year. We provide separate ratings for each group.

Online *Guide* users see a summary cost comparison table for their group, and then have the option to look at tables providing more detailed cost comparisons. Readers of the printed *Guide* see both summary and detailed cost comparison information for their group in one set of tables for all national plans and local plans available in the DC area, and summary cost comparison information on all local plans in a table covering "Cost and Special Features of All Plans" in all states at the end of *Guide*. The online information is by far more detailed and complete than we can provide in the print version.

Our comparisons take into account not only premiums and potential health care costs, but also plan financial features such as Health Savings Accounts and Wellness benefits that involve cash rewards. We also include dental benefits built into some health plans and, in our separate Chapter on "Dental, Vision, and Hearing," the costs and benefits of standalone dental plans. For annuitants, our estimates and comparisons also take into account both Medicare benefits and Medicare premiums, depending on choices about Medicare enrollment. Online, we also allow for comparisons for those using Flexible Spending Accounts (FSAs). In summary, we provide a comprehensive set of financial comparisons that allow users to make "apple to apple" comparisons of costs for both premiums and likely health care expenses under each plan and across all plans.

Understanding Health Insurance

Individuals and families buy automobile, life, fire, and health insurance policies to protect themselves from catastrophic financial harm from rare events. No one buys "food insurance" because food costs, though large, are unavoidable and predictable. Why pay a middle-man overhead costs to reimburse us for our grocery bills? Nor do we buy rent insurance, or clothes insurance.

We buy life insurance during our working years, because death is very unlikely but financially ruinous to our families if it occurs. For a few thousand dollars a year we can buy support for our families worth hundreds of thousands of dollars if we die. We buy automobile liability insurance because we can protect ourselves from losing huge amounts if we cause an accident.

True health insurance protects our families from ruinous costs of illness. Like most employers, the Federal Government does not offer employees this kind of insurance alone. Instead, it offers various combinations of true insurance and "prepaid" health care. The part of your premium that prepays health care by making advance payment for routine bills will generally equal about what you would have spent by paying the bills directly. However, you wind up paying far less than this because prepaid health care isn't counted as taxable income. Most Federal employees save as much as one-third of their premium costs because of this exclusion, as explained in our chapter on "Premiums and Taxes."

Unfortunately, prepaid health care creates incentives for enrollees to waste money because the insurance company pays the bill. Prepaid health care may be the single largest cause of wasteful health care spending which, according to some estimates, may be as high as one third of all health care expenditures. There are two major ways to reduce waste. First, health maintenance organizations (HMOs) and other managed care arrangements such as preferred provider organizations (PPOs) use payment incentives for doctors and hospitals to contain costs. Second, high deductible (HDHP) and consumer-driven plans with savings accounts create incentives for enrollees to save costs through prudent shopping decisions. We analyze the advantages and disadvantages of these plans in our analysis of "Plan Types and Flexibility."

How much and what kind of coverage is true insurance? How much is prepaid health care? These questions have no simple answer. A policy protecting against catastrophic medical expense for one family is simply a prepaid health care policy for another family. To a GS-5 with three dependents, $5,000 is a hardship, and $20,000 a heavy burden. To a GS-15 with no dependents, even $20,000 may not be a hardship.

Risk, Premium, and Choice

Since you do not know in advance how high your medical bills will be, there is no way to know which plan will leave you with the lowest total costs. You have to gamble just as you do with any insurance, or indeed with many other choices you make. On sunny mornings you probably won't take an umbrella to work, and sometimes you get wet. In a good year the best policy, in hindsight, would have been no policy, and your total costs would have been zero. In an expensive year, the best policy would have been one that covered every dollar. But we usually don't know whether we'll have a good year or a bad year, which is precisely why we buy insurance. No one but you can decide how much risk you want to bear. Our cost comparisons give you a menu of risk as well as plan choices. They help you think about the level of risk each plan involves, and how much that will cost or save you.

Do not pick a plan either because it has the lowest premium (a seeming best buy) or the highest premium (a seeming set of terrific benefits). As our ratings show, a low premium may hide major coverage gaps, and a high premium may simply reflect expensive enrollees rather than the best benefits. Only some plans have both low premiums and excellent coverage. Pick one of these based on our ratings, which combine both premium and coverage in determining the best buys.

Also, do not pick a plan because it has a lower deductible despite a higher coinsurance amount, or vice versa, and do not try to compare these benefits directly. We use computer programs to perform these calculations, and there are many complexities. For example, whether a plan with a low deductible and a high coinsurance rate is better for you than a plan with the opposites depends on the amount of your expenses, which may not be what you expect. A large body of research shows that very few people are able to juggles cost-sharing variables to pick plans that are the best buys.

Our Ratings

Our cost comparisons cover medical, hospital, dental, and prescription drug costs. They show how you are likely to fare under every national and local plan available to Federal employees. We show how each plan handles various levels of financial risk for you.

Plans are of several main types and a number of variations—combined Preferred Provider Organization (PPO) and Fee-for-Service (FFS) plans, High Deductible (HDHP) and Consumer-Driven (CDHP) plans, and Health Maintenance Organization (HMO) plans, some of which have Point-of-Service (POS) benefits outside the plan network. Most of these options are available in both national and local area plans. Historically, PPO-FFS and HMO plans are distinct approaches. The decision as to which type to join involves service delivery as well as financial factors. The preferred provider or

PPO approach now central to most Fee-for-Service plans goes part way toward the HMO model by reducing your cost if you restrict yourself to a network of providers. One national plan, the Blue Cross Basic option, is like many PPOs and most HMOs in providing no coverage except in emergencies if you use out-of-network providers. The HDHP plans follow the PPO and FFS model of the national plans, even when they are local. Thus, the differences among plan types are blurring.

Our cost ratings tell you how much you are likely to pay for premiums and out-of-pocket (unreimbursed) medical expenses added together. The tables assume that your bills may be for almost any type or size of expense, including:

- Hospital room and board for surgical or medical care for any illness;
- Other types of hospital services (operating room, anesthesia);
- Surgery, in or out of a hospital;
- Diagnostic tests, X-rays, and lab tests in or out of a hospital;
- Doctor visits in or out of a hospital when you are ill;
- Mental health treatment, outpatient and inpatient;
- Mammograms, Pap smears, and routine immunizations;
- Maternity, even if you are in a self-only plan;
- Emergency care in or out of a hospital;
- Prescription drugs, including insulin and syringes for diabetics;
- Nursing care after an illness;
- Chemotherapy and radiation therapy;
- Physical and rehabilitation therapy;
- Cosmetic ("plastic") surgery or oral surgery—only after an accident;
- Dental care;
- Preventive care including physical examinations and vaccines; and
- **All of these expenses are covered even if you have a preexisting condition or are hospitalized on the date when your enrollment begins.**

With rare exceptions, no plan will pay for any of the following expenses, and we do not cover them in our comparisons (however, some of these expenses can be covered by Flexible Spending Accounts and Health Savings Accounts):

- Care that the plan does not cover such as expensive drugs or dental expenses;
- Cosmetic or plastic surgery, except after some accidents or a disfiguring illness;
- Custodial nursing home care, or any kind of rest care;
- Personal comfort items such as telephone or television while in the hospital;
- Care that is fully paid by another insurance provider;
- Care that is not medically necessary;
- Experimental care (clinical trials are partly excepted);
- Charges that are higher than the plan "allowance" or what the plan has determined to be "reasonable;" and
- Expenses incurred before joining or after leaving a plan.

All plans cover routine exams without deductibles or copayments. Only some plans cover dental care. And most plans expose you to significant out-of-pocket costs, such as not including all prescription drugs in their formularies. Even among plans that cover all services generously, however, there are always some limitations, such as coinsurance and deductibles. Our tables take the major benefit limitations such as these into account in estimating costs. However, we cannot deal with every single coverage nuance or difference (such as which organs are eligible for transplantation, which models of particular medical devices are covered, or which specific medicines are covered). Nor can we assure that all plans will make identical medical necessity decisions in close cases—and they won't. Nor can we reflect extra benefits the plan may provide if, for example, it can save money by giving you more home nursing than its normal limitation on this benefit.

Hence, all of our calculations should be considered approximations that will be broadly accurate in the great majority of situations but that cannot provide precise predictions that cover every possible situation. What our calculations can do, and you cannot do for yourself even if you try to predict your costs, is take into account the risks of ruinously high health care costs from an unexpected illness or accident.

Using the Cost Comparison Tables

There are many separate sets of comparisons, one for each major group facing different premiums, coverage, or likely medical costs. We generally provide comparisons for self-only, self plus one, and families of sizes two through five. However, we limit certain tables to conserve space and because some situations are very uncommon: for older employees, annuitants, part-time employees, and several small enrollment groups we present only self-only, self plus one, and families of two or three rather than larger family sizes. In all family comparisons, the rankings would not change substantially with an additional child. Comparisons for employees and annuitants include:

- Employees who pay **GS premiums** (e.g., General Schedule, special rate, most Congressional, most Postal, Foreign Service, and Native American tribal employees).
- **Older employees,** whose costs are much higher on average.
- For **part-time employees**, we cover half-time workers. In almost all agencies, these employees pay part of the "employer share" as well as the regular employee share.
- Former spouses, children turning age 26 who are not covered by a parental FEHB plan, and other **persons who pay full premiums** (both employer and employee share). These persons are not eligible for tax sheltering, and we do not reduce premiums from the nominal rate.
- **Annuitants without Medicare**. Again, there are no tax savings in premium rates.
- **Annuitants with Medicare Parts A and B**. These tables include not only the FEHB plan premium, but also the Part B Medicare premium. We cover situations where high income retirees pay more, often far more, than the regular Part B premium.
- Finally, we present tables for **annuitants who have only Part A of Medicare**, the hospital benefit. We also compare these with the preceding ratings to see how much you gain, or in most cases lose, by paying the Part B premium.

There are many comparisons, but **only one cost comparison table applies to your current situation**. Of course, your situation may change if your family changes, if you retire, and if you change your Medicare decisions—and you can compare tables to see those differences. Each cost comparison table presents several columns of cost data. Each column except the one for published premium assumes a different level and mix of medical bills, described in the heading. These columns show what your likely costs will be under each plan, including both premium costs and out-of-pocket costs not paid by the plan.

By looking at the different columns in a table, you can find how you will come out under each plan. The columns display:

- The "Published premium" (including when applicable the Medicare Part B premium) that you will pay biweekly or monthly, expressed as an annual cost;
- The actual premium you will pay when you incur "No costs" for health care. This takes into account savings from premium conversion for employees, offsetting savings from money the plan puts in your Health Savings Account or Health Reimbursement Arrangement, and any dues;
- Your premium and out of pocket costs at "Low costs" usage with bills of about $1,000 (self-only) or $3,000 (families);
- Costs for "Average" usage with medical and dental bills averaged over a wide range of expense taking into account the statistical likelihood of costs at each level;
- Costs for "High" usage with bills of about $30,000; and
- The yearly "Limit to you" showing the maximum you will ever be expected to pay for medical (but not dental) bills, also reflecting both premium and out of pocket costs.

We present two different premium columns to reduce confusion over two issues. First, many employees do not understand Premium Conversion. For almost all employees, this tax preference creates close to a one-third saving in premium cost. The dollar amount of this saving is never provided to employees, and only shows up indirectly through a lowered taxable income number. Your average tax rate is much lower, but for those "marginal" income dollars most employees pay close to 33 percent, including Federal income tax, State income tax, and the employee share of Social Security and Medicare taxes. Annuitants are not eligible for Premium Conversion.

Second, many persons find High Deductible plans hard to understand. We believe that the best way to analyze them is to consider the Health Savings Account (HSA) as the equivalent of a reduction in premium. If you don't spend that account at the end of the year you will have a bank balance in that amount. It is therefore possible for you to have "free" health insurance in some High Deductible or Consumer-Driven plans. If your published premium is about $3,000 you actually pay only about $2,000 after Premium Conversion. However, the plan provides you with a savings account that is in your name. If that account is $2,000 you actually come out ahead if you have no medical expenses. In fact, since these plans all provide a free physical exam and routine vaccinations, you come out ahead this much even after your preventive care. The HSA is your money and can earn interest and grow like any other savings account (in this case, grow tax-free). You can save the HSA as an investment, or you can use it to pay your medical bills now or in old age.

If you join a Consumer-Driven plan with a "personal account" or Health Reimbursement Arrangement (HRA), the account belongs to the plan, and must be spent rather than saved if you incur expense, but still has the effect of reducing your "up front and for sure" premium cost. All HDHP and CDHP plans offer similar net savings, or greatly reduced premiums paid. Even retirees get an offset from these savings accounts if they join one of these plans.

Therefore, the "No costs" column includes your yearly premium adjusted, as pertinent, for Premium Conversion, HSA or HRA account, and any membership dues. These will be your only out-of-pocket costs if you have no medical bills.

We also indicate the percentage chance that you and your family will have bills that are "Low" or "High"—for instance, how likely you are to have bills of about $3,000 or less, or $30,000 or more.

We rank the plans in order of average cost to emphasize the importance of each plan's treatment of "average" expenses for a family of a particular size and type. Most families fall far below the average in most years, but very expensive cases pull the average up. Because almost all plans reimburse 80 percent or more of average or high expenses, the premium counts for most of this average cost, regardless of medical expenses. Very importantly, the "average" includes costs for the entirely unexpected medical problems that can affect any family, such as a heart attack, automobile accident, or onset of an expensive disease. Moreover, the "High costs" and "Limit to you" columns directly portray the insurance value of these plans. You should not select a plan based primarily on the relatively low costs that most of us can predict. It does not make sense to estimate expected costs by doctor visits you expect to make next year—it is the doctor and hospital and drug costs after some major health problem that you do not expect that need to be taken into account in a plan comparison.

You begin by making profile choices to find the one table that relates to families of your age, premium category, and size. Assuming that you don't know something to the contrary, you should expect average expenses in the coming year. The plans that are likely to cost families the least have the lowest dollar figures in this column. **Our cost comparisons assume that you use preferred, network providers exclusively**. You should select a plan primarily based on using network providers, and plan to use non-network providers only in rare instances. You can see some of the financial consequences of using non-network providers in the online *Guide*, but plans' cost-sharing for non-network providers do not include any payment for charges that may be double or triple or even higher multiples of the plan "allowance," except in emergencies. The "Surprise Billing" law does not protect you from your choice of an expensive non-network provider. (Retirees have additional protection, with or without Medicare, from a law that prohibits Medicare-participating physicians from charging age-65 federal retirees more than a "Medicare-approved" limiting charge amount).

But do not choose the highest-ranked plan until you consider whether there is some reason the average column does not apply to you or your family.

First, **consider your particular health situation**. Medical problems are mostly a matter of good or bad luck. However, some people are much more likely than others to have high expenses. In these cases, you should compare plans using the "High cost" or "Limit to you" column. A hip replacement is a large expense. A diabetic may have several expensive ailments. A history of cancer or heart disease worsens your odds. You can use the $30,000 ("High") cost comparisons if you have information that suggests you are much likely to face much higher health expenses than others of your age and family size.

Second, **consider your attitude about risk**. If you are willing to spend a few hundred dollars extra to be sure you will not have heavy out-of-pocket expenses, you may want to pick one of the plans that is lowest cost for a person with high medical bills. However, **all plans have such good coverage that you are well protected from most catastrophic expenses**. Most have a dollar limit on the annual hospital, doctor, and prescription drug expenses you must pay—as noted under the heading "Limit to you." Even where there is a gap, the effect of the generous benefit structure is to create a *de facto* limit.

In your cost table you will notice that differences among closely ranked plans are often very small. Differences of $100 or $200 are not important. A different mix of bills from those we use to compare plans could overcome these. Larger differences, however, reflect significant variations in how expensively the plans handle most cases as well as the "for sure" premium expense.

Notice that most of the higher-ranked plans will save you money in every year—whether your expenses are high or low—compared to the plans ranked lower. Again, this is because you have to pay the premium whether your medical expenses are high or low.

Using Preferred Providers

We rate plan costs based on the assumption that you will always or almost always want to use preferred providers, also known as "staying in the network". Your cost is always lower, usually far lower, when you do. However, all but one of the national PPO plans and all CDHP and HDHP plans allow you to obtain care out of network. This can sometimes be a valuable flexibility. But you face not only a higher copayment, but also an additional risk. The plans set limits on the fee they will recognize. For example, the plan may charge a flat amount of $20 to PPO users. For doctors outside the PPO, the plan may pay 70 percent of the cost up to $80 for a particular procedure, but if the physician charges $100 you will pay $30 plus the extra $20, or half the total bill compared to only $20 if you use the preferred provider. You can sometimes negotiate fees down, and we urge this strategy for non-preferred providers. This problem often goes away if you have Medicare Parts A and B, since most of the national plans and many local plans waive most doctor and hospital cost-sharing whether you obtain care in or out of the network. Even in HMOs that don't waive these costs, you can use Medicare to go out of network. Therefore, **for retirees who participate in Medicare Parts A and B preferred provider restrictions largely disappear when enrolled in most plans.** You can go to any hospital and almost any doctor without penalty. Moreover, annuitants over age 65 have the limiting charge protection described above when using doctors who participate in Medicare, even if cost sharing is not eliminated.

Catastrophic Coverage

The most important reason for buying health insurance is to protect you against financial catastrophe. You may, therefore, wish to approach plan selection by comparing plans on the basis of potential financial risk, rather than average cost. To facilitate this, our cost comparisons include a "Limit to you" column. Our "Limit" calculation includes both the annual premium and the claimed guarantee provided by each plan for hospital, medical, and prescription drug expenses. We combine these

---

Bargain with Out of Network Providers

Most plans have very low payments for non-preferred providers. You MUST negotiate with these doctors before any expensive procedure in order to protect yourself. One good tactic is to ask for either their "preferred" or Medicare rate.

two types of expenses because you are sure to incur premium costs and there is little point in picking a plan with $1,000 less in claimed limit if its premium is $2,000 higher. However, no plan includes dental expenses in its guarantee. The "Limits" column, therefore, cannot include these costs. Our figures use a 33 percent premium reduction for tax savings for employees under Premium Conversion (but not for retirees or those paying full premiums, who are ineligible). We also take account of the ability of enrollees in High Deductible plans to reduce costs by using their HSA or HRA accounts. We have not, however, included estimates for additional tax savings from funding high expenses through additional contributions to HSA accounts (see Cost and Taxes). Therefore, these are conservative estimates for High Deductible plans.

Because some plans present catastrophic limits in confusing ways, we attempt to make our limit calculations comparable among plans. For example, we take account of deductibles if these are not included in the claimed limit. A few plans put prescription drug payments under separate limits and we adjust for this difference. Plans calculate limits differently and the dollar numbers published in a plan's "Summary of Benefits" do not necessarily reflect the loopholes and exclusions listed under "Your cost for covered services"). The adjustments we make are necessary to make comparisons that are not inaccurate "apples to oranges."

How We Adjust Catastrophic Limits to Make Them Comparable Across Plans		
Illustrative plans	Brand X HDHP	Brand Y High Option Plan
Limit stated in plan's summary of benefits	$5,000	$3,000
Excluded amounts:		
Deductibles	None	None
Hospital copays*	None	$900
Prescription copays*	None	$1,000
Specialty drug limit	None	None
Physician copays*	None	$1,500
Subtotal	$5,000	$6,400
Premium	$1,000	$1,600
Health savings account	−$1,000	None
Total "limit" to you	$5,000	$6,400

* We assume three hospital stays at $300, 50 prescriptions at $20, and 50 physician visits at $30; typical values in many plans.

Although we included dental costs in most columns, we had to leave dental costs out of the "Limits" column because no plan includes dental costs in its guarantee. Aside from dental, all FEHB plans have a limit and cover nearly all hospital, medical, and prescription drug expenses if you use preferred providers.

The cost tables can be used to find those plans with the lowest limits. From this group, you can select plans with lower average costs. Or you might wish to select one of the plans with the very best catastrophic coverage and accept somewhat higher out-of-pocket costs as the price of that guarantee. Importantly, because we include premiums in the calculation of the most you can pay, we help you avoid the mistake of paying many thousands in higher premiums for a saving of fewer thousands in catastrophic limits.

If You Have Other Insurance

You cannot use our cost rankings directly if you have health insurance coverage from another source. The best FEHB plan for you depends on the cost and benefit structure of the other plan, though your best choice will almost always be a low premium plan to minimize unnecessary premium payments. But do not assume that you need not enroll in an FEHB plan just because you have other coverage.

If your spouse has a low-cost health plan through a private employer, or you have a health plan from prior employment, check to be sure that it covers you and your children, and has a benefit package as good as the Federal plans. Even if your spouse's plan is every bit as good as any of the Federal plans, consider the cost of this coverage compared to some of the lower-premium Federal plans. Remember that you must be covered under an FEHB plan continuously for the five years preceding retirement to continue enrollment after retirement (there are some very rare exceptions, such as certain agency downsizing situations). You don't have to be in the same plan in each year, but you must be covered continuously by some FEHB plan or, in the special case of former military, TRICARE.

Most importantly, if you should die while you are not enrolled in an FEHB family plan, your spouse will lose eligibility for the program. Since most employers do not continue coverage past retirement, or cannot be counted on to do so, your only guarantee that your spouse can keep this entitlement is to be continuously enrolled. There is an excellent strategy for doing so at minimum cost. All of the plans showing a very low or negative number in the "No Costs" column are Consumer-Driven or High Deductible plans that give you a savings account as large or larger than the premium. With double coverage, you will probably not ever reach the high deductible and will realize this saving in most circumstances. In other words, these plans really are almost "free" if they supplement other coverage from your spouse.

Chapter 3

Cost Comparisons and Advice for Employees and Former Employees

As explained in Chapter 2 on "Comparing Plan Costs," we rate and compare health plans based on their likely cost to you, taking into account your pay system, employment or retirement status, family size, age, health status, location, and other factors. A key element of our ratings are estimates of likely out-of-pocket costs under each plan, based on actuarial estimates of the size and likelihood of low, average, and high spending for families of different sizes and ages. This chapter focuses on current employees and former employees who are not annuitants. Annuitants are covered in the next chapter.

Readers of the printed *Guide* see both summary and detailed cost comparison information for their group in one set of tables for all national plans and local plans available in the DC area, and summary cost comparison information on all local plans in a table covering "Cost and Special Features of All Plans" in all states at the end of *Guide*.

All of these comparisons take into account not only premiums and potential health care costs, but also plan features such as Health Savings Accounts, personal accounts, and Wellness benefits that involve cash rewards. We also include dental benefits and premiums, both for dental benefits built into some health plans and for the costs and benefits of standalone dental plans. For annuitants, our estimates and comparisons also take into account both Medicare benefits and Medicare premiums (and any Medicare premium rebates), depending on choices about Medicare enrollment. In summary, we provide a comprehensive set of financial comparisons that allow users to make "apple to apple" comparisons of costs for both premiums and likely health care expenses under each plan and across all plans for which they are eligible.

Very importantly, our comparisons take into account that some plans provide both a Medicare "wraparound" and will pay part of the Medicare Part B premium. We discuss these changes in our advice for annuitants.

All of our calculations should be considered approximations that will be broadly accurate in the great majority of situations but that cannot provide precise predictions that cover every possible situation. What our calculations also do, therefore, is take into account the risks of ruinously high health care costs from an unexpected illness or accident and compare the maximum out-of-pocket and premium costs under each plan.

Using the Cost Comparison Tables for Employees and Former Employees

There are many separate sets of comparisons, one for each major group facing different premiums, coverage, or likely medical costs. We generally provide comparisons for self-only, self plus one, and families of sizes two through five. However, in the print version of the *Guide* we limit certain tables to conserve space and because some situations are very uncommon: for older employees, annuitants, part-time employees, and several small enrollment groups we present only self-only, self plus one, and families of two or three rather than larger family sizes. In all family comparisons the rankings would not change substantially with an additional child. Comparisons for employees include:

- Employees who pay **GS premiums** (e.g., General Schedule, special rate, Congressional, and Foreign Service employees).
- Employees who pay lower premiums, including **FDIC and SEC employees**. FDIC and SEC results are shown only online. (Postal employees now pay the same rates as GS employees.)
- **Older employees,** whose costs are much higher on average.
- For **part-time employees**, we cover half-time workers. In almost all agencies, these employees pay part of the "employer share" as well as the regular employee share.
- Former spouses, children turning age 26 who are not covered by a parental FEHBP plan, and other **persons who pay full premiums** (both employer and employee share). These persons are not eligible for tax sheltering, and we do not reduce premiums from the nominal rate.

There are many comparisons, but **only one cost comparison table applies to your current situation**. Of course, your situation may change if your family changes, or if you retire—and you can compare tables to see those differences. Each plan cost comparison table presents several columns of cost data. Each column except the one for published premium assumes a different level and mix of medical bills, described in the heading. These columns show what your likely costs will be under each plan, including both premium costs and out-of-pocket costs not paid by the plan.

By looking at the different columns in a table, you can find how you will come out under each plan if your expenses range from none to the maximum you could pay in a year. The details are explained in our chapter on "Comparing Plan Costs." Very importantly, the columns other than "Published premium" all include the tax savings you get from Premium Conversion for employees. These columns also credit you with the savings you gain from a Health Savings Account (HSA) or personal care account or Health Reimbursement Arrangement (HRA) in plans that give you these benefits. HSAs and HRAs are the equivalent of a reduction in premium. If you don't spend that account at the end of the year you will have a bank balance in that amount that carries over to the next year. Therefore, the "No costs" column includes your yearly premium adjusted, as pertinent, for Premium Conversion, HSA or personal care account or HRA, and any membership dues. These will be your only out-of-pocket costs if you have no medical bills. We rank the plans in order of average cost to emphasize the importance of each plan's treatment of "average" expenses for a family of a particular size and type.

You begin by making profile choices to find the table that relates to families of your age, premium category, and size. Assuming that you don't know something to the contrary, you should expect average expenses in the coming year. The plans that are likely to cost families the least have the lowest dollar figures in this column. But do not choose the highest-ranked plan until you consider whether there is some reason the average column does not apply to you or your family.

In your cost table you will notice that differences among closely ranked plans are often very small. Differences of $100 or $200 are not important. A different mix of bills from those we use to compare plans could overcome these. Differences of several hundred dollars or more, however, reflect significant variations in how expensively the plans handle most cases.

Notice that most of the higher-ranked plans will save you money in every situation—whether your expenses are high or low—compared to the plans ranked lower. You can also see that most but not all CDHP and HDHP plans will save you hundreds of dollars compared to most national PPO plans.

Avoid a Big Risk

Many people who are covered by their spouse's insurance drop FEHBP. This saves premium costs. However, if you are not enrolled and die suddenly, your spouse cannot ever enroll again. Your best option is to carry a family policy and drop the spousal insurance.

Savings for Couples Using Self Only Enrollments

For a husband and wife who are **both** employed by the Federal Government and who have no dependent children, it is possible to save on premium costs by enrolling separately as self only rather than together as a self plus one. The premiums for two self only enrollments are usually less than the self plus one premium. This option can be particularly valuable in cases where each spouse prefers a different plan, perhaps because no one plan covers both family physicians in its network.

Be cautious, however, because each person will have to meet a separate catastrophic limit rather than the single limit that applies to self plus one. Most plans do not increase your risk because they include individual limits of about half the amount of the overall self plus one or family limit. Moreover, while you are still technically subject to meeting two catastrophic limits if you both enroll self-only, the fee structure of most HMOs makes it almost impossible to reach those limits. For these reasons you are usually safe with two self only enrollments. But do check the plan brochure's catastrophic limits carefully before making this decision.

Savings for Couples or Single Parents with One Child Under Self Plus One

Married couples with no children to cover, and single parents with one child to cover, can enroll as self plus one rather than as a family and, depending on the plan chosen, usually save two or three hundred dollars a year in premium costs, and often more. Since the benefits of the plan are the same regardless of which enrollment type is chosen, this is a clear saving. You should use our comparison table for self plus one with adults of your age to make your initial plan comparison.

Is Self Plus One for You?

In most cases the self plus one premium is lower than the family premium by one or two hundred dollars a year. So check your plan to be sure it gives you this saving and, while you are at it, check our ratings to see if you can't save even more by changing plans.

If You or Your Spouse Has Other Employer Insurance

If your spouse has a low-cost health plan through a private employer, or you have a health plan from prior employment, check to be sure that it covers you and your children, and has a benefit package as good as the Federal plans. Even if your spouse's plan is every bit as good as any of the Federal plans, consider the cost of this coverage compared to some of the lower-premium Federal plans. Remember that you must be covered under the FEHBP continuously for the five years preceding retirement to be eligible for enrollment after retirement (there are some very rare exceptions, such as certain agency downsizing situations). You don't have to be in the same plan in each year, but you must be covered continuously by some FEHBP plan or, in the special case of military dependents, TRICARE.

If you should die while you are not enrolled in the FEHBP in a family plan, your spouse will lose eligibility for the program. Since most other employers do not continue coverage past retirement, or cannot be counted on to do so, your only guarantee that your spouse can keep this entitlement is to be continuously enrolled. There is an excellent strategy for doing so at minimum cost. All of the plans showing a very low or negative number in the "No Costs" column are Consumer-Driven or High Deductible plans that give you a savings account as large or larger than the premium. With double coverage you will probably not ever reach the high deductible and will realize this saving in most circumstances. In other words, these plans really are almost "free" if they supplement other coverage from your spouse.

Part-Time Employees

Many career Federal employees work part-time schedules. In these cases, most government agencies do not pay the regular share of the premium. Instead, employees receive a *pro rata* amount based on their work schedules. For example, an employee scheduled to work 40 hours per biweekly pay period receives only one half of the regular government contribution and must pay the regular employee contribution plus the extra one half, or about two thirds of the total premium cost for the plan. There are many possible part-time schedules. We present comparisons based on 50 percent of a regular work schedule. Almost all part-time employees are reasonably close to one of these scenarios. (A few agencies, including the Postal Service and the FDIC, give part-time employees the same rates as full-time employees.)

Persons Who Pay Full Premiums

The FEHBP also provides coverage for former spouses, former employees, children turning age 26, and others, but the enrollee must pay the full premium without government contribution. This often results, nonetheless, in a better price than is available for non-group insurance purchased individually, which is the only other insurance available to some. In most cases, however, a marketplace exchange option is worth considering and for those eligible for premium tax subsidies is often a better buy.

Persons eligible for continuing coverage for as long as needed include:

- Those **former spouses** who have a qualifying court order and meet other conditions. They may enroll in any plan on the same basis as employees and annuitants, except for premiums.
- **Temporary employees** who have worked for one full year also may enroll on the same basis as employees, except for premium cost. (Such employees should switch to permanent employment, if at all possible, to reduce premium costs by three-fourths.)

Time-limited coverage is also available for several categories of persons. They pay a small surcharge—two percent of the premium—and are eligible only for a limited time:

- **Employees separating from Federal service** for any reason may continue their coverage for 18 months.
- **Children reaching age 26** are, unless severely handicapped, no longer eligible for coverage under their parents' family plan. They may obtain coverage in their own name for 36 months.
- **Former spouses without a qualifying court order** also may enroll for 36 months.

For all purposes except premium contribution, tax shelter, and time limit, a temporary enrollee is treated like a regular enrollee. For example, there is no disqualification for preexisting conditions. There is a 60-day time limit for applying after the qualifying event, but once enrolled a person may switch plans in the next Open Season just like any employee or annuitant. At the end of the temporary period, these persons may switch to a "conversion" plan that is not part of the FEHB program and is sold at individual rather than group rates. However, the costs and coverages of these conversion plans are generally far worse than one can get by shopping on the private market. Some young adults will not have a parent with a family plan or will become ineligible for family coverage upon reaching age 26. **You can usually (but not always) get better deals from marketplace exchange plans than you would from paying full premiums for the regular FEHBP plans but must pay careful attention because bronze and silver plans have much higher deductibles and other cost-sharing than FEHBP plans.**

For persons who pay full premiums, we compare plans based on paying both the government and employee share. Although some of these persons must pay a two percent surcharge, we have omitted this factor to avoid the need for extra tables. Under any of the less-costly plans, the surcharge would be under $100 per year for singles and $200 per year for families. These tables do not include premium tax savings because persons who are not current employees are not eligible for this benefit. Of particular importance to former spouses turning age 65, joining Medicare Parts A and B, suspending FEHB enrollment, and enrolling in a Medicare Advantage plan will reduce premium costs by two thirds or more, and provide benefits very nearly as good as those in FEHB plans. And of particular importance for former spouses who are younger, the market-place exchanges are better buys in almost all cases since most enrollees get tax subsidies and don't have to pay full premium.

Employees Under Age 55		Self Only					
		Plan type	Published premium	Estimated yearly out-of-pocket costs, including premium and typical hospital, medical, drug, and dental bills near:			
Plan code	Plan name			No costs[1]	Low use: $1,000 or less	Average cost	High use: $30,000 or more	Limit to you

D.C. Area Plans When You Use Preferred Providers

Plan code	Plan name	Plan type	Published premium	No costs[1]	Low use: $1,000 or less	Average cost	High use: $30,000 or more	Limit to you
T71	Kaiser Prosper	HMO	1110	740	990	1750	4740	4740
E34	Kaiser-Std	HMO	1820	1220	1360	1900	4720	4720
B61	CareFirst HDHP	HDHP	1810	310	1010	1950	6210	6210
V41	United HDHP	HDHP	1990	570	1170	2070	5320	5320
E31	Kaiser-Hi	HMO	2710	1810	1910	2280	4060	4060
L91	United Choice Plus Advanced	PPO-FEE	1990	1330	1860	2430	4330	4330
Y81	United Choice Primary	HMO	1740	1160	1540	2500	8510	8510
AS1	United Choice Plus Primary	PPO-FEE	1950	1300	1680	2640	8650	8650
B64	CareFirst Blue Value Plus	HMO-POS	2320	1550	1880	2780	7550	7550
JN4	Aetna Open Access Basic	HMO	2510	1670	1930	2990	7670	7670
QQ4	Aetna Saver	HMO	1790	1190	1890	3010	7690	7690
F51	Aetna HealthFund CDHP	CDHP	4080	1720	2320	3200	7720	7720
LR1	United Choice Open Access	HMO	3500	2330	2520	3260	7330	7330
2G4	CareFirst-Std	HMO-POS	4500	3000	3140	3910	8000	8000
F54	Aetna Value Plan	PPO-FEE	4380	2920	3550	4450	8920	8920
JP1	MD-IPA	HMO	5780	3850	3980	4660	8440	8850
JN1	Aetna Open Access-Hi	HMO	8650	5770	5840	6400	9210	10770

National Plans When You Use Preferred Providers

Plan code	Plan name	Plan type	Published premium	No costs[1]	Low use: $1,000 or less	Average cost	High use: $30,000 or more	Limit to you
324	NALC CDHP	CDHP	1420	-250	450	1610	7040	7550
341	GEHA HDHP	HDHP	1640	200	800	1660	5240	6100
254	GEHA Elevate	PPO-FEE	1270	850	1000	1860	7830	7850
474	APWU CDHP	CDHP	1810	10	680	1890	6920	7710
481	MHBP HDHP	HDHP	1990	120	820	1890	5820	7320
401	Foreign Service	PPO-FEE	1900	1270	1490	2120	5160	6270
N61	Aetna Direct CDHP	CDHP	1880	360	1060	2140	7260	7260
111	Blue Cross Basic	PPO	2080	1390	1500	2240	6130	7890
131	Blue Cross FEP Blue Focus	PPO	1380	920	1530	2350	8890	9420
251	GEHA Elevate Plus	PPO-FEE	2060	1370	1590	2430	7240	7370
KM1	NALC Value Plan	PPO-FEE	1170	680	1380	2500	7380	7380
421	Compass Rose	PPO-FEE	2760	1840	1980	2520	5470	6840
314	GEHA-Std	PPO-FEE	1630	1090	1570	2570	7590	7590
454	MHBP-Std	PPO-FEE	2030	1360	1750	2640	7360	7360
321	NALC-Hi	PPO-FEE	2560	1700	2160	2860	6930	8300
444	SAMBA-Std	PPO-FEE	2130	1420	1940	2880	7420	7420
Z24	Aetna Advantage	PPO-FEE	1500	1000	1700	3070	8500	8500
414	MHBP Value Plan	PPO-FEE	1460	970	1530	3090	7570	7570
471	APWU-Hi	HMO	2770	1850	2370	3090	7630	8350
311	GEHA-Hi	PPO-FEE	2730	1820	2340	3100	6820	6820
381	Rural Carrier	PPO-FEE	3400	2270	2510	3210	7270	7270
224	Aetna HealthFund HDHP	HDHP	3530	1550	2150	3410	9250	9250
104	Blue Cross-Std	PPO-FEE	3310	2210	2650	3430	8060	8210
441	SAMBA-Hi	PPO-FEE	4130	2750	3220	4010	7750	7750

[1] These are the premiums after tax savings, offset by savings accounts for plans that offer them. If you have no or low health-care costs with these plans, it can result in actual saving to you, which we indicate with a negative number.

Employees Under Age 55		Self Plus One						
				Estimated yearly out-of-pocket costs, including premium and typical hospital, medical, drug, and dental bills near:				
Plan code	Plan name	Plan type	Published premium	No costs[1]	Low use: $3,000 or less	Average cost	High use: $30,000 or more	Limit to you
D.C. Area Plans When You Use Preferred Providers								
T73	Kaiser Prosper	HMO	2600	1730	2710	3690	7470	9730
B63	CareFirst HDHP	HDHP	3630	620	3020	3700	7570	12420
E36	Kaiser-Std	HMO	4190	2790	3350	4070	6700	9790
V43	United HDHP	HDHP	4270	1350	3550	4510	9280	9700
Y83	United Choice Primary	HMO	3750	2500	3780	4850	9370	17200
L93	United Choice Plus Advanced	PPO-FEE	3980	2660	4170	4890	8660	8660
B66	CareFirst Blue Value Plus	HMO-POS	4340	2900	4050	5010	9100	14900
AS3	United Choice Plus Primary	PPO-FEE	4200	2800	4080	5150	9670	17500
E33	Kaiser-Hi	HMO	7240	4830	5260	5690	7350	9330
JN6	Aetna Open Access Basic	HMO	5010	3340	4340	5770	10990	15340
QQ6	Aetna Saver	HMO	3750	2500	4900	6050	12420	15500
LR3	United Choice Open Access	HMO	7570	5050	5870	6710	10200	15050
2G6	CareFirst-Std	HMO-POS	8090	5400	6140	6870	9690	15400
F53	Aetna HealthFund CDHP	CDHP	9950	4630	6530	7520	12270	16630
JP3	MD-IPA	HMO	10080	6720	7400	8160	11230	16720
F56	Aetna Value Plan	PPO-FEE	10490	6990	8650	9740	14400	18990
JN3	Aetna Open Access-Hi	HMO	19790	13200	13720	14310	16580	23200
National Plans When You Use Preferred Providers								
326	NALC CDHP	CDHP	3130	-310	2090	3380	8520	15290
343	GEHA HDHP	HDHP	3530	560	2760	3440	6650	12360
256	GEHA Elevate	PPO-FEE	2910	1940	2620	3530	7070	15940
483	MHBP HDHP	HDHP	4400	530	2930	3940	7950	14930
476	APWU CDHP	CDHP	3940	230	2580	3950	8940	15630
133	Blue Cross FEP Blue Focus	PPO	2970	1980	3460	4220	8120	18980
N63	Aetna Direct CDHP	CDHP	4130	960	3360	4350	9130	14760
403	Foreign Service	PPO-FEE	4820	3220	4340	4760	7280	10220
113	Blue Cross Basic	PPO	5100	3400	4120	4900	8060	16400
316	GEHA-Std	PPO-FEE	3500	2340	3660	5030	10520	15340
253	GEHA Elevate Plus	PPO-FEE	4750	3170	4050	5060	8960	15170
KM3	NALC Value Plan	PPO-FEE	2570	1520	3920	5190	10350	14920
423	Compass Rose	PPO-FEE	6440	4290	4860	5470	7870	11290
456	MHBP-Std	PPO-FEE	5090	3400	4630	5580	9840	15400
446	SAMBA-Std	PPO-FEE	4640	3100	4570	5720	10760	15100
473	APWU-Hi	HMO	5540	3690	5080	5930	9720	16690
383	Rural Carrier	PPO-FEE	6430	4290	5190	6010	9260	14290
323	NALC-Hi	PPO-FEE	6090	4060	5370	6100	9510	13060
Z26	Aetna Advantage	PPO-FEE	3300	2200	4600	6270	13250	17200
313	GEHA-Hi	PPO-FEE	6360	4240	5580	6630	11100	14240
416	MHBP Value Plan	PPO-FEE	3450	2300	5300	6660	15500	15500
226	Aetna HealthFund HDHP	HDHP	7750	3570	5770	7130	12500	18970
106	Blue Cross-Std	PPO-FEE	7530	5020	6360	7190	11050	17020
443	SAMBA-Hi	PPO-FEE	9450	6300	7640	8520	12430	16300

[1] These are the premiums after tax savings, offset by savings accounts for plans that offer them. If you have no or low health-care costs with these plans, it can result in actual saving to you, which we indicate with a negative number.

				Family of Two				

Employees Under Age 55

Plan code	Plan name	Plan type	Published premium	No costs[1]	Low use: $3,000 or less	Average cost	High use: $30,000 or more	Limit to you
D.C. Area Plans When You Use Preferred Providers								
T72	Kaiser Prosper	HMO	3150	2100	3080	4060	7840	10100
E35	Kaiser-Std	HMO	4190	2790	3350	4070	6700	9790
B62	CareFirst HDHP	HDHP	4310	1070	3470	4150	8020	12870
V42	United HDHP	HDHP	4540	1530	3730	4690	9460	9880
E32	Kaiser-Hi	HMO	5960	3970	4400	4830	6490	8470
Y82	United Choice Primary	HMO	4120	2750	4030	5100	9620	17450
L92	United Choice Plus Advanced	PPO-FEE	4760	3170	4680	5400	9170	9170
AS2	United Choice Plus Primary	PPO-FEE	4620	3080	4360	5430	9950	17780
B65	CareFirst Blue Value Plus	HMO-POS	5710	3810	4960	5920	10010	15810
JN5	Aetna Open Access Basic	HMO	5380	3590	4590	6020	11240	15590
QQ5	Aetna Saver	HMO	4090	2730	5130	6280	12650	15730
F52	Aetna HealthFund CDHP	CDHP	8890	3930	5830	6820	11570	15930
LR2	United Choice Open Access	HMO	8460	5640	6460	7300	10790	15640
2G5	CareFirst-Std	HMO-POS	10890	7260	8000	8730	11550	17260
F55	Aetna Value Plan	PPO-FEE	9680	6460	8120	9210	13870	18460
JN2	Aetna Open Access-Hi	HMO	18840	12560	13080	13670	15940	22560
JP2	MD-IPA	HMO	19120	12760	13440	14200	17270	22760
National Plans When You Use Preferred Providers								
325	NALC CDHP	CDHP	3330	-180	2220	3510	8650	15420
255	GEHA Elevate	PPO-FEE	3550	2370	3050	3960	7500	16370
342	GEHA HDHP	HDHP	4340	1100	3300	3980	7190	12900
482	MHBP HDHP	HDHP	4620	680	3080	4090	8100	15080
475	APWU CDHP	CDHP	4290	460	2810	4180	9170	15860
132	Blue Cross FEP Blue Focus	PPO	3270	2180	3660	4420	8320	19180
402	Foreign Service	PPO-FEE	4710	3140	4260	4680	7200	10140
N62	Aetna Direct CDHP	CDHP	4750	1370	3770	4760	9540	15170
112	Blue Cross Basic	PPO	5520	3680	4400	5180	8340	16680
252	GEHA Elevate Plus	PPO-FEE	4960	3310	4190	5200	9100	15310
KM2	NALC Value Plan	PPO-FEE	2740	1630	4030	5300	10460	15030
455	MHBP-Std	PPO-FEE	4730	3150	4380	5330	9590	15150
322	NALC-Hi	PPO-FEE	5250	3500	4810	5540	8950	12500
315	GEHA-Std	PPO-FEE	4290	2860	4180	5550	11040	15860
422	Compass Rose	PPO-FEE	6980	4650	5220	5830	8230	11650
382	Rural Carrier	PPO-FEE	6160	4110	5010	5830	9080	14110
445	SAMBA-Std	PPO-FEE	4850	3230	4700	5850	10890	15230
225	Aetna HealthFund HDHP	HDHP	6890	3000	5200	6560	11930	18400
415	MHBP Value Plan	PPO-FEE	3520	2350	5350	6710	15550	15550
Z25	Aetna Advantage	PPO-FEE	3980	2650	5050	6720	13700	17650
472	APWU-Hi	HMO	6990	4660	6050	6900	10690	17660
105	Blue Cross-Std	PPO-FEE	8170	5450	6790	7620	11480	17450
312	GEHA-Hi	PPO-FEE	7860	5240	6580	7630	12100	15240
442	SAMBA-Hi	PPO-FEE	10260	6850	8190	9070	12980	16850

[1] These are the premiums after tax savings, offset by savings accounts for plans that offer them. If you have no or low health-care costs with these plans, it can result in actual saving to you, which we indicate with a negative number.

Employees Under Age 55		Family of Three						
				Estimated yearly out-of-pocket costs, including premium and typical hospital, medical, drug, and dental bills near:				
		Plan type	Published premium	No costs[1]	Low use: $3,000 or less	Average cost	High use: $30,000 or more	Limit to you
Plan code	Plan name							

D.C. Area Plans When You Use Preferred Providers

Plan code	Plan name	Plan type	Published premium	No costs[1]	Low use: $3,000 or less	Average cost	High use: $30,000 or more	Limit to you
E35	Kaiser-Std	HMO	4190	2790	3350	4270	6700	9790
T72	Kaiser Prosper	HMO	3150	2100	3080	4350	7840	10100
B62	CareFirst HDHP	HDHP	4310	1070	3470	4510	8020	12870
E32	Kaiser-Hi	HMO	5960	3970	4400	4960	6490	8470
V42	United HDHP	HDHP	4540	1530	3730	5080	9460	9880
Y82	United Choice Primary	HMO	4120	2750	4030	5420	9620	17450
L92	United Choice Plus Advanced	PPO-FEE	4760	3170	4680	5680	9170	9170
AS2	United Choice Plus Primary	PPO-FEE	4620	3080	4360	5750	9950	17780
B65	CareFirst Blue Value Plus	HMO-POS	5710	3810	4960	6210	10010	15810
JN5	Aetna Open Access Basic	HMO	5380	3590	4590	6370	11240	15590
QQ5	Aetna Saver	HMO	4090	2730	5130	6720	12650	15730
F52	Aetna HealthFund CDHP	CDHP	8890	3930	5830	7180	11570	15930
LR2	United Choice Open Access	HMO	8460	5640	6460	7540	10790	15640
2G5	CareFirst-Std	HMO-POS	10890	7260	8000	8950	11550	17260
F55	Aetna Value Plan	PPO-FEE	9680	6460	8120	9550	13870	18460
JN2	Aetna Open Access-Hi	HMO	18840	12560	13080	13850	15940	22560
JP2	MD-IPA	HMO	19120	12760	13440	14410	17270	22760

National Plans When You Use Preferred Providers

Plan code	Plan name	Plan type	Published premium	No costs[1]	Low use: $3,000 or less	Average cost	High use: $30,000 or more	Limit to you
325	NALC CDHP	CDHP	3330	-180	2220	3970	8650	15420
255	GEHA Elevate	PPO-FEE	3550	2370	3050	4200	7500	16370
342	GEHA HDHP	HDHP	4340	1100	3300	4310	7190	12900
482	MHBP HDHP	HDHP	4620	680	3080	4490	8100	15080
475	APWU CDHP	CDHP	4290	460	2810	4650	9170	15860
132	Blue Cross FEP Blue Focus	PPO	3270	2180	3660	4700	8320	19180
402	Foreign Service	PPO-FEE	4710	3140	4260	4880	7200	10140
N62	Aetna Direct CDHP	CDHP	4750	1370	3770	5170	9540	15170
112	Blue Cross Basic	PPO	5520	3680	4400	5410	8340	16680
252	GEHA Elevate Plus	PPO-FEE	4960	3310	4190	5470	9100	15310
455	MHBP-Std	PPO-FEE	4730	3150	4380	5630	9590	15150
KM2	NALC Value Plan	PPO-FEE	2740	1630	4030	5750	10460	15030
322	NALC-Hi	PPO-FEE	5250	3500	4810	5800	8950	12500
315	GEHA-Std	PPO-FEE	4290	2860	4180	5910	11040	15860
422	Compass Rose	PPO-FEE	6980	4650	5220	6000	8230	11650
382	Rural Carrier	PPO-FEE	6160	4110	5010	6060	9080	14110
445	SAMBA-Std	PPO-FEE	4850	3230	4700	6190	10890	15230
225	Aetna HealthFund HDHP	HDHP	6890	3000	5200	7010	11930	18400
472	APWU-Hi	HMO	6990	4660	6050	7180	10690	17660
Z25	Aetna Advantage	PPO-FEE	3980	2650	5050	7250	13700	17650
415	MHBP Value Plan	PPO-FEE	3520	2350	5350	7300	15550	15550
105	Blue Cross-Std	PPO-FEE	8170	5450	6790	7900	11480	17450
312	GEHA-Hi	PPO-FEE	7860	5240	6580	7940	12100	15240
442	SAMBA-Hi	PPO-FEE	10260	6850	8190	9350	12980	16850

[1] These are the premiums after tax savings, offset by savings accounts for plans that offer them. If you have no or low health-care costs with these plans, it can result in actual saving to you, which we indicate with a negative number.

Employees Under Age 55		Family of Four						
				Estimated yearly out-of-pocket costs, including premium and typical hospital, medical, drug, and dental bills near:				
Plan code	Plan name	Plan type	Published premium	No costs[1]	Low use: $3,000 or less	Average cost	High use: $30,000 or more	Limit to you
D.C. Area Plans When You Use Preferred Providers								
E35	Kaiser-Std	HMO	4190	2790	3350	4450	6700	9790
T72	Kaiser Prosper	HMO	3150	2100	3080	4610	7840	10100
B62	CareFirst HDHP	HDHP	4310	1070	3470	4830	8020	12870
E32	Kaiser-Hi	HMO	5960	3970	4400	5080	6490	8470
V42	United HDHP	HDHP	4540	1530	3730	5430	9460	9880
Y82	United Choice Primary	HMO	4120	2750	4030	5720	9620	17450
L92	United Choice Plus Advanced	PPO-FEE	4760	3170	4680	5930	9170	9170
AS2	United Choice Plus Primary	PPO-FEE	4620	3080	4360	6050	9950	17780
B65	CareFirst Blue Value Plus	HMO-POS	5710	3810	4960	6490	10010	15810
JN5	Aetna Open Access Basic	HMO	5380	3590	4590	6720	11240	15590
QQ5	Aetna Saver	HMO	4090	2730	5130	7150	12650	15730
F52	Aetna HealthFund CDHP	CDHP	8890	3930	5830	7500	11570	15930
LR2	United Choice Open Access	HMO	8460	5640	6460	7780	10790	15640
2G5	CareFirst-Std	HMO-POS	10890	7260	8000	9150	11550	17260
F55	Aetna Value Plan	PPO-FEE	9680	6460	8120	9880	13870	18460
JN2	Aetna Open Access-Hi	HMO	18840	12560	13080	14010	15940	22560
JP2	MD-IPA	HMO	19120	12760	13440	14620	17270	22760
National Plans When You Use Preferred Providers								
325	NALC CDHP	CDHP	3330	-180	2220	4380	8650	15420
255	GEHA Elevate	PPO-FEE	3550	2370	3050	4440	7500	16370
342	GEHA HDHP	HDHP	4340	1100	3300	4610	7190	12900
482	MHBP HDHP	HDHP	4620	680	3080	4850	8100	15080
132	Blue Cross FEP Blue Focus	PPO	3270	2180	3660	4960	8320	19180
475	APWU CDHP	CDHP	4290	460	2810	5060	9170	15860
402	Foreign Service	PPO-FEE	4710	3140	4260	5070	7200	10140
N62	Aetna Direct CDHP	CDHP	4750	1370	3770	5550	9540	15170
112	Blue Cross Basic	PPO	5520	3680	4400	5620	8340	16680
252	GEHA Elevate Plus	PPO-FEE	4960	3310	4190	5740	9100	15310
455	MHBP-Std	PPO-FEE	4730	3150	4380	5900	9590	15150
322	NALC-Hi	PPO-FEE	5250	3500	4810	6040	8950	12500
422	Compass Rose	PPO-FEE	6980	4650	5220	6170	8230	11650
KM2	NALC Value Plan	PPO-FEE	2740	1630	4030	6170	10460	15030
315	GEHA-Std	PPO-FEE	4290	2860	4180	6260	11040	15860
382	Rural Carrier	PPO-FEE	6160	4110	5010	6270	9080	14110
445	SAMBA-Std	PPO-FEE	4850	3230	4700	6520	10890	15230
225	Aetna HealthFund HDHP	HDHP	6890	3000	5200	7440	11930	18400
472	APWU-Hi	HMO	6990	4660	6050	7440	10690	17660
Z25	Aetna Advantage	PPO-FEE	3980	2650	5050	7740	13700	17650
415	MHBP Value Plan	PPO-FEE	3520	2350	5350	7860	15550	15550
105	Blue Cross-Std	PPO-FEE	8170	5450	6790	8180	11480	17450
312	GEHA-Hi	PPO-FEE	7860	5240	6580	8230	12100	15240
442	SAMBA-Hi	PPO-FEE	10260	6850	8190	9620	12980	16850

[1] These are the premiums after tax savings, offset by savings accounts for plans that offer them. If you have no or low health-care costs with these plans, it can result in actual saving to you, which we indicate with a negative number.

Employees Under Age 55		Family of Five						
		Plan type	Published premium	Estimated yearly out-of-pocket costs, including premium and typical hospital, medical, drug, and dental bills near:				
Plan code	Plan name			No costs[1]	Low use: $3,000 or less	Average cost	High use: $30,000 or more	Limit to you

<table>
<tr><td colspan="9">D.C. Area Plans When You Use Preferred Providers</td></tr>
</table>

Plan code	Plan name	Plan type	Published premium	No costs[1]	Low use: $3,000 or less	Average cost	High use: $30,000 or more	Limit to you
E35	Kaiser-Std	HMO	4190	2790	3350	4630	6700	9790
T72	Kaiser Prosper	HMO	3150	2100	3080	4870	7840	10100
B62	CareFirst HDHP	HDHP	4310	1070	3470	5120	8020	12870
E32	Kaiser-Hi	HMO	5960	3970	4400	5190	6490	8470
V42	United HDHP	HDHP	4540	1530	3730	5760	9460	9880
Y82	United Choice Primary	HMO	4120	2750	4030	6020	9620	17450
L92	United Choice Plus Advanced	PPO-FEE	4760	3170	4680	6160	9170	9170
AS2	United Choice Plus Primary	PPO-FEE	4620	3080	4360	6350	9950	17780
B65	CareFirst Blue Value Plus	HMO-POS	5710	3810	4960	6750	10010	15810
JN5	Aetna Open Access Basic	HMO	5380	3590	4590	7050	11240	15590
QQ5	Aetna Saver	HMO	4090	2730	5130	7550	12650	15730
F52	Aetna HealthFund CDHP	CDHP	8890	3930	5830	7810	11570	15930
LR2	United Choice Open Access	HMO	8460	5640	6460	8000	10790	15640
2G5	CareFirst-Std	HMO-POS	10890	7260	8000	9350	11550	17260
F55	Aetna Value Plan	PPO-FEE	9680	6460	8120	10180	13870	18460
JN2	Aetna Open Access-Hi	HMO	18840	12560	13080	14160	15940	22560
JP2	MD-IPA	HMO	19120	12760	13440	14810	17270	22760

<table>
<tr><td colspan="9">National Plans When You Use Preferred Providers</td></tr>
</table>

Plan code	Plan name	Plan type	Published premium	No costs[1]	Low use: $3,000 or less	Average cost	High use: $30,000 or more	Limit to you
255	GEHA Elevate	PPO-FEE	3550	2370	3050	4670	7500	16370
325	NALC CDHP	CDHP	3330	-180	2220	4760	8650	15420
342	GEHA HDHP	HDHP	4340	1100	3300	4880	7190	12900
482	MHBP HDHP	HDHP	4620	680	3080	5170	8100	15080
132	Blue Cross FEP Blue Focus	PPO	3270	2180	3660	5210	8320	19180
402	Foreign Service	PPO-FEE	4710	3140	4260	5250	7200	10140
475	APWU CDHP	CDHP	4290	460	2810	5450	9170	15860
112	Blue Cross Basic	PPO	5520	3680	4400	5830	8340	16680
N62	Aetna Direct CDHP	CDHP	4750	1370	3770	5900	9540	15170
252	GEHA Elevate Plus	PPO-FEE	4960	3310	4190	5990	9100	15310
455	MHBP-Std	PPO-FEE	4730	3150	4380	6170	9590	15150
322	NALC-Hi	PPO-FEE	5250	3500	4810	6270	8950	12500
422	Compass Rose	PPO-FEE	6980	4650	5220	6320	8230	11650
382	Rural Carrier	PPO-FEE	6160	4110	5010	6480	9080	14110
KM2	NALC Value Plan	PPO-FEE	2740	1630	4030	6550	10460	15030
315	GEHA-Std	PPO-FEE	4290	2860	4180	6600	11040	15860
445	SAMBA-Std	PPO-FEE	4850	3230	4700	6830	10890	15230
472	APWU-Hi	HMO	6990	4660	6050	7700	10690	17660
225	Aetna HealthFund HDHP	HDHP	6890	3000	5200	7830	11930	18400
Z25	Aetna Advantage	PPO-FEE	3980	2650	5050	8200	13700	17650
415	MHBP Value Plan	PPO-FEE	3520	2350	5350	8380	15550	15550
105	Blue Cross-Std	PPO-FEE	8170	5450	6790	8440	11480	17450
312	GEHA-Hi	PPO-FEE	7860	5240	6580	8500	12100	15240
442	SAMBA-Hi	PPO-FEE	10260	6850	8190	9870	12980	16850

[1] These are the premiums after tax savings, offset by savings accounts for plans that offer them. If you have no or low health-care costs with these plans, it can result in actual saving to you, which we indicate with a negative number.

Employees Age 55 to 64		Self Only						
				Estimated yearly out-of-pocket costs, including premium and typical hospital, medical, drug, and dental bills near:				
Plan code	Plan name	Plan type	Published premium	No costs[1]	Low use: $1,000 or less	Average cost	High use: $30,000 or more	Limit to you
D.C. Area Plans When You Use Preferred Providers								
T71	Kaiser Prosper	HMO	1110	740	990	2300	4740	4740
E34	Kaiser-Std	HMO	1820	1220	1360	2310	4720	4720
E31	Kaiser-Hi	HMO	2710	1810	1910	2560	4060	4060
B61	CareFirst HDHP	HDHP	1810	310	1010	2680	6210	6210
V41	United HDHP	HDHP	1990	570	1170	2720	5320	5320
L91	United Choice Plus Advanced	PPO-FEE	1990	1330	1860	2870	4330	4330
Y81	United Choice Primary	HMO	1740	1160	1540	3230	8510	8510
AS1	United Choice Plus Primary	PPO-FEE	1950	1300	1680	3370	8650	8650
B64	CareFirst Blue Value Plus	HMO-POS	2320	1550	1880	3450	7550	7550
JN4	Aetna Open Access Basic	HMO	2510	1670	1930	3750	7670	7670
LR1	United Choice Open Access	HMO	3500	2330	2520	3790	7330	7330
QQ4	Aetna Saver	HMO	1790	1190	1890	3860	7690	7690
F51	Aetna HealthFund CDHP	CDHP	4080	1720	2320	3890	7720	7720
2G4	CareFirst-Std	HMO-POS	4500	3000	3140	4460	8000	8000
JP1	MD-IPA	HMO	5780	3850	3980	5150	8440	8850
F54	Aetna Value Plan	PPO-FEE	4380	2920	3550	5160	8920	8920
JN1	Aetna Open Access-Hi	HMO	8650	5770	5840	6800	9210	10770
National Plans When You Use Preferred Providers								
341	GEHA HDHP	HDHP	1640	200	800	2330	5240	6100
324	NALC CDHP	CDHP	1420	-250	450	2490	7040	7550
254	GEHA Elevate	PPO-FEE	1270	850	1000	2520	7830	7850
401	Foreign Service	PPO-FEE	1900	1270	1490	2580	5160	6270
481	MHBP HDHP	HDHP	1990	120	820	2680	5820	7320
474	APWU CDHP	CDHP	1810	10	680	2780	6920	7710
111	Blue Cross Basic	PPO	2080	1390	1500	2780	6130	7890
421	Compass Rose	PPO-FEE	2760	1840	1980	2920	5470	6840
N61	Aetna Direct CDHP	CDHP	1880	360	1060	2960	7260	7260
131	Blue Cross FEP Blue Focus	PPO	1380	920	1530	3050	8890	9420
251	GEHA Elevate Plus	PPO-FEE	2060	1370	1590	3060	7240	7370
454	MHBP-Std	PPO-FEE	2030	1360	1750	3310	7360	7360
314	GEHA-Std	PPO-FEE	1630	1090	1570	3330	7590	7590
KM1	NALC Value Plan	PPO-FEE	1170	680	1380	3340	7380	7380
321	NALC-Hi	PPO-FEE	2560	1700	2160	3430	6930	8300
444	SAMBA-Std	PPO-FEE	2130	1420	1940	3610	7420	7420
471	APWU-Hi	HMO	2770	1850	2370	3690	7630	8350
311	GEHA-Hi	PPO-FEE	2730	1820	2340	3700	6820	6820
381	Rural Carrier	PPO-FEE	3400	2270	2510	3730	7270	7270
104	Blue Cross-Std	PPO-FEE	3310	2210	2650	4050	8060	8210
Z24	Aetna Advantage	PPO-FEE	1500	1000	1700	4080	8500	8500
414	MHBP Value Plan	PPO-FEE	1460	970	1530	4160	7570	7570
224	Aetna HealthFund HDHP	HDHP	3530	1550	2150	4340	9250	9250
441	SAMBA-Hi	PPO-FEE	4130	2750	3220	4600	7750	7750

[1] These are the premiums after tax savings, offset by savings accounts for plans that offer them. If you have no or low health-care costs with these plans, it can result in actual saving to you, which we indicate with a negative number.

Employees Age 55 to 64		Self Plus One						
				Estimated yearly out-of-pocket costs, including premium and typical hospital, medical, drug, and dental bills near:				
		Plan type	Published premium	No costs[1]	Low use: $3,000 or less	Average cost	High use: $30,000 or more	Limit to you
Plan code	Plan name							
D.C. Area Plans When You Use Preferred Providers								
T73	Kaiser Prosper	HMO	2600	1730	2710	4830	7470	9730
E36	Kaiser-Std	HMO	4190	2790	3350	4880	6700	9790
B63	CareFirst HDHP	HDHP	3630	620	3020	5100	7570	12420
L93	United Choice Plus Advanced	PPO-FEE	3980	2660	4170	5930	8660	8660
V43	United HDHP	HDHP	4270	1350	3550	5980	9280	9700
E33	Kaiser-Hi	HMO	7240	4830	5260	6210	7350	9330
Y83	United Choice Primary	HMO	3750	2500	3780	6230	9370	17200
B66	CareFirst Blue Value Plus	HMO-POS	4340	2900	4050	6250	9100	14900
AS3	United Choice Plus Primary	PPO-FEE	4200	2800	4080	6530	9670	17500
JN6	Aetna Open Access Basic	HMO	5010	3340	4340	7260	10990	15340
LR3	United Choice Open Access	HMO	7570	5050	5870	7740	10200	15050
2G6	CareFirst-Std	HMO-POS	8090	5400	6140	7820	9690	15400
QQ6	Aetna Saver	HMO	3750	2500	4900	7860	12420	15500
F53	Aetna HealthFund CDHP	CDHP	9950	4630	6530	8970	12270	16630
JP3	MD-IPA	HMO	10080	6720	7400	9070	11230	16720
F56	Aetna Value Plan	PPO-FEE	10490	6990	8650	11160	14400	18990
JN3	Aetna Open Access-Hi	HMO	19790	13200	13720	15040	16580	23200
National Plans When You Use Preferred Providers								
256	GEHA Elevate	PPO-FEE	2910	1940	2620	4630	7070	15940
343	GEHA HDHP	HDHP	3530	560	2760	4700	6650	12360
326	NALC CDHP	CDHP	3130	-310	2090	5200	8520	15290
133	Blue Cross FEP Blue Focus	PPO	2970	1980	3460	5440	8120	18980
483	MHBP HDHP	HDHP	4400	530	2930	5450	7950	14930
403	Foreign Service	PPO-FEE	4820	3220	4340	5580	7280	10220
476	APWU CDHP	CDHP	3940	230	2580	5780	8940	15630
113	Blue Cross Basic	PPO	5100	3400	4120	5850	8060	16400
N63	Aetna Direct CDHP	CDHP	4130	960	3360	6000	9130	14760
423	Compass Rose	PPO-FEE	6440	4290	4860	6200	7870	11290
253	GEHA Elevate Plus	PPO-FEE	4750	3170	4050	6240	8960	15170
316	GEHA-Std	PPO-FEE	3500	2340	3660	6570	10520	15340
456	MHBP-Std	PPO-FEE	5090	3400	4630	6800	9840	15400
383	Rural Carrier	PPO-FEE	6430	4290	5190	6960	9260	14290
KM3	NALC Value Plan	PPO-FEE	2570	1520	3920	6970	10350	14920
473	APWU-Hi	HMO	5540	3690	5080	7130	9720	16690
446	SAMBA-Std	PPO-FEE	4640	3100	4570	7150	10760	15100
323	NALC-Hi	PPO-FEE	6090	4060	5370	7150	9510	13060
313	GEHA-Hi	PPO-FEE	6360	4240	5580	7890	11100	14240
Z26	Aetna Advantage	PPO-FEE	3300	2200	4600	8390	13250	17200
106	Blue Cross-Std	PPO-FEE	7530	5020	6360	8400	11050	17020
416	MHBP Value Plan	PPO-FEE	3450	2300	5300	8960	15500	15500
226	Aetna HealthFund HDHP	HDHP	7750	3570	5770	8970	12500	18970
443	SAMBA-Hi	PPO-FEE	9450	6300	7640	9680	12430	16300

[1] These are the premiums after tax savings, offset by savings accounts for plans that offer them. If you have no or low health-care costs with these plans, it can result in actual saving to you, which we indicate with a negative number.

Employees Age 55 to 64		Family of Two						
				Estimated yearly out-of-pocket costs, including premium and typical hospital, medical, drug, and dental bills near:				
		Plan type	Published premium	No costs[1]	Low use: $3,000 or less	Average cost	High use: $30,000 or more	Limit to you
Plan code	Plan name							
D.C. Area Plans When You Use Preferred Providers								
E35	Kaiser-Std	HMO	4190	2790	3350	4880	6700	9790
T72	Kaiser Prosper	HMO	3150	2100	3080	5200	7840	10100
E32	Kaiser-Hi	HMO	5960	3970	4400	5350	6490	8470
B62	CareFirst HDHP	HDHP	4310	1070	3470	5550	8020	12870
V42	United HDHP	HDHP	4540	1530	3730	6160	9460	9880
L92	United Choice Plus Advanced	PPO-FEE	4760	3170	4680	6440	9170	9170
Y82	United Choice Primary	HMO	4120	2750	4030	6480	9620	17450
AS2	United Choice Plus Primary	PPO-FEE	4620	3080	4360	6810	9950	17780
B65	CareFirst Blue Value Plus	HMO-POS	5710	3810	4960	7160	10010	15810
JN5	Aetna Open Access Basic	HMO	5380	3590	4590	7510	11240	15590
QQ5	Aetna Saver	HMO	4090	2730	5130	8090	12650	15730
F52	Aetna HealthFund CDHP	CDHP	8890	3930	5830	8270	11570	15930
LR2	United Choice Open Access	HMO	8460	5640	6460	8330	10790	15640
2G5	CareFirst-Std	HMO-POS	10890	7260	8000	9680	11550	17260
F55	Aetna Value Plan	PPO-FEE	9680	6460	8120	10630	13870	18460
JN2	Aetna Open Access-Hi	HMO	18840	12560	13080	14400	15940	22560
JP2	MD-IPA	HMO	19120	12760	13440	15110	17270	22760
National Plans When You Use Preferred Providers								
255	GEHA Elevate	PPO-FEE	3550	2370	3050	5060	7500	16370
342	GEHA HDHP	HDHP	4340	1100	3300	5240	7190	12900
325	NALC CDHP	CDHP	3330	-180	2220	5330	8650	15420
402	Foreign Service	PPO-FEE	4710	3140	4260	5500	7200	10140
482	MHBP HDHP	HDHP	4620	680	3080	5600	8100	15080
132	Blue Cross FEP Blue Focus	PPO	3270	2180	3660	5640	8320	19180
475	APWU CDHP	CDHP	4290	460	2810	6010	9170	15860
112	Blue Cross Basic	PPO	5520	3680	4400	6130	8340	16680
252	GEHA Elevate Plus	PPO-FEE	4960	3310	4190	6380	9100	15310
N62	Aetna Direct CDHP	CDHP	4750	1370	3770	6410	9540	15170
455	MHBP-Std	PPO-FEE	4730	3150	4380	6550	9590	15150
422	Compass Rose	PPO-FEE	6980	4650	5220	6560	8230	11650
322	NALC-Hi	PPO-FEE	5250	3500	4810	6590	8950	12500
382	Rural Carrier	PPO-FEE	6160	4110	5010	6780	9080	14110
KM2	NALC Value Plan	PPO-FEE	2740	1630	4030	7080	10460	15030
315	GEHA-Std	PPO-FEE	4290	2860	4180	7090	11040	15860
445	SAMBA-Std	PPO-FEE	4850	3230	4700	7280	10890	15230
472	APWU-Hi	HMO	6990	4660	6050	8100	10690	17660
225	Aetna HealthFund HDHP	HDHP	6890	3000	5200	8400	11930	18400
105	Blue Cross-Std	PPO-FEE	8170	5450	6790	8830	11480	17450
Z25	Aetna Advantage	PPO-FEE	3980	2650	5050	8840	13700	17650
312	GEHA-Hi	PPO-FEE	7860	5240	6580	8890	12100	15240
415	MHBP Value Plan	PPO-FEE	3520	2350	5350	9010	15550	15550
442	SAMBA-Hi	PPO-FEE	10260	6850	8190	10230	12980	16850

[1] These are the premiums after tax savings, offset by savings accounts for plans that offer them. If you have no or low health-care costs with these plans, it can result in actual saving to you, which we indicate with a negative number.

				Family of Three				
Employees Age 55 to 64		Plan type	Published premium	Estimated yearly out-of-pocket costs, including premium and typical hospital, medical, drug, and dental bills near:				
Plan code	Plan name			No costs[1]	Low use: $3,000 or less	Average cost	High use: $30,000 or more	Limit to you
D.C. Area Plans When You Use Preferred Providers								
E35	Kaiser-Std	HMO	4190	2790	3350	5040	6700	9790
T72	Kaiser Prosper	HMO	3150	2100	3080	5430	7840	10100
E32	Kaiser-Hi	HMO	5960	3970	4400	5450	6490	8470
B62	CareFirst HDHP	HDHP	4310	1070	3470	5800	8020	12870
V42	United HDHP	HDHP	4540	1530	3730	6440	9460	9880
L92	United Choice Plus Advanced	PPO-FEE	4760	3170	4680	6650	9170	9170
Y82	United Choice Primary	HMO	4120	2750	4030	6750	9620	17450
AS2	United Choice Plus Primary	PPO-FEE	4620	3080	4360	7080	9950	17780
B65	CareFirst Blue Value Plus	HMO-POS	5710	3810	4960	7410	10010	15810
JN5	Aetna Open Access Basic	HMO	5380	3590	4590	7810	11240	15590
QQ5	Aetna Saver	HMO	4090	2730	5130	8440	12650	15730
LR2	United Choice Open Access	HMO	8460	5640	6460	8530	10790	15640
F52	Aetna HealthFund CDHP	CDHP	8890	3930	5830	8540	11570	15930
2G5	CareFirst-Std	HMO-POS	10890	7260	8000	9860	11550	17260
F55	Aetna Value Plan	PPO-FEE	9680	6460	8120	10910	13870	18460
JN2	Aetna Open Access-Hi	HMO	18840	12560	13080	14530	15940	22560
JP2	MD-IPA	HMO	19120	12760	13440	15290	17270	22760
National Plans When You Use Preferred Providers								
255	GEHA Elevate	PPO-FEE	3550	2370	3050	5280	7500	16370
342	GEHA HDHP	HDHP	4340	1100	3300	5460	7190	12900
325	NALC CDHP	CDHP	3330	-180	2220	5660	8650	15420
402	Foreign Service	PPO-FEE	4710	3140	4260	5660	7200	10140
482	MHBP HDHP	HDHP	4620	680	3080	5860	8100	15080
132	Blue Cross FEP Blue Focus	PPO	3270	2180	3660	5870	8320	19180
112	Blue Cross Basic	PPO	5520	3680	4400	6320	8340	16680
475	APWU CDHP	CDHP	4290	460	2810	6330	9170	15860
252	GEHA Elevate Plus	PPO-FEE	4960	3310	4190	6610	9100	15310
422	Compass Rose	PPO-FEE	6980	4650	5220	6710	8230	11650
N62	Aetna Direct CDHP	CDHP	4750	1370	3770	6710	9540	15170
455	MHBP-Std	PPO-FEE	4730	3150	4380	6790	9590	15150
322	NALC-Hi	PPO-FEE	5250	3500	4810	6800	8950	12500
382	Rural Carrier	PPO-FEE	6160	4110	5010	6970	9080	14110
315	GEHA-Std	PPO-FEE	4290	2860	4180	7390	11040	15860
KM2	NALC Value Plan	PPO-FEE	2740	1630	4030	7410	10460	15030
445	SAMBA-Std	PPO-FEE	4850	3230	4700	7560	10890	15230
472	APWU-Hi	HMO	6990	4660	6050	8330	10690	17660
225	Aetna HealthFund HDHP	HDHP	6890	3000	5200	8730	11930	18400
105	Blue Cross-Std	PPO-FEE	8170	5450	6790	9060	11480	17450
312	GEHA-Hi	PPO-FEE	7860	5240	6580	9140	12100	15240
Z25	Aetna Advantage	PPO-FEE	3980	2650	5050	9240	13700	17650
415	MHBP Value Plan	PPO-FEE	3520	2350	5350	9470	15550	15550
442	SAMBA-Hi	PPO-FEE	10260	6850	8190	10460	12980	16850

[1] These are the premiums after tax savings, offset by savings accounts for plans that offer them. If you have no or low health-care costs with these plans, it can result in actual saving to you, which we indicate with a negative number.

Half-Time Employees Under Age 55		Self Only						
				Estimated yearly out-of-pocket costs, including premium and typical hospital, medical, drug, and dental bills near:				
Plan code	Plan name	Plan type	Published premium	No costs[1]	Low use: $1,000 or less	Average cost	High use: $30,000 or more	Limit to you
D.C. Area Plans When You Use Preferred Providers								
T71	Kaiser Prosper	HMO	2770	1850	2100	2860	5850	5850
E34	Kaiser-Std	HMO	4550	3040	3180	3730	6540	6540
B61	CareFirst HDHP	HDHP	4530	2120	2820	3760	8020	8020
V41	United HDHP	HDHP	4960	2560	3160	4050	7310	7310
Y81	United Choice Primary	HMO	4360	2910	3290	4240	10260	10260
E31	Kaiser-Hi	HMO	5900	3930	4030	4410	6180	6180
L91	United Choice Plus Advanced	PPO-FEE	4980	3320	3850	4420	6320	6320
AS1	United Choice Plus Primary	PPO-FEE	4880	3260	3640	4590	10610	10610
QQ4	Aetna Saver	HMO	4460	2980	3680	4800	9480	9480
B64	CareFirst Blue Value Plus	HMO-POS	5500	3670	4000	4900	9670	9670
JN4	Aetna Open Access Basic	HMO	5690	3800	4060	5120	9800	9800
F51	Aetna HealthFund CDHP	CDHP	7260	3850	4450	5330	9850	9850
LR1	United Choice Open Access	HMO	6680	4460	4650	5380	9460	9460
2G4	CareFirst-Std	HMO-POS	7680	5130	5270	6040	10130	10130
F54	Aetna Value Plan	PPO-FEE	7560	5040	5670	6570	11040	11040
JP1	MD-IPA	HMO	8960	5980	6110	6790	10570	10980
JN1	Aetna Open Access-Hi	HMO	11840	7890	7960	8510	11330	12890
National Plans When You Use Preferred Providers								
324	NALC CDHP	CDHP	3550	1170	1870	3030	8460	8970
254	GEHA Elevate	PPO-FEE	3170	2110	2260	3130	9090	9110
341	GEHA HDHP	HDHP	4110	1840	2440	3310	6880	7740
KM1	NALC Value Plan	PPO-FEE	2910	1840	2540	3660	8540	8540
474	APWU CDHP	CDHP	4530	1820	2490	3700	8730	9520
131	Blue Cross FEP Blue Focus	PPO	3450	2300	2910	3730	10270	10800
481	MHBP HDHP	HDHP	4970	2110	2810	3870	7810	9310
N61	Aetna Direct CDHP	CDHP	4710	2240	2940	4020	9140	9140
401	Foreign Service	PPO-FEE	4760	3170	3390	4020	7060	8170
314	GEHA-Std	PPO-FEE	4070	2720	3200	4200	9220	9220
111	Blue Cross Basic	PPO	5210	3480	3590	4330	8220	9980
251	GEHA Elevate Plus	PPO-FEE	5140	3430	3650	4490	9300	9430
414	MHBP Value Plan	PPO-FEE	3640	2430	2990	4540	9030	9030
Z24	Aetna Advantage	PPO-FEE	3750	2500	3200	4570	10000	10000
421	Compass Rose	PPO-FEE	5940	3960	4100	4630	7590	8960
454	MHBP-Std	PPO-FEE	5090	3390	3780	4670	9390	9390
321	NALC-Hi	PPO-FEE	5740	3830	4290	4990	9060	10430
444	SAMBA-Std	PPO-FEE	5310	3540	4060	5000	9540	9540
311	GEHA-Hi	PPO-FEE	5910	3940	4460	5220	8940	8940
471	APWU-Hi	HMO	5950	3970	4490	5220	9750	10470
381	Rural Carrier	PPO-FEE	6580	4390	4630	5330	9390	9390
224	Aetna HealthFund HDHP	HDHP	6710	3670	4270	5530	11370	11370
104	Blue Cross-Std	PPO-FEE	6500	4330	4770	5550	10180	10330
441	SAMBA-Hi	PPO-FEE	7310	4880	5350	6130	9880	9880

[1] These are the premiums after tax savings, offset by savings accounts for plans that offer them. If you have no or low health-care costs with these plans, it can result in actual saving to you, which we indicate with a negative number.

Half-Time Employees Under Age 55		Self Plus One					
		Plan type	Published premium	Estimated yearly out-of-pocket costs, including premium and typical hospital, medical, drug, and dental bills near:			
Plan code	Plan name			No costs[1]	Low use: $3,000 or less	Average cost	High use: $30,000 or more	Limit to you

Plan code	Plan name	Plan type	Published premium	No costs[1]	Low use: $3,000 or less	Average cost	High use: $30,000 or more	Limit to you
D.C. Area Plans When You Use Preferred Providers								
T73	Kaiser Prosper	HMO	6500	4340	5320	6300	10080	12340
B63	CareFirst HDHP	HDHP	9060	4250	6650	7330	11200	16050
E36	Kaiser-Std	HMO	10470	6990	7550	8270	10900	13990
Y83	United Choice Primary	HMO	9370	6250	7530	8600	13120	20950
V43	United HDHP	HDHP	10670	5620	7820	8780	13550	13970
L93	United Choice Plus Advanced	PPO-FEE	9960	6640	8150	8870	12640	12640
AS3	United Choice Plus Primary	PPO-FEE	10500	7000	8280	9350	13870	21700
B66	CareFirst Blue Value Plus	HMO-POS	10850	7240	8390	9350	13440	19240
QQ6	Aetna Saver	HMO	9380	6260	8660	9810	16180	19260
E33	Kaiser-Hi	HMO	14060	9380	9810	10240	11900	13880
JN6	Aetna Open Access Basic	HMO	11830	7890	8890	10320	15540	19890
LR3	United Choice Open Access	HMO	14390	9600	10420	11260	14750	19600
2G6	CareFirst-Std	HMO-POS	14910	9950	10690	11420	14240	19950
F53	Aetna HealthFund CDHP	CDHP	16770	9180	11080	12070	16820	21180
JP3	MD-IPA	HMO	16900	11270	11950	12710	15780	21270
F56	Aetna Value Plan	PPO-FEE	17310	11540	13200	14290	18950	23540
JN3	Aetna Open Access-Hi	HMO	26610	17750	18270	18860	21130	27750
National Plans When You Use Preferred Providers								
256	GEHA Elevate	PPO-FEE	7290	4860	5540	6450	9990	18860
326	NALC CDHP	CDHP	7840	2830	5230	6520	11660	18430
343	GEHA HDHP	HDHP	8830	4090	6290	6970	10180	15890
133	Blue Cross FEP Blue Focus	PPO	7430	4950	6430	7190	11090	21950
KM3	NALC Value Plan	PPO-FEE	6430	4090	6490	7760	12920	17490
476	APWU CDHP	CDHP	9840	4160	6510	7880	12870	19560
483	MHBP HDHP	HDHP	10990	4930	7330	8340	12350	19330
N63	Aetna Direct CDHP	CDHP	10330	5090	7490	8480	13260	18890
316	GEHA-Std	PPO-FEE	8760	5840	7160	8530	14020	18840
403	Foreign Service	PPO-FEE	11640	7770	8890	9310	11830	14770
113	Blue Cross Basic	PPO	11920	7950	8670	9450	12610	20950
Z26	Aetna Advantage	PPO-FEE	8250	5500	7900	9570	16550	20500
253	GEHA Elevate Plus	PPO-FEE	11570	7710	8590	9600	13500	19710
423	Compass Rose	PPO-FEE	13260	8840	9410	10020	12420	15840
416	MHBP Value Plan	PPO-FEE	8620	5750	8750	10110	18950	18950
456	MHBP-Std	PPO-FEE	11910	7950	9180	10130	14390	19950
446	SAMBA-Std	PPO-FEE	11460	7650	9120	10270	15310	19650
473	APWU-Hi	HMO	12360	8240	9630	10480	14270	21240
383	Rural Carrier	PPO-FEE	13250	8840	9740	10560	13810	18840
323	NALC-Hi	PPO-FEE	12910	8610	9920	10650	14060	17610
313	GEHA-Hi	PPO-FEE	13180	8790	10130	11180	15650	18790
226	Aetna HealthFund HDHP	HDHP	14570	8120	10320	11680	17050	23520
106	Blue Cross-Std	PPO-FEE	14350	9570	10910	11740	15600	21570
443	SAMBA-Hi	PPO-FEE	16270	10850	12190	13070	16980	20850

[1] These are the premiums after tax savings, offset by savings accounts for plans that offer them. If you have no or low health-care costs with these plans, it can result in actual saving to you, which we indicate with a negative number.

Half-Time Employees Under Age 55		Family of Three						
				Estimated yearly out-of-pocket costs, including premium and typical hospital, medical, drug, and dental bills near:				
		Plan type	Published premium	No costs[1]	Low use: $1,000 or less	Average cost	High use: $30,000 or more	Limit to you
Plan code	Plan name							

D.C. Area Plans When You Use Preferred Providers

Plan code	Plan name	Plan type	Published premium	No costs[1]	Low use: $1,000 or less	Average cost	High use: $30,000 or more	Limit to you
T72	Kaiser Prosper	HMO	7880	5260	6240	7510	11000	13260
E35	Kaiser-Std	HMO	10470	6990	7550	8470	10900	13990
B62	CareFirst HDHP	HDHP	10770	5380	7780	8820	12330	17180
Y82	United Choice Primary	HMO	10310	6880	8160	9550	13750	21580
V42	United HDHP	HDHP	11360	6070	8270	9620	14000	14420
E32	Kaiser-Hi	HMO	13420	8950	9380	9940	11470	13450
AS2	United Choice Plus Primary	PPO-FEE	11550	7700	8980	10370	14570	22400
L92	United Choice Plus Advanced	PPO-FEE	11900	7940	9450	10440	13940	13940
QQ5	Aetna Saver	HMO	10220	6810	9210	10810	16730	19810
B65	CareFirst Blue Value Plus	HMO-POS	13170	8780	9930	11180	14980	20780
JN5	Aetna Open Access Basic	HMO	12840	8570	9570	11360	16220	20570
F52	Aetna HealthFund CDHP	CDHP	16360	8910	10810	12150	16550	20910
LR2	United Choice Open Access	HMO	15920	10620	11440	12520	15770	20620
2G5	CareFirst-Std	HMO-POS	18360	12240	12980	13930	16530	22240
F55	Aetna Value Plan	PPO-FEE	17140	11440	13100	14530	18850	23440
JN2	Aetna Open Access-Hi	HMO	26300	17540	18060	18830	20920	27540
JP2	MD-IPA	HMO	26590	17730	18410	19380	22240	27730

National Plans When You Use Preferred Providers

Plan code	Plan name	Plan type	Published premium	No costs[1]	Low use: $1,000 or less	Average cost	High use: $30,000 or more	Limit to you
325	NALC CDHP	CDHP	8330	3160	5560	7300	11990	18760
255	GEHA Elevate	PPO-FEE	8870	5920	6600	7750	11050	19920
132	Blue Cross FEP Blue Focus	PPO	8170	5450	6930	7970	11590	22450
KM2	NALC Value Plan	PPO-FEE	6840	4360	6760	8480	13190	17760
342	GEHA HDHP	HDHP	10850	5440	7640	8650	11530	17240
475	APWU CDHP	CDHP	10730	4760	7110	8940	13470	20160
482	MHBP HDHP	HDHP	11540	5300	7700	9110	12720	19700
402	Foreign Service	PPO-FEE	11770	7850	8970	9590	11910	14850
N62	Aetna Direct CDHP	CDHP	11880	6130	8530	9930	14300	19930
315	GEHA-Std	PPO-FEE	10720	7150	8470	10200	15330	20150
455	MHBP-Std	PPO-FEE	11820	7880	9110	10350	14320	19880
112	Blue Cross Basic	PPO	12980	8660	9380	10390	13320	21660
252	GEHA Elevate Plus	PPO-FEE	12390	8260	9140	10430	14050	20260
322	NALC-Hi	PPO-FEE	12720	8480	9790	10780	13930	17480
415	MHBP Value Plan	PPO-FEE	8790	5860	8860	10810	19060	19060
422	Compass Rose	PPO-FEE	14440	9630	10200	10980	13210	16630
445	SAMBA-Std	PPO-FEE	12110	8080	9550	11040	15740	20080
382	Rural Carrier	PPO-FEE	13620	9090	9990	11040	14060	19090
Z25	Aetna Advantage	PPO-FEE	9940	6630	9030	11230	17680	21630
225	Aetna HealthFund HDHP	HDHP	14360	7970	10170	11990	16900	23370
472	APWU-Hi	HMO	14450	9640	11030	12160	15670	22640
105	Blue Cross-Std	PPO-FEE	15630	10430	11770	12890	16460	22430
312	GEHA-Hi	PPO-FEE	15320	10220	11560	12920	17080	20220
442	SAMBA-Hi	PPO-FEE	17730	11820	13160	14320	17950	21820

[1] These are the premiums after tax savings, offset by savings accounts for plans that offer them. If you have no or low health-care costs with these plans, it can result in actual saving to you, which we indicate with a negative number.

Persons Under Age 55 Who Pay Full Premiums		Self Only						
		Plan type	Published premium	Estimated yearly out-of-pocket costs, including premium and typical hospital, medical, drug, and dental bills near:				
Plan code	Plan name			No costs[1]	Low use: $3,000 or less	Average cost	High use: $30,000 or more	Limit to you
D.C. Area Plans When You Use Preferred Providers								
T71	Kaiser Prosper	HMO	4430	4430	4680	5440	8430	8430
E34	Kaiser-Std	HMO	7290	7290	7430	7970	10790	10790
B61	CareFirst HDHP	HDHP	7250	6350	7050	7990	12250	12250
Y81	United Choice Primary	HMO	6980	6980	7360	8310	14330	14330
V41	United HDHP	HDHP	7940	7190	7790	8690	11940	11940
QQ4	Aetna Saver	HMO	7140	7140	7840	8960	13640	13640
L91	United Choice Plus Advanced	PPO-FEE	7970	7970	8500	9070	10970	10970
AS1	United Choice Plus Primary	PPO-FEE	7810	7810	8190	9150	15160	15160
E31	Kaiser-Hi	HMO	9080	9080	9180	9550	11330	11330
B64	CareFirst Blue Value Plus	HMO-POS	8680	8680	9010	9920	14680	14680
JN4	Aetna Open Access Basic	HMO	8870	8870	9130	10190	14870	14870
LR1	United Choice Open Access	HMO	9870	9870	10060	10790	14870	14870
F51	Aetna HealthFund CDHP	CDHP	10450	9450	10050	10930	15450	15450
2G4	CareFirst-Std	HMO-POS	10870	10870	11010	11780	15870	15870
F54	Aetna Value Plan	PPO-FEE	10750	10750	11380	12270	16750	16750
JP1	MD-IPA	HMO	12140	12140	12270	12950	16730	17140
JN1	Aetna Open Access-Hi	HMO	15020	15020	15090	15650	18460	20020
National Plans When You Use Preferred Providers								
254	GEHA Elevate	PPO-FEE	5070	5070	5220	6080	12050	12070
324	NALC CDHP	CDHP	5680	4480	5180	6340	11770	12280
KM1	NALC Value Plan	PPO-FEE	4660	4560	5260	6390	11260	11260
131	Blue Cross FEP Blue Focus	PPO	5530	5530	6140	6960	13500	14030
341	GEHA HDHP	HDHP	6570	5670	6270	7140	10710	11570
474	APWU CDHP	CDHP	7240	6040	6710	7930	12950	13740
414	MHBP Value Plan	PPO-FEE	5820	5820	6380	7940	12420	12420
314	GEHA-Std	PPO-FEE	6520	6520	7000	8000	13020	13020
Z24	Aetna Advantage	PPO-FEE	6000	6000	6700	8070	13500	13500
N61	Aetna Direct CDHP	CDHP	7540	6640	7340	8420	13540	13540
401	Foreign Service	PPO-FEE	7610	7610	7830	8460	11500	12610
481	MHBP HDHP	HDHP	7950	6750	7450	8510	12450	13950
111	Blue Cross Basic	PPO	8340	8340	8450	9190	13080	14840
251	GEHA Elevate Plus	PPO-FEE	8230	8230	8450	9290	14100	14230
454	MHBP-Std	PPO-FEE	8140	8140	8530	9420	14140	14140
421	Compass Rose	PPO-FEE	9130	9130	9270	9810	12760	14130
444	SAMBA-Std	PPO-FEE	8500	8500	9020	9960	14500	14500
321	NALC-Hi	PPO-FEE	8920	8920	9380	10080	14150	15520
311	GEHA-Hi	PPO-FEE	9090	9090	9610	10370	14090	14090
471	APWU-Hi	HMO	9130	9130	9650	10380	14910	15630
381	Rural Carrier	PPO-FEE	9770	9770	10010	10710	14770	14770
104	Blue Cross-Std	PPO-FEE	9680	9680	10120	10900	15530	15680
224	Aetna HealthFund HDHP	HDHP	9890	9090	9690	10950	16790	16790
441	SAMBA-Hi	PPO-FEE	10500	10500	10970	11750	15500	15500

[1] These are the premiums after tax savings, offset by savings accounts for plans that offer them. If you have no or low health-care costs with these plans, it can result in actual saving to you, which we indicate with a negative number.

Persons Under Age 55 Who Pay Full Premiums		Self Plus One						
				Estimated yearly out-of-pocket costs, including premium and typical hospital, medical, drug, and dental bills near:				
		Plan type	Published premium	No costs[1]	Low use: $3,000 or less	Average cost	High use: $30,000 or more	Limit to you
Plan code	Plan name							
D.C. Area Plans When You Use Preferred Providers								
T73	Kaiser Prosper	HMO	10400	10400	11380	12360	16140	18400
B63	CareFirst HDHP	HDHP	14500	12700	15100	15780	19650	24500
Y83	United Choice Primary	HMO	15000	15000	16280	17350	21870	29700
E36	Kaiser-Std	HMO	16760	16760	17320	18040	20670	23760
L93	United Choice Plus Advanced	PPO-FEE	15930	15930	17440	18160	21930	21930
QQ6	Aetna Saver	HMO	15010	15010	17410	18560	24930	28010
V43	United HDHP	HDHP	17070	15570	17770	18730	23500	23920
AS3	United Choice Plus Primary	PPO-FEE	16790	16790	18070	19140	23660	31490
B66	CareFirst Blue Value Plus	HMO-POS	17370	17370	18520	19480	23570	29370
JN6	Aetna Open Access Basic	HMO	18650	18650	19650	21080	26300	30650
E33	Kaiser-Hi	HMO	20880	20880	21310	21740	23400	25380
LR3	United Choice Open Access	HMO	21210	21210	22030	22870	26360	31210
2G6	CareFirst-Std	HMO-POS	21730	21730	22470	23200	26020	31730
F53	Aetna HealthFund CDHP	CDHP	23590	21590	23490	24480	29230	33590
JP3	MD-IPA	HMO	23720	23720	24400	25160	28230	33720
F56	Aetna Value Plan	PPO-FEE	24130	24130	25790	26880	31540	36130
JN3	Aetna Open Access-Hi	HMO	33430	33430	33950	34540	36810	43430
National Plans When You Use Preferred Providers								
256	GEHA Elevate	PPO-FEE	11660	11660	12340	13250	16790	25660
KM3	NALC Value Plan	PPO-FEE	10290	10090	12490	13760	18920	23490
326	NALC CDHP	CDHP	12540	10140	12540	13830	18970	25740
133	Blue Cross FEP Blue Focus	PPO	11880	11880	13360	14120	18020	28880
343	GEHA HDHP	HDHP	14130	12330	14530	15210	18420	24130
316	GEHA-Std	PPO-FEE	14010	14010	15330	16700	22190	27010
476	APWU CDHP	CDHP	15740	13340	15690	17060	22050	28740
Z26	Aetna Advantage	PPO-FEE	13200	13200	15600	17270	24250	28200
N63	Aetna Direct CDHP	CDHP	16530	14730	17130	18120	22900	28530
416	MHBP Value Plan	PPO-FEE	13790	13790	16790	18150	26990	26990
483	MHBP HDHP	HDHP	17580	15180	17580	18590	22600	29580
403	Foreign Service	PPO-FEE	18460	18460	19580	20000	22520	25460
113	Blue Cross Basic	PPO	18740	18740	19460	20240	23400	31740
253	GEHA Elevate Plus	PPO-FEE	18390	18390	19270	20280	24180	30390
446	SAMBA-Std	PPO-FEE	18280	18280	19750	20900	25940	30280
456	MHBP-Std	PPO-FEE	18730	18730	19960	20910	25170	30730
423	Compass Rose	PPO-FEE	20080	20080	20650	21260	23660	27080
473	APWU-Hi	HMO	19180	19180	20570	21420	25210	32180
323	NALC-Hi	PPO-FEE	19730	19730	21040	21770	25180	28730
383	Rural Carrier	PPO-FEE	20080	20080	20980	21800	25050	30080
313	GEHA-Hi	PPO-FEE	20000	20000	21340	22390	26860	30000
106	Blue Cross-Std	PPO-FEE	21170	21170	22510	23340	27200	33170
226	Aetna HealthFund HDHP	HDHP	21390	19790	21990	23350	28720	35190
443	SAMBA-Hi	PPO-FEE	23090	23090	24430	25310	29220	33090

[1] These are the premiums after tax savings, offset by savings accounts for plans that offer them. If you have no or low health-care costs with these plans, it can result in actual saving to you, which we indicate with a negative number.

Persons Under Age 55 Who Pay Full Premiums		Family of Three						
		Plan type	Published premium	Estimated yearly out-of-pocket costs, including premium and typical hospital, medical, drug, and dental bills near:				
Plan code	Plan name			No costs[1]	Low use: $1,000 or less	Average cost	High use: $30,000 or more	Limit to you
D.C. Area Plans When You Use Preferred Providers								
T72	Kaiser Prosper	HMO	12620	12620	13600	14860	18360	20620
E35	Kaiser-Std	HMO	16760	16760	17320	18230	20670	23760
B62	CareFirst HDHP	HDHP	17230	15430	17830	18870	22380	27230
Y82	United Choice Primary	HMO	16500	16500	17780	19170	23370	31200
V42	United HDHP	HDHP	18170	16670	18870	20220	24600	25020
QQ5	Aetna Saver	HMO	16350	16350	18750	20340	26270	29350
AS2	United Choice Plus Primary	PPO-FEE	18470	18470	19750	21140	25340	33170
L92	United Choice Plus Advanced	PPO-FEE	19040	19040	20550	21540	25040	25040
E32	Kaiser-Hi	HMO	20880	20880	21310	21870	23400	25380
B65	CareFirst Blue Value Plus	HMO-POS	20630	20630	21780	23040	26830	32630
JN5	Aetna Open Access Basic	HMO	20310	20310	21310	23090	27960	32310
F52	Aetna HealthFund CDHP	CDHP	23820	21820	23720	25070	29460	33820
LR2	United Choice Open Access	HMO	23380	23380	24200	25280	28530	33380
2G5	CareFirst-Std	HMO-POS	25820	25820	26560	27500	30110	35820
F55	Aetna Value Plan	PPO-FEE	24610	24610	26270	27700	32020	36610
JN2	Aetna Open Access-Hi	HMO	33760	33760	34280	35050	37140	43760
JP2	MD-IPA	HMO	34050	34050	34730	35710	38560	44050
National Plans When You Use Preferred Providers								
T72	Kaiser Prosper	HMO	12620	12620	13600	14860	18360	20620
E35	Kaiser-Std	HMO	16760	16760	17320	18230	20670	23760
B62	CareFirst HDHP	HDHP	17230	15430	17830	18870	22380	27230
Y82	United Choice Primary	HMO	16500	16500	17780	19170	23370	31200
V42	United HDHP	HDHP	18170	16670	18870	20220	24600	25020
QQ5	Aetna Saver	HMO	16350	16350	18750	20340	26270	29350
AS2	United Choice Plus Primary	PPO-FEE	18470	18470	19750	21140	25340	33170
L92	United Choice Plus Advanced	PPO-FEE	19040	19040	20550	21540	25040	25040
E32	Kaiser-Hi	HMO	20880	20880	21310	21870	23400	25380
B65	CareFirst Blue Value Plus	HMO-POS	20630	20630	21780	23040	26830	32630
JN5	Aetna Open Access Basic	HMO	20310	20310	21310	23090	27960	32310
F52	Aetna HealthFund CDHP	CDHP	23820	21820	23720	25070	29460	33820
LR2	United Choice Open Access	HMO	23380	23380	24200	25280	28530	33380
2G5	CareFirst-Std	HMO-POS	25820	25820	26560	27500	30110	35820
F55	Aetna Value Plan	PPO-FEE	24610	24610	26270	27700	32020	36610
JN2	Aetna Open Access-Hi	HMO	33760	33760	34280	35050	37140	43760
JP2	MD-IPA	HMO	34050	34050	34730	35710	38560	44050
382	Rural Carrier	PPO-FEE	21090	21090	21990	23030	26060	31090
422	Compass Rose	PPO-FEE	21900	21900	22470	23250	25480	28900
225	Aetna HealthFund HDHP	HDHP	21820	20220	22420	24240	29150	35620
472	APWU-Hi	HMO	21920	21920	23310	24440	27950	34920
312	GEHA-Hi	PPO-FEE	22790	22790	24130	25490	29650	32790
105	Blue Cross-Std	PPO-FEE	23090	23090	24430	25550	29120	35090
442	SAMBA-Hi	PPO-FEE	25190	25190	26530	27690	31320	35190

[1] These are the premiums after tax savings, offset by savings accounts for plans that offer them. If you have no or low health-care costs with these plans, it can result in actual saving to you, which we indicate with a negative number.

Chapter 4

Cost Comparisons and Advice for Annuitants

As explained in Chapter 2 "Comparing Plan Costs," we rate and compare health plans based on their likely cost to you, taking into account your pay system, employment or retirement status, family size, age, health status, location, and other factors. A key element of our ratings are estimates of likely out-of-pocket costs under each plan, based on actuarial estimates of the size and likelihood of low, average, and high spending for families of different sizes and ages. Our ratings also reflect varying premium levels and tax situations faced by different eligibility groups. For example, unlike employees, annuitants do not obtain "Premium Conversion" tax advantages.

Online *Guide* users see a summary cost comparison table for their group, and then have the option to look at tables providing more detailed cost comparisons. Readers of the printed *Guide* see both summary and detailed cost information for their comparison group for all national plans and local plans available in the DC area.

All of these comparisons take into account not only premiums and potential health care costs, but also plan features such as Health Savings Accounts, personal accounts, and Wellness benefits that involve cash rewards. We also include dental benefits and premiums, both for dental benefits built into some health plans and for the costs and benefits of standalone dental plans. For annuitants, our estimates and comparisons also take into account both Medicare benefits and Medicare premiums, depending on choices about Medicare enrollment. In summary, we provide a comprehensive set of financial comparisons that allow users to make "apple to apple" comparisons of costs for both premiums and likely health care expenses under each plan and across all plans for which they are eligible.

Very importantly, our comparisons take into account that some plans provide both a Medicare "wraparound" benefit and a fund that will pay part or most of the Medicare Part B premium. National plans that provide a complete wraparound for hospital and doctor costs and also reimburse a substantial part of the Part B premium cost include Aetna Advantage, APWU high option, Blue Cross Basic option, Compass Rose, GEHA High option, MHBP standard option, and Rural Carrier. Most Kaiser and many UnitedHealthcare and Humana plans offer substantial Part B premium rebates if you join their Medicare Advantage plans, as do many other plans around the country. The amounts these and some other plans pay is almost as high as the 2022 Part B premium and in some cases covers the entire premium cost. The plans with the highest Part B rebates do, however, require that you join their Medicare Advantage options. Those options are tailored to FEHB enrollees and all have rich benefit packages.

All of our calculations should be considered approximations that will be broadly accurate in the great majority of situations but that cannot provide precise predictions that cover every possible situation. What our calculations also do, therefore, is take into account the risks of ruinously high health care costs from an unexpected illness or accident and compare the maximum out-of-pocket and premium costs under each plan.

Using the Cost Comparison Tables for Annuitants

We provide rating comparisons for self-only, self plus one, and families of two for annuitants in the print Guide, and additionally for families of sizes three through five online. Comparisons include:

- **Annuitants without Medicare**.
- **Annuitants with Medicare Parts A and B who pay regular premium rates**. These tables include not only the FEHB premium, but also the Part B Medicare premium.
- **Annuitants with Medicare Parts A and B who pay higher "income-tested" rates** (online only).
- A**nnuitants who have only Part A of Medicare**, the hospital benefit. You can compare these with the preceding ratings to see how much you gain or lose by enrolling in Part B and paying the Part B premium.

There are many comparisons, but **only one cost comparison table applies to your current situation**. Of course, your situation may change if your family changes or if you change your Medicare decisions—and you can compare tables to see those differences. For example, if you are trying to decide whether to enroll in Medicare Part B or not, you can compare plans with or without this option—but be careful to read our advice on this decision, since there are important advantages to Part B enrollment that for most annuitants outweigh its premium costs.

By looking at the different columns in a table, you can find how you will come out under each plan if your expenses range from none to the maximum you could pay in a year. Very importantly for those with Medicare Part B, the "Published premium" column, as well as following columns, includes both FEHB and Part B premiums. These columns also credit you with the savings you gain from a Health Savings Account (HSA) or personal health care account or Health Reimbursement Arrangement (HRA) in plans that give you these benefits (annuitants get the HSA amount as an HRA contribution, as explained in our chapter on "Plan Types and Flexibility"). Personal care accounts and HRAs are the equivalent of a reduction in premium. If you don't spend that account at the end of the year you will have a bank balance in that amount that carries over to the next year. Therefore, the "No costs" column includes your yearly premium adjusted, as pertinent, for the Medicare Part B Premium and HSA or HRA account. These will be your only out-of-pocket costs if you have no medical bills. We rank the plans in order of average cost to emphasize the importance of each plan's treatment of "average" expenses for a family of a particular size and type.

You begin by making profile choices to find the table that relates to families of your age, premium category, and size. Unless you know something to the contrary, you should expect average expenses in the coming year. The plans that are likely to cost families the least have the lowest dollar figures in this column. But do not choose the highest-ranked plan until you consider whether there is some reason the average column does not apply to you or your family.

In your cost table you will notice that differences among closely ranked plans are often very small. Differences of $100 or $200 are not important. A different mix of bills from those we use to compare plans could overcome these. Differences that are much higher, however, reflect significant variations in how expensively the plans handle most cases.

Notice that our tables show that most of the higher-ranked plans will save you money in every situation—whether your expenses are high or low—compared to the plans ranked lower in each group on your comparison. You can also see that many HMOs and CDHP and HDHP plans will save you hundreds of dollars compared to most national PPO plans, but that many will not.

Preferred Providers and Annuitants Over Age 65

We rate plan costs based on the assumption that you will always or almost always want to use preferred providers, also known as "staying in the network". However, network problems largely disappear if you have Medicare Parts A and B, since most of the national plans waive doctor and hospital cost-sharing whether you obtain care in or out of the network. Even in HMOs that don't waive these costs, you can use Medicare to go out of network and pay only the 20% coinsurance under Medicare. Therefore, **for retirees who participate in Medicare Parts A and B preferred provider restrictions largely disappear when enrolled in almost all plans.** You can go to any hospital and almost any doctor without losing coverage. Moreover, persons over age 65 are by law guaranteed a Medicare rate "limiting charge" rate when using any Medicare-participating physician, whether or not in the plan network, and can use all doctors who have not opted out of Medicare without fearing very high charges, even while enrolled in plans that offer no reduced cost sharing for those with Part B of Medicare.

You should be aware, however, that there are many complexities. For example, some doctors do not accept new Medicare patients, even if the patients are in a plan whose network includes these doctors. Some doctors accept no insurance of any kind. And still others will accept new Medicare patients but do not "take assignment" and have their patients pay in full and submit Medicare claims. In such cases the 15% higher Medicare rate called the "limiting charge" will still apply. The great majority of doctors do not present such problems, so your best option will often be to avoid those who do.

Savings for Couples Using Self Only Enrollments

For a husband and wife who are **both** Federal annuitants and who have no dependent children, it is possible to save on premium costs by enrolling separately as self only rather than together as self plus one. The premiums for two self only enrollments are usually less than the self plus one premium. This option can be particularly valuable in cases where each spouse prefers a different plan, perhaps because no one plan covers both family physicians in its network.

Be cautious, however, because each person will have to meet a separate catastrophic limit rather than the single limit that applies to self plus one. Most plans do not increase your risk because they include individual limits of about half the amount of the overall self plus one or family limit. Moreover, while you are still technically subject to meeting two catastrophic limits if you both enroll self-only, the fee structure of most HMOs makes it almost impossible to reach those limits. Finally, if two Federal annuitants both have Medicare Parts A and B your risk exposure is low in all plans, and very low in plans that offer a Part B wrap-around. For these reasons, you are almost always safe with two self only enrollments. But do check the plan brochure's catastrophic limits carefully before making this decision.

However, couples in which one is a federal annuitant and the other still federally employed should almost never use two self only enrollments. It is always less expensive for the employed spouse to enroll in a self plus one or family option and get about a one-third savings from Premium Conversion.

You Can Keep Flexibility Only at a Price

Good arguments for paying the Medicare Part B premium are to preserve your choices over time, as both FEHB and Medicare evolve, to get you low costs for providers who are not in your plan network, and to reduce cost-sharing. However, to use this choice choose a plan designed to keep these costs low.

Savings for Couples or Single Parents with One Child Under Self Plus One Enrollment

Married couples with no children to cover, and single parents with one child to cover, can enroll as self plus one rather than as a family and, depending on the plan chosen, usually save two or three hundred dollars a year in premium costs, and often more. Since the benefits of the plan are identical (or in a few cases even better) in the self plus one plan, this is a clear saving. You should use our comparison table for self plus one with adults of your age to make your initial plan comparison.

In addition to the regular Open Season, where you can switch plans or enrollment category or both, OPM allows annuitants to switch "down" to from family to self plus one at any time during the year. This can only be used for the plan you are already enrolled in, not to switch plans, unless there is a "qualifying life event" such as death of family member or divorce.

Annuitants Without Medicare Part B

Older persons, on average, incur much higher expenses than do younger persons. Children's expenses average about $2,000 a year, and those of an adult below 55 years of age about $6,000 per year. Expenses for people aged 65 and older average over $12,000 per year. Of course, most enrollees have much lower bills. The average cost is pulled up by a small fraction that has much higher bills, a fraction that rises sharply with age. To reflect these large differences, our cost tables for annuitants compare plans on the basis of expenses faced by older persons. We provide separate results for annuitants aged 55 to 64, and over age 65, as their expense profiles are quite different. In either age group, the plans with better coverage tend to rank higher despite bigger premiums. In using our print comparisons, a safe approach for couples in which only one member has Medicare coverage is to use the cost comparisons for retirees without Medicare (in the online Guide we provide specific estimates for these situations).

Once you reach age 65, a special rule applies whether or not you enroll in Medicare Part B. **It is illegal for doctors who have not opted out entirely from Medicare to charge patients covered by Medicare more than a "limiting charge." This restriction applies to all FEHB annuitants over age 65, whether or not they have Medicare.** Under this provision, you will not be exposed to high charges that neither Medicare nor your FEHB plan recognizes as reasonable. You do **not** have to sign up for Medicare Part B to get this guarantee. Therefore, unlike employees, if you are over 65 you can use non-preferred providers without fear of being charged substantially more than the plan will recognize as reasonable. You also usually have to pay higher deductibles and coinsurance if the provider is not in your plan's network.

Annuitants with Medicare Part A or Parts A and B

Obviously, if Medicare covers you, the rankings in our regular cost comparisons do not apply, since Medicare is "primary" for retirees and will pay most expenses. Therefore, we present tables for single persons and couples with either both Parts A and B of Medicare, or Part A only. Since couples can choose either self plus one or family enrollments, we provide comparisons for both. Although these tables are presented in terms of preferred providers, it is important to understand that the main advantage of preferred providers, guaranteed low rates, is available once you reach age 65 from almost any doctor you might use, whether or not you have Medicare Part B. The online *Guide* also presents a comparison for couples in which one spouse does not have Medicare and the other has both Parts A and B. Each comparison takes into account:

Huge Annuitant Cost Saving

Annuitants with Medicare Parts A and B can suspend their FEHBP enrollment, join a Medicare Advantage plan, and pay only the Medicare premium. They can reenroll in an FEHBP plan in the future without penalty, and in the meantime enjoy good catastrophic protection, have low copays, and save thousands in premium costs.

- Premium costs for the FEHB plan and, in the "both Part A and B" tables, for Medicare Part B (Part A has no premium for Federal annuitants who retired after 1983);
- Each plan's coverage for services, such as prescription drugs and dental care, that are not covered by Medicare Parts A and B; and
- Elimination of all or most hospital and medical cost-sharing offered by many plans for Medicare Part A and B enrollees.

Should You Stay Enrolled in the FEHB Program After Age 65?

You could drop the FEHB program once you enroll in Parts A and B. But this would be a bad decision. Medicare Part B requires you to pay 20 percent of the cost of doctors' fees, and deductibles, with no upper limit. The Medicare Part A hospital deductible is about $1,500 and the Part B medical deductible is over $200. To obtain Medicare coverage roughly comparable to FEHB plans you would have to pay a Part B premium of over $150 a month, or over $1,900 for the year (many pay more, as discussed below), and a Part D premium for drug coverage of about $30 a month and $400 for the year (there is a wide range of prescription drug premiums, some lower and some higher). The total

Continues on page 52

Annuitants Age 55 to 64 Without Medicare		Self Only						
		Plan type	Published premium	Estimated yearly out-of-pocket costs, including premium and typical hospital, medical, drug, and dental bills near:				
Plan code	Plan name			No costs[1]	Low use: $3,000 or less	Average cost	High use: $30,000 or more	Limit to you
D.C. Area Plans When You Use Preferred Providers								
T71	Kaiser Prosper	HMO	1110	1110	1360	2670	5110	5110
E34	Kaiser-Std	HMO	1820	1820	1960	2910	5320	5320
B61	CareFirst HDHP	HDHP	1810	910	1610	3280	6810	6810
V41	United HDHP	HDHP	1990	1240	1840	3390	5990	5990
E31	Kaiser-Hi	HMO	2710	2710	2810	3460	4960	4960
L91	United Choice Plus Advanced	PPO-FEE	1990	1990	2520	3540	4990	4990
Y81	United Choice Primary	HMO	1740	1740	2120	3810	9090	9090
AS1	United Choice Plus Primary	PPO-FEE	1950	1950	2330	4020	9300	9300
B64	CareFirst Blue Value Plus	HMO-POS	2320	2320	2650	4220	8320	8320
QQ4	Aetna Saver	HMO	1790	1790	2490	4450	8290	8290
JN4	Aetna Open Access Basic	HMO	2510	2510	2770	4590	8510	8510
LR1	United Choice Open Access	HMO	3500	3500	3690	4960	8500	8500
F51	Aetna HealthFund CDHP	CDHP	4080	3080	3680	5250	9080	9080
2G4	CareFirst-Std	HMO-POS	4500	4500	4640	5960	9500	9500
F54	Aetna Value Plan	PPO-FEE	4380	4380	5010	6620	10380	10380
JP1	MD-IPA	HMO	5780	5780	5910	7080	10370	10780
JN1	Aetna Open Access-Hi	HMO	8650	8650	8720	9690	12090	13650
National Plans When You Use Preferred Providers								
341	GEHA HDHP	HDHP	1640	740	1340	2870	5780	6640
254	GEHA Elevate	PPO-FEE	1270	1270	1420	2940	8250	8270
324	NALC CDHP	CDHP	1420	220	920	2960	7510	8020
401	Foreign Service	PPO-FEE	1900	1900	2120	3220	5790	6900
481	MHBP HDHP	HDHP	1990	790	1490	3340	6490	7990
474	APWU CDHP	CDHP	1810	610	1280	3380	7520	8310
111	Blue Cross Basic	PPO	2080	2080	2190	3470	6820	8580
131	Blue Cross FEP Blue Focus	PPO	1380	1380	1990	3520	9350	9880
N61	Aetna Direct CDHP	CDHP	1880	980	1680	3590	7880	7880
KM1	NALC Value Plan	PPO-FEE	1170	1070	1770	3720	7770	7770
251	GEHA Elevate Plus	PPO-FEE	2060	2060	2280	3740	7930	8060
421	Compass Rose	PPO-FEE	2760	2760	2900	3840	6390	7760
314	GEHA-Std	PPO-FEE	1630	1630	2110	3870	8130	8130
454	MHBP-Std	PPO-FEE	2030	2030	2420	3990	8030	8030
321	NALC-Hi	PPO-FEE	2560	2560	3020	4290	7790	9160
444	SAMBA-Std	PPO-FEE	2130	2130	2650	4320	8130	8130
Z24	Aetna Advantage	PPO-FEE	1500	1500	2200	4580	9000	9000
311	GEHA-Hi	PPO-FEE	2730	2730	3250	4600	7730	7730
471	APWU-Hi	HMO	2770	2770	3290	4610	8550	9270
414	MHBP Value Plan	PPO-FEE	1460	1460	2020	4650	8060	8060
381	Rural Carrier	PPO-FEE	3400	3400	3640	4860	8400	8400
104	Blue Cross-Std	PPO-FEE	3310	3310	3750	5150	9160	9310
224	Aetna HealthFund HDHP	HDHP	3530	2730	3330	5520	10430	10430
441	SAMBA-Hi	PPO-FEE	4130	4130	4600	5980	9130	9130

[1] These are the premiums after tax savings, offset by savings accounts for plans that offer them. If you have no or low health-care costs with these plans, it can result in actual saving to you, which we indicate with a negative number.

Annuitants Age 55 to 64 Without Medicare				Self Plus One				
		Plan type	Published premium	Estimated yearly out-of-pocket costs, including premium and typical hospital, medical, drug, and dental bills near:				
Plan code	Plan name			No costs[1]	Low use: $3,000 or less	Average cost	High use: $30,000 or more	Limit to you
D.C. Area Plans When You Use Preferred Providers								
T73	Kaiser Prosper	HMO	2600	2600	3580	5700	8340	10600
E36	Kaiser-Std	HMO	4190	4190	4750	6280	8100	11190
B63	CareFirst HDHP	HDHP	3630	1830	4230	6310	8780	13630
L93	United Choice Plus Advanced	PPO-FEE	3980	3980	5490	7250	9980	9980
V43	United HDHP	HDHP	4270	2770	4970	7400	10700	11120
Y83	United Choice Primary	HMO	3750	3750	5030	7480	10620	18450
B66	CareFirst Blue Value Plus	HMO-POS	4340	4340	5490	7690	10540	16340
AS3	United Choice Plus Primary	PPO-FEE	4200	4200	5480	7930	11070	18900
E33	Kaiser-Hi	HMO	7240	7240	7670	8620	9760	11740
JN6	Aetna Open Access Basic	HMO	5010	5010	6010	8930	12660	17010
QQ6	Aetna Saver	HMO	3750	3750	6150	9110	13670	16750
LR3	United Choice Open Access	HMO	7570	7570	8390	10260	12720	17570
2G6	CareFirst-Std	HMO-POS	8090	8090	8830	10510	12380	18090
F53	Aetna HealthFund CDHP	CDHP	9950	7950	9850	12290	15590	19950
JP3	MD-IPA	HMO	10080	10080	10760	12430	14590	20080
F56	Aetna Value Plan	PPO-FEE	10490	10490	12150	14660	17900	22490
JN3	Aetna Open Access-Hi	HMO	19790	19790	20310	21630	23170	29790
National Plans When You Use Preferred Providers								
256	GEHA Elevate	PPO-FEE	2910	2910	3590	5600	8040	16910
343	GEHA HDHP	HDHP	3530	1730	3930	5870	7820	13530
326	NALC CDHP	CDHP	3130	730	3130	6240	9560	16330
133	Blue Cross FEP Blue Focus	PPO	2970	2970	4450	6430	9110	19970
483	MHBP HDHP	HDHP	4400	2000	4400	6920	9420	16400
476	APWU CDHP	CDHP	3940	1540	3890	7090	10250	16940
403	Foreign Service	PPO-FEE	4820	4820	5940	7180	8880	11820
N63	Aetna Direct CDHP	CDHP	4130	2330	4730	7370	10500	16130
113	Blue Cross Basic	PPO	5100	5100	5820	7550	9760	18100
316	GEHA-Std	PPO-FEE	3500	3500	4820	7730	11680	16500
253	GEHA Elevate Plus	PPO-FEE	4750	4750	5630	7820	10540	16750
KM3	NALC Value Plan	PPO-FEE	2570	2370	4770	7820	11200	15770
423	Compass Rose	PPO-FEE	6440	6440	7010	8350	10020	13440
456	MHBP-Std	PPO-FEE	5090	5090	6320	8490	11530	17090
446	SAMBA-Std	PPO-FEE	4640	4640	6110	8690	12300	16640
473	APWU-Hi	HMO	5540	5540	6930	8980	11570	18540
383	Rural Carrier	PPO-FEE	6430	6430	7330	9100	11400	16430
323	NALC-Hi	PPO-FEE	6090	6090	7400	9180	11540	15090
Z26	Aetna Advantage	PPO-FEE	3300	3300	5700	9490	14350	18300
313	GEHA-Hi	PPO-FEE	6360	6360	7700	10010	13220	16360
416	MHBP Value Plan	PPO-FEE	3450	3450	6450	10110	16650	16650
106	Blue Cross-Std	PPO-FEE	7530	7530	8870	10910	13560	19530
226	Aetna HealthFund HDHP	HDHP	7750	6150	8350	11550	15080	21550
443	SAMBA-Hi	PPO-FEE	9450	9450	10790	12830	15580	19450

[1] These are the premiums after tax savings, offset by savings accounts for plans that offer them. If you have no or low health-care costs with these plans, it can result in actual saving to you, which we indicate with a negative number.

Annuitants Age 55 to 64 Without Medicare		Family of Two						
				Estimated yearly out-of-pocket costs, including premium and typical hospital, medical, drug, and dental bills near:				
		Plan type	Published premium	No costs[1]	Low use: $3,000 or less	Average cost	High use: $30,000 or more	Limit to you
Plan code	Plan name							

D.C. Area Plans When You Use Preferred Providers

Plan code	Plan name	Plan type	Published premium	No costs[1]	Low use: $3,000 or less	Average cost	High use: $30,000 or more	Limit to you
T72	Kaiser Prosper	HMO	3150	3150	4130	6260	8890	11150
E35	Kaiser-Std	HMO	4190	4190	4750	6280	8100	11190
B62	CareFirst HDHP	HDHP	4310	2510	4910	6990	9460	14310
E32	Kaiser-Hi	HMO	5960	5960	6390	7330	8480	10460
V42	United HDHP	HDHP	4540	3040	5240	7670	10970	11390
Y82	United Choice Primary	HMO	4120	4120	5400	7850	10990	18820
L92	United Choice Plus Advanced	PPO-FEE	4760	4760	6270	8030	10760	10760
AS2	United Choice Plus Primary	PPO-FEE	4620	4620	5900	8340	11490	19320
B65	CareFirst Blue Value Plus	HMO-POS	5710	5710	6860	9060	11910	17710
JN5	Aetna Open Access Basic	HMO	5380	5380	6380	9300	13030	17380
QQ5	Aetna Saver	HMO	4090	4090	6490	9440	14010	17090
LR2	United Choice Open Access	HMO	8460	8460	9280	11150	13610	18460
F52	Aetna HealthFund CDHP	CDHP	8890	6890	8790	11230	14530	18890
2G5	CareFirst-Std	HMO-POS	10890	10890	11630	13310	15180	20890
F55	Aetna Value Plan	PPO-FEE	9680	9680	11340	13850	17090	21680
JN2	Aetna Open Access-Hi	HMO	18840	18840	19360	20670	22220	28840
JP2	MD-IPA	HMO	19120	19120	19800	21480	23630	29120

National Plans When You Use Preferred Providers

Plan code	Plan name	Plan type	Published premium	No costs[1]	Low use: $3,000 or less	Average cost	High use: $30,000 or more	Limit to you
255	GEHA Elevate	PPO-FEE	3550	3550	4230	6240	8680	17550
325	NALC CDHP	CDHP	3330	930	3330	6440	9760	16530
342	GEHA HDHP	HDHP	4340	2540	4740	6690	8630	14340
132	Blue Cross FEP Blue Focus	PPO	3270	3270	4750	6730	9410	20270
402	Foreign Service	PPO-FEE	4710	4710	5830	7070	8770	11710
482	MHBP HDHP	HDHP	4620	2220	4620	7130	9640	16620
475	APWU CDHP	CDHP	4290	1890	4240	7440	10600	17290
112	Blue Cross Basic	PPO	5520	5520	6240	7970	10180	18520
N62	Aetna Direct CDHP	CDHP	4750	2950	5350	7990	11120	16750
KM2	NALC Value Plan	PPO-FEE	2740	2540	4940	7990	11370	15940
252	GEHA Elevate Plus	PPO-FEE	4960	4960	5840	8030	10750	16960
455	MHBP-Std	PPO-FEE	4730	4730	5960	8130	11170	16730
322	NALC-Hi	PPO-FEE	5250	5250	6560	8340	10700	14250
315	GEHA-Std	PPO-FEE	4290	4290	5610	8510	12470	17290
382	Rural Carrier	PPO-FEE	6160	6160	7060	8830	11130	16160
445	SAMBA-Std	PPO-FEE	4850	4850	6320	8890	12510	16850
422	Compass Rose	PPO-FEE	6980	6980	7550	8890	10560	13980
Z25	Aetna Advantage	PPO-FEE	3980	3980	6380	10160	15030	18980
415	MHBP Value Plan	PPO-FEE	3520	3520	6520	10170	16720	16720
472	APWU-Hi	HMO	6990	6990	8380	10430	13020	19990
225	Aetna HealthFund HDHP	HDHP	6890	5290	7490	10690	14220	20690
312	GEHA-Hi	PPO-FEE	7860	7860	9200	11510	14720	17860
105	Blue Cross-Std	PPO-FEE	8170	8170	9510	11540	14200	20170
442	SAMBA-Hi	PPO-FEE	10260	10260	11600	13650	16390	20260

[1] These are the premiums after tax savings, offset by savings accounts for plans that offer them. If you have no or low health-care costs with these plans, it can result in actual saving to you, which we indicate with a negative number.

Annuitants Age 65 and Older with Medicare Part A Only		Self Only						
				Estimated yearly out-of-pocket costs, including premium and typical hospital, medical, drug, and dental bills near:				
		Plan type	Published premium	No costs[1]	Low use: $3,000 or less	Average cost	High use: $30,000 or more	Limit to you
Plan code	Plan name							
D.C. Area Plans When You Use Preferred Providers								
T71	Kaiser Prosper	HMO	1110	1110	1360	2670	5110	5110
E34	Kaiser-Std	HMO	1820	1820	1960	2910	5320	5320
B61	CareFirst HDHP	HDHP	1810	910	1610	3280	6050	6810
V41	United HDHP	HDHP	1990	1240	1840	3390	5990	5990
E31	Kaiser-Hi	HMO	2710	2710	2810	3460	4960	4960
L91	United Choice Plus Advanced	PPO-FEE	1990	1990	2520	3540	4990	4990
Y81	United Choice Primary	HMO	1740	1740	2120	3810	7660	9090
AS1	United Choice Plus Primary	PPO-FEE	1950	1950	2330	4020	7870	9300
B64	CareFirst Blue Value Plus	HMO-POS	2320	2320	2650	4220	7950	8320
QQ4	Aetna Saver	HMO	1790	1790	2490	4450	8290	8290
JN4	Aetna Open Access Basic	HMO	2510	2510	2770	4590	8510	8510
LR1	United Choice Open Access	HMO	3500	3500	3690	4960	8420	8500
F51	Aetna HealthFund CDHP	CDHP	4080	3080	3680	5250	9080	9080
2G4	CareFirst-Std	HMO-POS	4500	4500	4640	5960	8390	9500
F54	Aetna Value Plan	PPO-FEE	4380	4380	5010	6620	10380	10380
JP1	MD-IPA	HMO	5780	5780	5910	7080	10070	10780
JN1	Aetna Open Access-Hi	HMO	8650	8650	8720	9690	12090	13650
National Plans When You Use Preferred Providers								
341	GEHA HDHP	HDHP	1640	740	1340	2870	5300	6640
254	GEHA Elevate	PPO-FEE	1270	1270	1420	2940	5850	8270
324	NALC CDHP	CDHP	1420	220	920	2960	7030	8020
401	Foreign Service	PPO-FEE	1900	1900	2120	3220	5790	6900
481	MHBP HDHP	HDHP	1990	790	1490	3340	6340	7990
474	APWU CDHP	CDHP	1810	610	1280	3380	7160	8310
111	Blue Cross Basic	PPO	2080	2080	2190	3470	6470	8580
131	Blue Cross FEP Blue Focus	PPO	1380	1380	1990	3520	6470	9880
N61	Aetna Direct CDHP	CDHP	1880	980	1680	3590	7450	7880
KM1	NALC Value Plan	PPO-FEE	1170	1070	1770	3720	7770	7770
251	GEHA Elevate Plus	PPO-FEE	2060	2060	2280	3740	7430	8060
421	Compass Rose	PPO-FEE	2760	2760	2900	3840	6190	7760
314	GEHA-Std	PPO-FEE	1630	1630	2110	3870	8130	8130
454	MHBP-Std	PPO-FEE	2030	2030	2420	3990	8030	8030
321	NALC-Hi	PPO-FEE	2560	2560	3020	4290	7790	9160
444	SAMBA-Std	PPO-FEE	2130	2130	2650	4320	8130	8130
Z24	Aetna Advantage	PPO-FEE	1500	1500	2200	4580	9000	9000
311	GEHA-Hi	PPO-FEE	2730	2730	3250	4600	7730	7730
471	APWU-Hi	HMO	2770	2770	3290	4610	8190	9270
414	MHBP Value Plan	PPO-FEE	1460	1460	2020	4650	8060	8060
381	Rural Carrier	PPO-FEE	3400	3400	3640	4860	8200	8400
104	Blue Cross-Std	PPO-FEE	3310	3310	3750	5150	8810	9310
224	Aetna HealthFund HDHP	HDHP	3530	2730	3330	5520	9820	10430
441	SAMBA-Hi	PPO-FEE	4130	4130	4600	5980	9130	9130

[1] These are the premiums after tax savings, offset by savings accounts for plans that offer them. If you have no or low health-care costs with these plans, it can result in actual saving to you, which we indicate with a negative number.

Annuitants Age 65 and Older with Medicare Part A Only		Self Plus One						
				Estimated yearly out-of-pocket costs, including premium and typical hospital, medical, drug, and dental bills near:				
		Plan type	Published premium	No costs[1]	Low use: $3,000 or less	Average cost	High use: $30,000 or more	Limit to you
Plan code	Plan name							

D.C. Area Plans When You Use Preferred Providers

Plan code	Plan name	Plan type	Published premium	No costs[1]	Low use: $3,000 or less	Average cost	High use: $30,000 or more	Limit to you
T73	Kaiser Prosper	HMO	2600	2600	3580	6390	8340	10600
B63	CareFirst HDHP	HDHP	3630	1830	4230	6700	8300	13630
E36	Kaiser-Std	HMO	4190	4190	4750	6750	8100	11190
L93	United Choice Plus Advanced	PPO-FEE	3980	3980	5490	7800	9980	9980
Y83	United Choice Primary	HMO	3750	3750	5030	7960	10140	18450
B66	CareFirst Blue Value Plus	HMO-POS	4340	4340	5490	8070	9940	16340
V43	United HDHP	HDHP	4270	2770	4970	8210	10700	11120
AS3	United Choice Plus Primary	PPO-FEE	4200	4200	5480	8410	10590	18900
E33	Kaiser-Hi	HMO	7240	7240	7670	8910	9760	11740
JN6	Aetna Open Access Basic	HMO	5010	5010	6010	9550	12180	17010
QQ6	Aetna Saver	HMO	3750	3750	6150	9870	12950	16750
2G6	CareFirst-Std	HMO-POS	8090	8090	8830	10690	11900	18090
LR3	United Choice Open Access	HMO	7570	7570	8390	10700	12420	17570
JP3	MD-IPA	HMO	10080	10080	10760	12800	14290	20080
F53	Aetna HealthFund CDHP	CDHP	9950	7950	9850	12900	15230	19950
F56	Aetna Value Plan	PPO-FEE	10490	10490	12150	15220	17420	22490
JN3	Aetna Open Access-Hi	HMO	19790	19790	20310	22040	23170	29790

National Plans When You Use Preferred Providers

Plan code	Plan name	Plan type	Published premium	No costs[1]	Low use: $3,000 or less	Average cost	High use: $30,000 or more	Limit to you
256	GEHA Elevate	PPO-FEE	2910	2910	3590	5730	7440	16910
343	GEHA HDHP	HDHP	3530	1730	3930	6380	7700	13530
133	Blue Cross FEP Blue Focus	PPO	2970	2970	4450	6520	8390	19970
326	NALC CDHP	CDHP	3130	730	3130	6840	9080	16330
483	MHBP HDHP	HDHP	4400	2000	4400	7570	9270	16400
403	Foreign Service	PPO-FEE	4820	4820	5940	7640	8880	11820
476	APWU CDHP	CDHP	3940	1540	3890	7700	9890	16940
113	Blue Cross Basic	PPO	5100	5100	5820	7900	9410	18100
N63	Aetna Direct CDHP	CDHP	4130	2330	4730	7950	10020	16130
253	GEHA Elevate Plus	PPO-FEE	4750	4750	5630	8230	10040	16750
316	GEHA-Std	PPO-FEE	3500	3500	4820	8460	11320	16500
KM3	NALC Value Plan	PPO-FEE	2570	2370	4770	8480	10720	15770
423	Compass Rose	PPO-FEE	6440	6440	7010	8650	9820	13440
456	MHBP-Std	PPO-FEE	5090	5090	6320	9060	11330	17090
473	APWU-Hi	HMO	5540	5540	6930	9380	11210	18540
446	SAMBA-Std	PPO-FEE	4640	4640	6110	9420	12100	16640
383	Rural Carrier	PPO-FEE	6430	6430	7330	9520	11200	16430
323	NALC-Hi	PPO-FEE	6090	6090	7400	9790	11540	15090
Z26	Aetna Advantage	PPO-FEE	3300	3300	5700	10350	13630	18300
313	GEHA-Hi	PPO-FEE	6360	6360	7700	10580	12890	16360
106	Blue Cross-Std	PPO-FEE	7530	7530	8870	11330	13210	19530
416	MHBP Value Plan	PPO-FEE	3450	3450	6450	11400	16520	16650
226	Aetna HealthFund HDHP	HDHP	7750	6150	8350	12270	14720	21550
443	SAMBA-Hi	PPO-FEE	9450	9450	10790	13380	15380	19450

[1] These are the premiums after tax savings, offset by savings accounts for plans that offer them. If you have no or low health-care costs with these plans, it can result in actual saving to you, which we indicate with a negative number.

Annuitants Age 65 and Older with Medicare Part A Only		Family of Two						
		Plan type	Published premium	Estimated yearly out-of-pocket costs, including premium and typical hospital, medical, drug, and dental bills near:				
Plan code	Plan name			No costs[1]	Low use: $3,000 or less	Average cost	High use: $30,000 or more	Limit to you
D.C. Area Plans When You Use Preferred Providers								
E35	Kaiser-Std	HMO	4190	4190	4750	6750	8100	11190
T72	Kaiser Prosper	HMO	3150	3150	4130	6940	8890	11150
B62	CareFirst HDHP	HDHP	4310	2510	4910	7380	8980	14310
E32	Kaiser-Hi	HMO	5960	5960	6390	7630	8480	10460
Y82	United Choice Primary	HMO	4120	4120	5400	8330	10510	18820
V42	United HDHP	HDHP	4540	3040	5240	8480	10970	11390
L92	United Choice Plus Advanced	PPO-FEE	4760	4760	6270	8580	10760	10760
AS2	United Choice Plus Primary	PPO-FEE	4620	4620	5900	8830	11010	19320
B65	CareFirst Blue Value Plus	HMO-POS	5710	5710	6860	9440	11310	17710
JN5	Aetna Open Access Basic	HMO	5380	5380	6380	9920	12550	17380
QQ5	Aetna Saver	HMO	4090	4090	6490	10210	13290	17090
LR2	United Choice Open Access	HMO	8460	8460	9280	11590	13310	18460
F52	Aetna HealthFund CDHP	CDHP	8890	6890	8790	11840	14170	18890
2G5	CareFirst-Std	HMO-POS	10890	10890	11630	13490	14700	20890
F55	Aetna Value Plan	PPO-FEE	9680	9680	11340	14410	16610	21680
JN2	Aetna Open Access-Hi	HMO	18840	18840	19360	21090	22220	28840
JP2	MD-IPA	HMO	19120	19120	19800	21840	23330	29120
National Plans When You Use Preferred Providers								
255	GEHA Elevate	PPO-FEE	3550	3550	4230	6370	8080	17550
132	Blue Cross FEP Blue Focus	PPO	3270	3270	4750	6820	8690	20270
325	NALC CDHP	CDHP	3330	930	3330	7040	9280	16530
342	GEHA HDHP	HDHP	4340	2540	4740	7190	8510	14340
402	Foreign Service	PPO-FEE	4710	4710	5830	7530	8770	11710
482	MHBP HDHP	HDHP	4620	2220	4620	7790	9490	16620
475	APWU CDHP	CDHP	4290	1890	4240	8050	10240	17290
112	Blue Cross Basic	PPO	5520	5520	6240	8320	9830	18520
252	GEHA Elevate Plus	PPO-FEE	4960	4960	5840	8440	10250	16960
N62	Aetna Direct CDHP	CDHP	4750	2950	5350	8570	10640	16750
KM2	NALC Value Plan	PPO-FEE	2740	2540	4940	8650	10890	15940
455	MHBP-Std	PPO-FEE	4730	4730	5960	8700	10970	16730
322	NALC-Hi	PPO-FEE	5250	5250	6560	8950	10700	14250
422	Compass Rose	PPO-FEE	6980	6980	7550	9190	10360	13980
315	GEHA-Std	PPO-FEE	4290	4290	5610	9250	12110	17290
382	Rural Carrier	PPO-FEE	6160	6160	7060	9250	10930	16160
445	SAMBA-Std	PPO-FEE	4850	4850	6320	9630	12310	16850
472	APWU-Hi	HMO	6990	6990	8380	10830	12660	19990
Z25	Aetna Advantage	PPO-FEE	3980	3980	6380	11030	14310	18980
225	Aetna HealthFund HDHP	HDHP	6890	5290	7490	11410	13860	20690
415	MHBP Value Plan	PPO-FEE	3520	3520	6520	11470	16590	16720
105	Blue Cross-Std	PPO-FEE	8170	8170	9510	11970	13850	20170
312	GEHA-Hi	PPO-FEE	7860	7860	9200	12080	14390	17860
442	SAMBA-Hi	PPO-FEE	10260	10260	11600	14190	16190	20260

[1] These are the premiums after tax savings, offset by savings accounts for plans that offer them. If you have no or low health-care costs with these plans, it can result in actual saving to you, which we indicate with a negative number.

Continued from page 45

premium cost for Medicare is about $2,400 a person—higher than in many FEHB plans and with cost-sharing worse than most and no protection against catastrophically high expenses. You could improve your protection by enrolling in what are called "Medigap" plans, but only at the cost of paying another $2,000 a year in premium, the exact amount depending on the Medigap plan chosen. Therefore, if paying both FEHB and Medicare premiums presses you financially, and you are not sure which program to retain, **the FEHB program alone is a better bargain than Medicare alone, unless you are willing to enroll in a Medicare Advantage plan** (discussed below). And even then, you should never drop the FEHB program completely, but "suspend" enrollment with the option of rejoining in the next Open Season. Moreover, almost all Federal annuitants over age 65 have premium-free Medicare Part A, and in combination with almost all FEHB plans will never have to pay more than a few hundred dollars for hospital costs. Finally, FEHB plans, unlike Medicare (except in parts of Canada and Mexico), cover you if you travel or live abroad.

Should You Enroll in Part B After Age 65?

There are advantages to enrolling in Part B as a complement to an FEHB plan (technically, Medicare is "primary" and pays first). Almost all of the national plans waive their hospital and medical deductibles, copays, and coinsurance for members enrolled in both Medicare Part A (hospital) and Part B (medical). In effect, they "wrap around" Medicare. HMOs generally have only nominal deductibles or copayments and most of them do not provide such waivers. However, an increasing number do. For example, in the Washington, DC area CareFirst and M.D. IPA provide wraparound benefits to retirees with both parts of Medicare. In other parts of the nation, the Humana plans offer similar savings. With Medicare Parts A and B and most national Federal plans, you will have close to 100 percent coverage of almost all medical expenses (a few services are not covered by either program and would not get this coverage). Coverage for dental and prescription drug expenses will still differ depending on which plan you choose.

However, Medicare Part B will rarely save you nearly as much money as you spend on the Part B premium. This is because the cost sharing for physician visits and tests in almost all FEHB plans is already so low. And as we discuss below, for those who pay more for Part B than the normal premium, it is almost always a bad buy in purely financial terms.

By comparing tables for those with Part A only, versus those with Parts A and B, you will see that in most plans you are likely to spend several hundred dollars a year more for this combination than by retaining the FEHB plan alone. Simply put, Medicare Part B is of limited dollar value to someone already covered by a good health plan. **If you join an HMO, the Medicare premium gains you very little in dollar benefits. If you are willing to use preferred providers in national plans, or to join an HMO and use its network, you can usually save several hundred dollars per year or more—often a thousand dollars a year or more—by not joining, or dropping, Medicare Part B.** Even if you do not use preferred providers, you will do almost as well without Medicare Part B, because of the special rate ceiling that limits what Medicare-participating doctors can charge to Medicare allowed charges.

Part B does have some important advantages. Perhaps most importantly, in almost all the plans that wrap around Part B, **enrollment in Part B gives you the freedom to go outside the plan's network** at **no cost**.

Even if you enroll in one of the plans that don't wrap around, you can use your Part B benefit to **go outside the plan's doctor network and pay only 20% of the Medicare allowed charge**. For example, for using a specialist at the Mayo Clinic, you could simply charge the visit to Part B without your HMO or PPO plan's permission,

Part B provides more generous benefits than most FEHB plans in a few categories, such as physical therapy and home health care, and it covers more of the costs of some injected specialty drugs, prostheses and durable medical equipment than many. Still, Medicare Part B rarely reduces overall costs enough to pay for the extra premium. For those plans that provide a wraparound, in almost all situations Part B will likely save you several hundred dollars a year and often as much as half the Part B premium—but rarely as much as the "for sure" premium expense.

Also importantly, Part B gives you the option of joining a Medicare Advantage plan your choice—either PPO or HMO—through Medicare and suspending your FEHB enrollment and premium payment. It also gives you the option under many plans of enrolling in both FEHB and MA plans simultaneously and getting a large premium reimbursement, with the MA plan specially designed to work with the FEHB plan of that same carrier.

Enrollment in Part B also gives you some "insurance" against the possibility that the Congress would enact some major adverse change to the FEHB program.

Finally, for many the value of "peace of mind" that you get from coverage under both programs exceeds the increase in premium costs.

There is an important innovation under way that reduces the cost of enrolling under both programs that will be attractive to many. The national Aetna Direct plan not only has a Medicare wraparound, but also lets you use your $900 a year per spouse personal care account to reimburse most of your Medicare Part B premium, or to offset dental and other expenses not covered by FEHB plans or Medicare. This gives you the advantage of wraparound coverage at a significantly lower cost than you would otherwise pay. Since the plan also waives its deductible and other cost sharing if you have parts A and B, this plan costs almost the same with Medicare as without Medicare for those who pay normal Part B premiums. Likewise, the Blue Cross Basic plan now provides both a wraparound benefit and an $800 yearly reimbursement for each spouse with Part B, and GEHA High has a $600 reimbursement for each. Some HDHP and CDHP plans, including the national MHBP HDHP plan, and the CareFirst HDHP plan in the DC metro area, offer similar premium and/or personal account advantages, including the wraparound benefit. But the examples above are just the beginning of your choices. Kaiser and UnitedHealthcare, for example, will in many of their plans reimburse enough to pay more or less the entire Part B of about $1,900 in 2022.

If you do decide to drop (or not start) Part B you can join it later. But there is a 10 percent a year penalty if you later decide to join or rejoin. As a financial matter, however many years you elect to do without Part B, you will be money ahead for approximately the first five or six years after joining or rejoining. After that, the penalty will outweigh your earlier savings (except for those who were once above, but now fall below, the income-tested premium). If you never join or rejoin, you will (on average) save annually roughly the amounts indicated in our tables showing costs with and without Parts B—generally about half the cost of the Part B premium, though this varies somewhat from plan to plan. Thus, either not joining or dropping Part B is not an irrevocable decision, and later rejoining Part B need not be highly costly.

There are some circumstances to which the conclusions above do not apply:

- **Working employees over age 65** with Medicare Parts A and B coverage face a different situation. The special waivers of deductibles and coinsurance do not apply, because Medicare is by law the secondary rather than primary payer (except for firms with fewer than 20 employees). Your best choice is to stay in your preferred FEHB plan and **postpone joining Medicare Part B until you actually retire. There is no penalty** for joining after age 65 if you were working and covered by employer insurance (subject to the same exception for small firms).
- **A few people over age 65 did not earn Medicare Part A and can join by paying** a very substantial premium—about $5,000 a year. We recommend strongly against this purchase. Almost all FEHB plans charge you at most a few hundred dollars for hospital admissions, far less than the Part A premium.

Income-Related Part B Premiums

Historically, the taxpayer has funded three-fourths of the Medicare Part B premium, and the enrollee has paid only one fourth of the cost. Under current law, however, some higher income enrollees pay more than the traditional one-fourth share.

This only affects individuals with Adjusted Gross Income (AGI) of $88,000 or more, and married couples filing jointly with income of $176,000 or more, for 2022. These thresholds are not in most years adjusted for inflation. The actual calculation includes adding some forms of income, such as

Continues on page 60

Annuitants Age 65 and Older with Medicare Parts A & B		Self Only						
				Estimated yearly out-of-pocket costs, including premium and typical hospital, medical, drug, and dental bills near:				
Plan code	Plan name	Plan type	Published premium	No costs[1]	Low use: $3,000 or less	Average cost	High use: $30,000 or more	Limit to you
D.C. Area Plans When You Use Preferred Providers								
Y81R[1]	United Choice Primary (Retiree Adv.)	PPO-FEE	3650	1860	1940	2760	3890	8910
AS1R[1]	United Choice Plus Primary (Ret. Adv.)	PPO-FEE	3850	2070	2150	2970	4100	9120
L91R[1]	United Choice Plus Advanced (Ret. Adv.)	PPO-FEE	3890	2110	2190	3010	4140	9160
E31R2[1]	Kaiser-Hi (Medicare Advantage 2)	HMO	4610	2710	2800	3590	4860	12010
B61	CareFirst HDHP	HDHP	3710	2810	2950	3860	5000	8710
LR1R[1]	United Choice Open Access (Ret. Adv.)	PPO-FEE	5400	3620	3700	4520	5650	10670
E34R[1]	Kaiser-Std (Medicare Advantage)	HMO	3720	3720	3830	4670	6090	13670
T71R[1]	Kaiser Prosper (Medicare Advantage)	HMO	3010	3010	3230	4780	7260	13560
T71	Kaiser Prosper	HMO	3010	3010	3260	4920	7010	7010
E34	Kaiser-Std	HMO	3720	3720	3860	5080	7220	7220
E31R1[1]	Kaiser-Hi (Medicare Advantage 1)	HMO	4610	4610	4660	5140	5810	13910
E31	Kaiser-Hi	HMO	4610	4610	4710	5540	6860	6860
B64	CareFirst Blue Value Plus	HMO-POS	4220	4220	4530	5610	7250	10220
V41	United HDHP	HDHP	3890	3140	3740	5680	7890	7890
L91	United Choice Plus Advanced	PPO-FEE	3890	3890	4420	5690	6890	6890
Y81	United Choice Primary	HMO	3650	3650	4030	5910	9570	11000
AS1	United Choice Plus Primary	PPO-FEE	3850	3850	4230	6110	9770	11200
QQ4	Aetna Saver	HMO	3690	3690	4390	6670	10190	10190
JP1R[1]	MD-IPA (Retiree Advantage)	PPO-FEE	7680	5900	6050	6790	7780	12450
JN4	Aetna Open Access Basic	HMO	4410	4410	4670	6850	10410	10410
LR1	United Choice Open Access	HMO	5400	5400	5590	7200	10320	10400
2G4	CareFirst-Std	HMO-POS	6400	6400	6540	7450	8590	11400
F51	Aetna HealthFund CDHP	CDHP	5980	4980	5580	7480	10980	10980
JP1	MD-IPA	HMO	7680	7680	7790	8610	9980	12680
F54	Aetna Value Plan	PPO-FEE	6280	6280	6910	8830	12280	12280
JN1	Aetna Open Access-Hi	HMO	10550	10550	10620	11850	13990	15550

[1] These are the premiums after tax savings, offset by savings accounts for plans that offer them. If you have no or low health-care costs with these plans, it can result in actual saving to you, which we indicate with a negative number.
[2] This Medicare Advantage plan has special enrollment procedures.

Annuitants Age 65 and Older with Medicare Parts A & B			Self Only				
		Plan type	Published premium	Estimated yearly out-of-pocket costs, including premium and typical hospital, medical, drug, and dental bills near:			
Plan code	Plan name			No costs[1]	Low use: $3,000 or less	Average cost	High use: $30,000 or more	Limit to you

Plan code	Plan name	Plan type	Published premium	No costs[1]	Low use: $3,000 or less	Average cost	High use: $30,000 or more	Limit to you
National Plans When You Use Preferred Providers								
Z24R[1]	Aetna Advantage (Medicare Adv.)	PPO	3400	2500	2650	3520	4610	8850
454R[1]	MHBP - Std (Medicare Advantage)	PPO-FEE	3940	3040	3070	3910	4910	10090
421R[1]	Compass Rose (Medicare Advantage)	PPO-FEE	4660	3460	3490	3920	4500	10510
N61	Aetna Direct CDHP	CDHP	3790	2890	3060	4040	5340	9790
111	Blue Cross Basic	PPO	3990	3190	3310	4260	5610	9690
131	Blue Cross FEP Blue Focus	PPO	3280	3280	3470	4480	5920	11780
481	MHBP HDHP	HDHP	3890	2690	2910	4610	7490	9890
254	GEHA Elevate	PPO-FEE	3170	3170	3320	4810	7750	10170
401	Foreign Service	PPO-FEE	3800	3800	3920	4860	6170	8800
381R[1]	Rural Carrier (Medicare Advantage)	PPO-FEE	5300	4400	4400	4880	5610	11450
454	MHBP-Std	PPO-FEE	3940	3940	4020	4960	6230	9940
471R[1]	APWU-Hi (Medicare Advantage)	HMO	4670	4070	4150	4970	6100	11120
341	GEHA HDHP	HDHP	3550	2650	3250	5060	7210	8550
251	GEHA Elevate Plus	PPO-FEE	3960	3960	4150	5270	6930	9960
324	NALC CDHP	CDHP	3320	2120	2820	5290	8930	9920
421	Compass Rose	PPO-FEE	4660	4660	4750	5290	6000	9660
444	SAMBA-Std	PPO-FEE	4030	4030	4260	5510	7700	10030
311	GEHA-Hi	PPO-FEE	4630	3830	4130	5540	7920	8830
314	GEHA-Std	PPO-FEE	3530	3530	3850	5640	8710	10030
474	APWU CDHP	CDHP	3710	2510	3180	5730	9060	10210
321	NALC-Hi	PPO-FEE	4460	4460	4630	5750	7450	11060
KM1	NALC Value Plan	PPO-FEE	3070	2970	3670	6090	9670	9670
471	APWU-Hi	HMO	4670	4670	5160	6310	8360	11170
104	Blue Cross-Std	PPO-FEE	5220	5220	5350	6360	7770	11220
381	Rural Carrier	PPO-FEE	5300	5300	5520	6410	7700	10300
Z24	Aetna Advantage	PPO-FEE	3400	3400	4100	6870	10900	10900
414	MHBP Value Plan	PPO-FEE	3360	3360	3920	7060	9960	9960
441	SAMBA-Hi	PPO-FEE	6030	6030	6230	7280	8760	11030
224	Aetna HealthFund HDHP	HDHP	5430	4630	5230	7820	11720	12330

[1] These are the premiums after tax savings, offset by savings accounts for plans that offer them. If you have no or low health-care costs with these plans, it can result in actual saving to you, which we indicate with a negative number.
[2] This Medicare Advantage plan has special enrollment procedures.

Annuitants Age 65 and Older with Medicare Parts A & B		Self Plus One						
				Estimated yearly out-of-pocket costs, including premium and typical hospital, medical, drug, and dental bills near:				
Plan code	Plan name	Plan type	Published premium	No costs[1]	Low use: $3,000 or less	Average cost	High use: $30,000 or more	Limit to you

D.C. Area Plans When You Use Preferred Providers

Plan code	Plan name	Plan type	Published premium	No costs[1]	Low use: $3,000 or less	Average cost	High use: $30,000 or more	Limit to you
Y83R[1]	United Choice Primary (Retiree Adv.)	PPO-FEE	7550	3990	4420	5460	6020	18090
L93R[1]	United Choice Plus Advanced (Ret. Adv.)	PPO-FEE	7790	4220	4650	5690	6250	18320
AS3R[1]	United Choice Plus Primary (Ret. Adv.)	PPO-FEE	8000	4440	4870	5910	6470	18540
B63	CareFirst HDHP	HDHP	7430	5630	6210	7280	7820	17430
E33R2[1]	Kaiser-Hi (Medicare Advantage 2)	HMO	11050	7240	7620	8690	9360	25840
LR3R[1]	United Choice Open Access (Ret. Adv.)	PPO-FEE	11380	7810	8240	9280	9840	21910
T73R[1]	Kaiser Prosper (Medicare Advantage)	HMO	6400	6400	7260	9280	10590	27500
E36R[1]	Kaiser-Std (Medicare Advantage)	HMO	7990	7990	8400	9580	10340	28090
T73	Kaiser Prosper	HMO	6400	6400	7380	10190	12140	14400
B66	CareFirst Blue Value Plus	HMO-POS	8150	8150	9040	10400	11250	20150
E36	Kaiser-Std	HMO	7990	7990	8550	10560	11900	14990
L93	United Choice Plus Advanced	PPO-FEE	7790	7790	9300	11610	13790	13790
JP3R[1]	MD-IPA (Retiree Advantage)	PPO-FEE	13880	10320	10820	11710	12200	23420
Y83	United Choice Primary	HMO	7550	7550	8830	11770	13940	22250
E33R1[1]	Kaiser-Hi (Medicare Advantage 1)	HMO	11050	11050	11300	11920	12250	29650
V43	United HDHP	HDHP	8070	6570	8770	12010	14500	14920
AS3	United Choice Plus Primary	PPO-FEE	8000	8000	9280	12220	14390	22700
E33	Kaiser-Hi	HMO	11050	11050	11480	12730	13570	15550
JN6	Aetna Open Access Basic	HMO	8810	8810	9810	13410	15980	20810
2G6	CareFirst-Std	HMO-POS	11900	11900	12480	13550	14090	21900
QQ6	Aetna Saver	HMO	7560	7560	9960	13680	16760	20560
LR3	United Choice Open Access	HMO	11380	11380	12200	14510	16230	21380
JP3	MD-IPA	HMO	13880	13880	14300	15440	16180	23880
F53	Aetna HealthFund CDHP	CDHP	13750	11750	13650	16760	19030	23750
F56	Aetna Value Plan	PPO-FEE	14290	14290	15950	19000	21220	26290
JN3	Aetna Open Access-Hi	HMO	23590	23590	24110	25810	26970	33590

[1] These are the premiums after tax savings, offset by savings accounts for plans that offer them. If you have no or low health-care costs with these plans, it can result in actual saving to you, which we indicate with a negative number.
[2] This Medicare Advantage plan has special enrollment procedures. Limit to you for Medicare Advantage plans includes medical and drug max where present.

Annuitants Age 65 and Older with Medicare Parts A & B		Self Plus One						
		Plan type	Published premium	Estimated yearly out-of-pocket costs, including premium and typical hospital, medical, drug, and dental bills near:				
Plan code	Plan name			No costs[1]	Low use: $3,000 or less	Average cost	High use: $30,000 or more	Limit to you
National Plans When You Use Preferred Providers								
Z26R[1]	Aetna Advantage (Medicare Adv.)	PPO	7100	5300	5890	6890	7410	18000
N63	Aetna Direct CDHP	CDHP	7940	6140	6770	7960	8590	19940
456R[1]	MHBP - Std (Medicare Advantage)	PPO-FEE	8900	7100	7460	8410	8870	21200
423R[1]	Compass Rose (Medicare Advantage)	PPO-FEE	10240	7840	8040	8600	8880	21940
133	Blue Cross FEP Blue Focus	PPO	6770	6770	7440	8670	9410	23770
113	Blue Cross Basic	PPO	8900	7300	7810	9040	9720	20300
483	MHBP HDHP	HDHP	8200	5800	6520	9150	10600	20200
383R[1]	Rural Carrier (Medicare Advantage)	PPO-FEE	10240	8440	8490	9180	9550	22540
256	GEHA Elevate	PPO-FEE	6720	6720	7400	9540	11250	20720
473R[1]	APWU-Hi (Medicare Advantage)	HMO	9340	8140	8570	9610	10170	22240
343	GEHA HDHP	HDHP	7340	5540	7740	10190	11510	17340
403	Foreign Service	PPO-FEE	8630	8630	9110	10260	10930	15630
456	MHBP-Std	PPO-FEE	8900	8900	9340	10470	11090	20900
326	NALC CDHP	CDHP	6940	4540	6940	10640	12890	20140
253	GEHA Elevate Plus	PPO-FEE	8550	8550	9170	10680	11520	20550
446	SAMBA-Std	PPO-FEE	8450	8450	9180	10890	12120	20450
316	GEHA-Std	PPO-FEE	7310	7310	8160	10910	12490	20310
423	Compass Rose	PPO-FEE	10240	10240	10590	11240	11580	17240
313	GEHA-Hi	PPO-FEE	10170	8570	9340	11440	12660	18570
476	APWU CDHP	CDHP	7740	5340	7690	11540	13690	20740
383	Rural Carrier	PPO-FEE	10240	10240	10920	12040	12680	20240
323	NALC-Hi	PPO-FEE	9900	9900	10530	12070	12890	18900
473	APWU-Hi	HMO	9340	9340	10530	12160	13380	22340
KM3	NALC Value Plan	PPO-FEE	6380	6180	8580	12280	14530	19580
106	Blue Cross-Std	PPO-FEE	11330	11330	11870	13120	13830	23330
Z26	Aetna Advantage	PPO-FEE	7100	7100	9500	14150	17430	22100
416	MHBP Value Plan	PPO-FEE	7250	7250	10250	15200	20320	20450
443	SAMBA-Hi	PPO-FEE	13260	13260	13940	15240	15990	23260
226	Aetna HealthFund HDHP	HDHP	11560	9960	12160	16100	18530	25360

[1] These are the premiums after tax savings, offset by savings accounts for plans that offer them. If you have no or low health-care costs with these plans, it can result in actual saving to you, which we indicate with a negative number.
[2] This Medicare Advantage plan has special enrollment procedures. Limit to you for Medicare Advantage plans includes medical and drug max where present.

Annuitants Age 65 and Older with Medicare Parts A & B		Family of Two					
		Plan type	Published premium	Estimated yearly out-of-pocket costs, including premium and typical hospital, medical, drug, and dental bills near:			
Plan code	Plan name			No costs[1]	Low use: $3,000 or less	Average cost	High use: $30,000 or more	Limit to you

Plan code	Plan name	Plan type	Published premium	No costs[1]	Low use: $3,000 or less	Average cost	High use: $30,000 or more	Limit to you
D.C. Area Plans When You Use Preferred Providers								
Y82R[1]	United Choice Primary (Retiree Adv.)	PPO-FEE	7930	4360	4790	5830	6390	18460
AS2R[1]	United Choice Plus Primary (Ret. Adv.)	PPO-FEE	8420	4860	5290	6330	6890	18960
L92R[1]	United Choice Plus Advanced (Ret. Adv.)	PPO-FEE	8560	5000	5430	6470	7030	19100
E32R2[1]	Kaiser-Hi (Medicare Advantage 2)	HMO	9760	5960	6340	7410	8080	24560
B62	CareFirst HDHP	HDHP	8110	6310	6890	7960	8500	18110
E35R[1]	Kaiser-Std (Medicare Advantage)	HMO	7990	7990	8400	9580	10340	28090
T72R[1]	Kaiser Prosper (Medicare Advantage)	HMO	6960	6960	7820	9840	11150	28060
LR2R[1]	United Choice Open Access (Ret. Adv.)	PPO-FEE	12260	8700	9130	10170	10730	22800
E35	Kaiser-Std	HMO	7990	7990	8550	10560	11900	14990
E32R1[1]	Kaiser-Hi (Medicare Advantage 1)	HMO	9760	9760	10010	10630	10960	28360
T72	Kaiser Prosper	HMO	6960	6960	7940	10750	12700	14960
E32	Kaiser-Hi	HMO	9760	9760	10190	11440	12280	14260
B65	CareFirst Blue Value Plus	HMO-POS	9510	9510	10400	11760	12610	21510
Y82	United Choice Primary	HMO	7930	7930	9210	12150	14320	22630
V42	United HDHP	HDHP	8350	6850	9050	12290	14780	15200
L92	United Choice Plus Advanced	PPO-FEE	8560	8560	10070	12380	14560	14560
AS2	United Choice Plus Primary	PPO-FEE	8420	8420	9700	12640	14810	23120
JN5	Aetna Open Access Basic	HMO	9180	9180	10180	13780	16350	21180
QQ5	Aetna Saver	HMO	7890	7890	10290	14010	17090	20890
LR2	United Choice Open Access	HMO	12260	12260	13080	15390	17110	22260
F52	Aetna HealthFund CDHP	CDHP	12700	10700	12600	15710	17980	22700
2G5	CareFirst-Std	HMO-POS	14700	14700	15280	16350	16890	24700
F55	Aetna Value Plan	PPO-FEE	13480	13480	15140	18190	20410	25480
JP2R[1]	MD-IPA (Retiree Advantage)	PPO-FEE	22930	19360	19860	20750	21240	32460
JP2	MD-IPA	HMO	22930	22930	23350	24490	25230	32930
JN2	Aetna Open Access-Hi	HMO	22640	22640	23160	24860	26020	32640

[1] These are the premiums after tax savings, offset by savings accounts for plans that offer them. If you have no or low health-care costs with these plans, it can result in actual saving to you, which we indicate with a negative number.
[2] This Medicare Advantage plan has special enrollment procedures. Limit to you for Medicare Advantage plans includes medical and drug max where present.

Annuitants Age 65 and Older with Medicare Parts A & B		Family of Two						
		Plan type	Published premium	Estimated yearly out-of-pocket costs, including premium and typical hospital, medical, drug, and dental bills near:				
Plan code	Plan name			No costs[1]	Low use: $3,000 or less	Average cost	High use: $30,000 or more	Limit to you
National Plans When You Use Preferred Providers								
Z25R[1]	Aetna Advantage (Medicare Adv.)	PPO	7780	5980	6570	7570	8090	18680
455R[1]	MHBP - Std (Medicare Advantage)	PPO-FEE	8530	6730	7090	8040	8500	20830
N62	Aetna Direct CDHP	CDHP	8560	6760	7390	8580	9210	20560
382R[1]	Rural Carrier (Medicare Advantage)	PPO-FEE	9960	8160	8210	8900	9270	22260
132	Blue Cross FEP Blue Focus	PPO	7070	7070	7740	8970	9710	24070
422R[1]	Compass Rose (Medicare Advantage)	PPO-FEE	10780	8380	8580	9140	9420	22480
482	MHBP HDHP	HDHP	8420	6020	6740	9370	10820	20420
112	Blue Cross Basic	PPO	9320	7720	8230	9460	10140	20720
455	MHBP-Std	PPO-FEE	8530	8530	8970	10100	10720	20530
402	Foreign Service	PPO-FEE	8510	8510	8990	10140	10810	15510
255	GEHA Elevate	PPO-FEE	7350	7350	8030	10170	11880	21350
325	NALC CDHP	CDHP	7140	4740	7140	10840	13090	20340
252	GEHA Elevate Plus	PPO-FEE	8760	8760	9380	10890	11730	20760
342	GEHA HDHP	HDHP	8150	6350	8550	11000	12320	18150
472R[1]	APWU-Hi (Medicare Advantage)	HMO	10790	9590	10020	11060	11620	23690
445	SAMBA-Std	PPO-FEE	8650	8650	9380	11090	12320	20650
322	NALC-Hi	PPO-FEE	9060	9060	9690	11230	12050	18060
315	GEHA-Std	PPO-FEE	8090	8090	8940	11690	13270	21090
382	Rural Carrier	PPO-FEE	9960	9960	10640	11760	12400	19960
422	Compass Rose	PPO-FEE	10780	10780	11130	11780	12120	17780
475	APWU CDHP	CDHP	8100	5700	8050	11900	14050	21100
KM2	NALC Value Plan	PPO-FEE	6540	6340	8740	12440	14690	19740
312	GEHA-Hi	PPO-FEE	11660	10060	10830	12930	14150	20060
472	APWU-Hi	HMO	10790	10790	11980	13610	14830	23790
105	Blue Cross-Std	PPO-FEE	11970	11970	12510	13760	14470	23970
Z25	Aetna Advantage	PPO-FEE	7780	7780	10180	14830	18110	22780
225	Aetna HealthFund HDHP	HDHP	10700	9100	11300	15240	17670	24500
415	MHBP Value Plan	PPO-FEE	7320	7320	10320	15270	20390	20520
442	SAMBA-Hi	PPO-FEE	14070	14070	14750	16050	16800	24070

[1] These are the premiums after tax savings, offset by savings accounts for plans that offer them. If you have no or low health-care costs with these plans, it can result in actual saving to you, which we indicate with a negative number.
[2] This Medicare Advantage plan has special enrollment procedures. Limit to you for Medicare Advantage plans includes medical and drug max where present.

Continued from page 53

tax-exempt interest income, to AGI. In 2022 the resulting annual Part B premium will range from about $2,700 for individual AGI of between $88,000 to $111,000 and increase in steps to over $6,000 for income of more than $500,000. The corresponding amounts for married couples filing jointly are twice as high.

There are additional factors that may determine whether this affects you. For example, if you marry or divorce or suffer a casualty loss you may become exempt. If your income fluctuates from year to year, you may be subject to the increase one year but not the next (generally, the calculation is based on your AGI two years previously). If you have just retired with previous income above these thresholds, it is very important to apply to the Social Security Administration to use your lower retirement income to reduce or eliminate the higher premium.

The premium calculation is made based on your income two years ago, which for many is a much higher pre-retirement amount, unless you apply for an adjustment. The "bottom line" is that if your income is above these thresholds and likely to remain there, the case for enrolling in Medicare Part B becomes far weaker. Dropping Part B will not affect your continued premium-free enrollment in Part A. The sensible solution for many high-income annuitants will be to drop out of Medicare Part B and rely on your FEHB plan. Why pay $3,000 or $4,000 or even more annually for a Part B benefit that rarely results in reduced cost sharing of more than a small fraction of that amount?

Joining Medicare Advantage

Over a third of Medicare beneficiaries now enroll in a Medicare Advantage plan, rather than sticking with Original Medicare. Medicare Advantage (MA) is a program designed to be very similar in operation to the FEHB program. Retirees can choose from a wide range of PPO and HMO plans in an annual Open Season. These plans' premiums are paid mainly through the Medicare Part A and B payments (with some adjustments) that the government would otherwise have paid in direct benefits. The enrollees continue to pay their Part B premium. Almost all of these plans include prescription drug coverage and various improvements over the original Medicare structure. For example, most eliminate most of the hospital deductible. In some cases, these plans charge no extra premium for drug coverage and other benefits. Very importantly, all of these plans now provide protection against catastrophic costs. The MA program is thoroughly described in the *Medicare & You* brochure mailed to all Medicare participants. The Medicare web site at *www.medicare.gov* contains additional information and provides an MA plan comparison tool that includes many of the same features as the online *Guide*, with a comparison of total costs including both premium and out-of-pocket expenses.

This is important to Federal retirees because if you have Parts A and B you can join an MA plan and pay only one premium instead of two, saving thousands of dollars a year. There are two ways to do this. First, you can temporarily suspend your FEHB enrollment and stop paying two sets of premiums. Under this "suspend" option you pay only the Part B premium and sometimes an extra premium charge (usually only a few hundred dollars per year and often nothing at all) that the Medicare Advantage plan charges Medicare enrollees for additional benefits such as prescription drug coverage. You can switch out of Medicare Advantage and rejoin the FEHB program as if you had never left during any future Open Season. This works equally well for a couple when both spouses are enrolled in Medicare, or if they are willing to pursue separate health insurance options. The other way to join an MA plan and pay one premium instead of two is to choose an FEHB plan that will let you enroll in both programs simultaneously and receive a Part B premium reimbursement that generally covers all or most of the Part B Premium. This option is now available in most parts of the country through UnitedHealthcare, Humana, Kaiser, and other plans. Under these "Medicare Advantage", "Senior Advantage", and "Retiree Advantage" options, you enroll in one of these carriers' own Medicare Advantage plan after joining its FEHB plan, and remain fully enrolled in its FEHB plan rather than suspending FEHB enrollment. You nominally pay both premiums but obtain a large Part B premium reimbursement equal to most or all of the cost of the regular Part B premium. In effect, you can enroll in both programs at the cost of one premium. You get much-reduced cost-sharing—close to zero cost to you for hospital and doctor services—if you use network providers.

Either approach generates substantial savings because you will in effect pay one premium instead of two. Some carriers, such as Aetna, offer both approaches. How much you will save depends on the precise benefits the MA plan offers to Medicare enrollees and whether or how much it charges in extra premium. Under the first approach, you will have a wide range of MA plan options. Most MA plans are comparable to FEHB plans in hospital and medical benefits, but the prescription drug benefits will not be as good because the plans have a "coverage gap" where you are responsible for all or most drug costs until you reach a catastrophic limit. Under the second approach the plans that offer a Part B premium rebate if you join their tailored MA plan (your only choice) are generally even better deals, because they have structured FEHB-specific MA plans that in most cases cover hospital and doctor bills 100% and provide strong drug benefits. Some of the newer offerings under the second approach come from national carriers like MHBP, Compass Rose, and Rural Carrier. These carriers' plans have been among the higher priced options in recent years, but with MA plans that pay all hospital and doctor costs they are much better choices than before.

Under the second approach you will need to carefully read Section 9 of the plan brochure, visit the plan website, and talk to a plan representative to make sure you understand what you are doing and how it will work. Under the first approach you will have to choose your MA plan on your own or with insurance vendor advice, or by using the good plan comparison tool at medicare.gov, and then make arrangements to suspend your FEHB enrollment through OPM.

Under either option for enrolling in an MA plan you will keep your FEHB enrollment status and legal right to make another decision at the next open season. But before the final decision, you should pay particular attention to drug benefits. A very important feature in the original Medicare Part D prescription drug program was a requirement that enrollees pay a large amount out-of-pocket for drugs before catastrophic protection against substantial additional drug costs kicked in. This "coverage gap" is phasing out. But all MA plans have not moved equally rapidly to eliminate it. And while most MA plans give you Part D benefits without paying any additional premium, not all do so. Finally, the drug formulary in some MA plans is more generous than in others. So before you make a final decision on enrolling in a particular MA plan, do check out its drug benefit details carefully to make sure they meet your needs.

Your Final Decision on Medicare Part B and the FEHB Program

Throughout our advice we have highlighted specific advantages and disadvantages of enrolling in Medicare Part B in addition to your FEHB enrollment. On the minus side, there is one large factor—paying two costly sets of premiums instead of one. For those who pay the higher part B income-tested premiums, this is a very considerable cost, at least $2,700 and for some almost $6,000 to join Part B, depending on exact income level. On the plus side there are several factors, including avoiding network restrictions, better coverage for a few services, and above all having the option to join FEHB plans that sponsor Medicare Advantage plans and saving much of the cost of the Part B premium.

By now, you should realize that you have many options, each with advantages and disadvantages. Taking into account dollar costs only, there are five good sets of options.

- The first option is to enroll in a Medicare Advantage plan and suspend FEHB enrollment. This is the lowest-cost option for many. Many MA plans have benefits as good as many FEHB plans and charge nothing beyond the regular Part B premium.
- A second option is to enroll in a plan that contributes a substantial amount toward your Medicare premium, such as Aetna Direct CDHP or Blue Cross Basic. In both CDHP and HDHP plans your special account will pay towards the Part B premium (or in the Aetna Direct plan for drug or dental costs not otherwise covered), and you also get a Medicare wraparound. Several HDHP plans give you an equivalent value through their Health Reimbursement Account. We rate MHBP HDHP and CareFirst HDHP as particularly good buys.
- A third option is to enroll simultaneously in a UnitedHealthcare, Kaiser or other FEHB plan with a plan-specific corresponding local Medicare Advantage plan to obtain a "Senior Advantage" or "Retiree Advantage" option that pays most or all of the Part B premium while dramatically lowering your cost-sharing for medical expenses.

Extra Cost of Enrolling in Both an FEHB Plan and Medicare Part B

Plan code	Plan name	Average cost for self only			Average cost for self plus one		
		With Medicare A only	With Medicare A & B	Extra cost of Part B	With Medicare A only	With Medicare A & B	Extra cost of Part B
D.C. Area Plans When You Use Preferred Providers							
Y81-3R[1]	United Choice Primary (Retiree Adv.)	2640	2760	120	5210	5460	250
AS1-3R[1]	United Choice Plus Primary (Ret. Adv.)	2850	2970	120	5660	5910	250
L91-3R[1]	United Choice Plus Advanced (Ret. Adv.)	2890	3010	120	5440	5690	250
E31-3R2[1]	Kaiser-Hi (Medicare Advantage 2)	3580	3590	10	8680	8690	10
B61-3	CareFirst HDHP	3480	3860	380	6700	7280	580
LR1-3R[1]	United Choice Open Access (Ret. Adv.)	4400	4520	120	9030	9280	250
E34-6R[1]	Kaiser-Std (Medicare Advantage)	2770	4670	1900	5770	9580	3810
T71-3R[1]	Kaiser Prosper (Medicare Advantage)	2880	4780	1900	5480	9280	3800
T71-3	Kaiser Prosper	3020	4920	1900	6390	10190	3800
E34-6	Kaiser-Std	3180	5080	1900	6750	10560	3810
E31-3R1[1]	Kaiser-Hi (Medicare Advantage 1)	3240	5140	1900	8110	11920	3810
E31-3	Kaiser-Hi	3640	5540	1900	8910	12730	3820
B64-6	CareFirst Blue Value Plus	4450	5610	1160	8070	10400	2330
V41-3	United HDHP	3780	5680	1900	8210	12010	3800
L91-3	United Choice Plus Advanced	3790	5690	1900	7800	11610	3810
Y81-3	United Choice Primary	4000	5910	1910	7960	11770	3810
AS1-3	United Choice Plus Primary	4210	6110	1900	8410	12220	3810
QQ4-6	Aetna Saver	4770	6670	1900	9870	13680	3810
JP1-3R[1]	MD-IPA (Retiree Advantage)	6660	6790	130	11460	11710	250
JN4-6	Aetna Open Access Basic	4950	6850	1900	9550	13410	3860
LR1-3	United Choice Open Access	5300	7200	1900	10700	14510	3810
2G4-6	CareFirst-Std	6050	7450	1400	10690	13550	2860
F51-3	Aetna HealthFund CDHP	5580	7480	1900	12900	16760	3860
JP1-3	MD-IPA	7360	8610	1250	12800	15440	2640
F54-6	Aetna Value Plan	6930	8830	1900	15220	19000	3780
JN1-3	Aetna Open Access-Hi	9950	11850	1900	22040	25810	3770

[1] This Medicare Advantage plan has special enrollment procedures.

Extra Cost of Enrolling in Both an FEHB Plan and Medicare Part B

Plan code	Plan name	Average cost for self only			Average cost for self plus one		
		With Medicare A only	With Medicare A & B	Extra cost of Part B	With Medicare A only	With Medicare A & B	Extra cost of Part B
National Plans When You Use Preferred Providers							
Z24-6R[1]	Aetna Advantage (Medicare Advantage)	2530	3520	990	4920	6890	1970
454-6R[1]	MHBP - Std (Medicare Advantage)	2900	3910	1010	6390	8410	2020
421-3R[1]	Compass Rose (Medicare Advantage)	3230	3920	690	7210	8600	1390
N61-3	Aetna Direct CDHP	3900	4040	140	7950	7960	10
111-3	Blue Cross Basic	3750	4260	510	7900	9040	1140
131-3	Blue Cross FEP Blue Focus	3400	4480	1080	6520	8670	2150
481-3	MHBP HDHP	3760	4610	850	7570	9150	1580
254-6	GEHA Elevate	2910	4810	1900	5730	9540	3810
401-3	Foreign Service	3510	4860	1350	7640	10260	2620
381-3R[1]	Rural Carrier (Medicare Advantage)	3880	4880	1000	7180	9180	2000
454-6	MHBP-Std	4350	4960	610	9060	10470	1410
471-3R[1]	APWU-Hi (Medicare Advantage)	3670	4970	1300	7000	9610	2610
341-3	GEHA HDHP	3150	5060	1910	6380	10190	3810
251-3	GEHA Elevate Plus	4070	5270	1200	8230	10680	2450
421-3	Compass Rose	4060	5290	1230	8650	11240	2590
324-6	NALC CDHP	3390	5290	1900	6840	10640	3800
444-6	SAMBA-Std	4650	5510	860	9420	10890	1470
311-3	GEHA-Hi	4960	5540	580	10580	11440	860
314-6	GEHA-Std	4270	5640	1370	8460	10910	2450
474-6	APWU CDHP	3830	5730	1900	7700	11540	3840
321-3	NALC-Hi	4670	5750	1080	9790	12070	2280
KM1-3	NALC Value Plan	4190	6090	1900	8480	12280	3800
471-3	APWU-Hi	4940	6310	1370	9380	12160	2780
104-6	Blue Cross-Std	5460	6360	900	11330	13120	1790
381-3	Rural Carrier	5170	6410	1240	9520	12040	2520
Z24-6	Aetna Advantage	4970	6870	1900	10350	14150	3800
414-6	MHBP Value Plan	5160	7060	1900	11400	15200	3800
441-3	SAMBA-Hi	6260	7280	1020	13380	15240	1860
224-6	Aetna HealthFund HDHP	5920	7820	1900	12270	16100	3830

[1] This Medicare Advantage plan has special enrollment procedures.

- A fourth cost-saving choice is to enroll in an FEHB plan with good benefits such as APWU, NALC, Kaiser Standard option, or a number of HMO, HDHP, and CDHP plans, and bypass Medicare Part B enrollment.
- As a fifth choice, you can enroll in a relatively low-premium plan like FEP Blue Focus, Aetna Advantage, Blue Cross Basic, CareFirst Blue Value, Aetna Direct or MHBP HDHP, along with Part B, and get either a rich Medicare wraparound benefit or simply the ability to use Medicare to go outside the plan's network should you choose to do so.
- All of these options and the plans that save the most money within each option vary in details that you can only assess after studying the brochure of several plans. All of them can provide most annuitants substantial annual savings.

What you should generally not do is stay in a high premium FEHB plan to get the Part B wraparound benefit when you can join a less costly FEHB plan with an equally good wraparound benefit. If your medical costs are close to zero in a number of plans, most offering this deal in or out of network, why pay a higher rather than lower premium? Of course, there are always cases where even the most expensive combination provides a benefit essential to you. And differences in prescription drug formularies or cost sharing can make a seemingly more expensive option actually a less expensive option. So, there is no simple "one size fits all" answer. What you should do, regardless, is at least be aware of the dollar costs or gains of whatever decision you reach.

Our table on the extra cost of enrolling in both an FEHB plan and Medicare Part B shows which plans are likely to cost you the least or save you the most by enrolling in Part B. We present the plans in national and local groups, and within each list the plans in order of the lowest cost for self only enrollment in both FEHB and Part B. Some plans cost very little extra for Part B, taking into account both premium and enhanced benefits, and Aetna Direct and Part B together reduce your costs considerably. The plans that save you the most are sometimes the plans that offer the best premium reimbursements, and sometimes not. The table does not include estimates for the options involving enrollment in a Medicare Advantage plan as your primary plan, but these are generally roughly equivalent to the better buys shown in the table, provided that you are willing to consider such a major change.

Medicare Part D

The Medicare Part D prescription drug program benefits millions of low-income elderly. It fills a major hole in Medicare that lasted fifty years. But it will rarely benefit those, like Federal retirees, who have good drug coverage from their former employer.

Few Federal retirees should join a Part D plan. A typical plan will cost four or five hundred dollars in premium and provide little improved benefit for most. Also, there is no penalty for joining Part D at a later time if you have current "creditable" coverage. This test is met by all FEHB plans. There are three exceptions. First, a few Federal annuitants have incomes and liquid assets low enough to qualify for special help. For example, a divorced former spouse may receive so little in pension that he or she qualifies for low-income assistance (the income cutoff is approximately $18,000, depending on state of residence). In such a case, the annuitant may be able to reduce drug costs to almost nothing. You apply to the Social Security Administration to obtain an official decision. Second, the Part D benefit can offer savings to annuitants in plans with relatively weak prescription drug coverage, like GEHA Standard option. This GEHA plan only reimburses half the cost of name brand drugs. An enrollee with a name brand drug costing at retail $2,000 a year would be out of pocket $1,000 under GEHA. Many Part D plans would pay most of this cost for a premium of $500 a year or less, and GEHA would pay half the rest. Third, a Part D plan will let enrollees in High Deductible and Consumer-Driven plans such as Aetna Direct, NALC CDHP, or MHBP HDHP avoid using their personal account for routine drug expenses.

Unfortunately, the national plans are not offering extra benefits such as copay waivers to those who join Part D, unlike their improved coverage for those with Parts A or B. They simply promise to "consider" paying part of your Part D costs, whatever that means. And having two drug plans involves a lot of paperwork. Hence, only if you can achieve substantial savings for your particular drugs is it worthwhile to join Part D. Also, before enrolling in Part D check whether or not you are subject to income-related premiums. The law now subjects Part D enrollees to the same income-tested levels as under Part B.

Chapter 5

Cost Sharing

Health insurance plans never pay 100 percent of all health-related expenses. For example, no plan pays for elective cosmetic surgery. Most plans pay little or nothing towards expensive dental procedures. Almost all plans charge something—usually $20 to $40—for physician visits. Many plans charge deductibles, either before reimbursing any expenses or before reimbursing particular categories of expenses, such as hospital or prescription drugs. These and other payment limitations are complicated and vary from plan to plan. We estimate these out-of-pocket costs for you using a complex computer model that takes into account all these various interactions, but in some cases, you may want to focus on particular coverages and copayments of concern to you.

Deductibles, Copayments, and Coinsurance

Cost sharing details can help you pinpoint a plan's strengths and weakenesses for cost items of particular concern to you. If you are especially concerned about a broad area of coverage, such as prescription drugs, copayment information can identify plans that are most acceptable to you and be used together with other cost rankings to narrow your choice. Our comparisons of deductibles, coinsurance, and copays display many of the cost sharing provisions taken into account in our overall cost comparisons. (In the printed *Guide,* we present a cost-sharing table for national plans and DC area local plans, but not for the local plans in other parts of the country that we are able to display online.)

Plans require you to pay more for "name brand" drugs than for "generic" drugs. Most plans now use at least a six-tier reimbursement structure for prescription drugs: generic, preferred name brand, and non-formulary name brand at the local pharmacy for a one-month supply; and the same three categories for a three-month supply by mail order (multi-thousand dollar "specialty drugs" are often yet another tier). Our overall cost comparisons reflect these differences, but if you have unusually high (or low) name brand drug costs, use our cost sharing tables to identify plans most likely to match your needs.

You should not rely primarily on cost sharing information to select a plan. Choosing a plan with the best rate for a particular benefit without taking into account its premium and all its other benefits would be a mistake. You could try to compare key factors two or three at a time, but this approach necessarily either omits other key factors or requires so many oversimplified comparisons as to become meaningless. For example, whether or not and how much a separate hospital deductible matters compared to premium dollars depends on a key unknown: your likelihood of one or more hospital stays. With few exceptions (e.g., routine visits and maintenance prescription drugs, and some planned operations if you avoid complications that lead to readmissions) you cannot forecast just what medical expenses of each type you will incur next year, and even if you could it is very complex to make all the interactive calculations involved. Furthermore, cost sharing can be and often is expressed in annual, monthly, biweekly, per dollar spent, and per service unit for different benefits in the same plan. It can be expressed as the dollar amount you pay, the dollar amount the plan pays, the percent you pay, or the percent the plan pays. Converting all these disparate measures to the common metric of annual cost is essential to making comparisons. Otherwise, you are comparing apples to oranges—how much biweekly premium equals how many annual physician visit copayments or what coinsurance percent for name brand prescriptions? We not only handle these messy computations for you, but also use actuarial information on the probability of different kinds and amounts of costs. **Most importantly, you cannot sensibly compare plans based only or primarily on expenses you already expect—that misses the main purpose of insurance: to protect you against unknown and potentially devastating future expenses.**

Cost Sharing for D.C. Area Plans		Savings account for self	Savings account for family	Deductibles			Extra for 2-day hospital stay
Plan code	Plan name (listed in alphabetical order within group)			Single	Family	Extra for drugs (self)	

D.C. Area Plans When You Use Preferred Providers

Plan code	Plan name	Savings account for self	Savings account for family	Single	Family	Extra for drugs (self)	Extra for 2-day hospital stay
F51-3	Aetna HealthFund CDHP	$1,000	$2,000	$1,000	$2,000	None	None
JN4-6	Aetna Open Access Basic	None	None	None	None	None	None
JN1-3	Aetna Open Access-Hi	None	None	None	None	None	$300
QQ4-6	Aetna Saver	None	None	$1,000	$2,000	None	None
F54-6	Aetna Value Plan	None	None	$700	$1,400	None	None
B64-6	CareFirst Blue Value Plus	None	None	None	None	$100	None
B61-3	CareFirst HDHP	$900	$1,800	$1,400	$2,800	None	None
2G4-6	CareFirst-Std	None	None	None	None	None	None
T71-3	Kaiser Prosper	None	None	$100	$200	None	$750
E31-3	Kaiser-Hi	None	None	None	None	None	$100
E34-6	Kaiser-Std	None	None	None	None	None	$500
JP1-3	MD-IPA	None	None	None	None	None	$300
LR1-3	United Choice Open Access	None	None	None	None	None	$300
L91-3	United Choice Plus Advanced	None	None	$500	$1,000	None	None
AS1-3	United Choice Plus Primary	None	None	$500	$1,000	$250	None
Y81-3	United Choice Primary	None	None	$500	$1,000	$250	None
V41-3	United HDHP	$750	$1,500	$1,500	$3,000	None	$500

D.C. Area Medicare Advantage Plans

Plan code	Plan name	Savings account for self	Savings account for family	Single	Family	Extra for drugs (self)	Extra for 2-day hospital stay
T71-3R[1]	Kaiser Prosper (Medicare Advantage)	None	None	None	None	None	$250
E31-3R1[1]	Kaiser-Hi (Medicare Advantage 1)	None	None	None	None	None	$75
E31-3R2[1]	Kaiser-Hi (Medicare Advantage 2)	None	None	None	None	None	$100
E34-6R[1]	Kaiser-Std (Medicare Advantage)	None	None	None	None	None	$150
JP1-3R[1]	MD-IPA (Retiree Adv.)	None	None	None	None	None	None
LR1-3R[1]	United Choice Open Access (Ret. Adv.)	None	None	None	None	None	None
L91-3R[1]	United Choice Plus Advanced (Ret. Adv.)	None	None	None	None	None	None
AS1-3R[1]	United Choice Plus Primary (Ret. Adv.)	None	None	None	None	None	None
Y81-3R[1]	United Choice Primary (Retiree Adv.)	None	None	None	None	None	None

[1] This Medicare Advantage plan has special enrollment procedures.

Hospital room & board (%)	Other hospital inpatient (%)	Visit to primary care ($ or %)	Visit to specialist ($ or %)	Prescription drugs ($) or (%)			
				Generic local pharmacy	Name brand local pharmacy	Generic mail order 90 day	Name brand mail order 90 day
You pay after deductible and after using savings account:							
15%	15%	15%	15%	$10	50%	$20	50%
20%	20%	$25	$55	$10	50%	$20	50%
None	None	$15	$30	$3	$35	$6	$70
30%	30%	30%	30%	$10	50%	$30	50%
20%	20%	$25	$40	$10	30%	$20	30%
25%	25%	$15	$50	$10	$50	$20	$100
20%	20%	None	$35	None	$50	None	$100
20%	20%	None	$40	None	$50	None	$100
None	None	$30	$40	$10	$45	$24	$129
None	None	$10	$20	$7	$30	$15	$84
None	None	$20	$30	$10	$40	$24	$114
None	None	$25	$40	$5	$40	$15	$120
None	None	$25	$35	$10	$40	$25	$100
20%	20%	$25	$50	$10	$35	$25	$88
20%	20%	None	$60	$5	$50	$13	$125
20%	20%	None	$60	$5	$50	$13	$125
None	None	$15	$30	$10	$40	$25	$100
None	None	$20	$30	$10	$35	$20	$70
None	None	None	None	$3.50	$20	$7	$40
None	None	$5	$15	$7	$30	$14	$60
None	None	$10	$10	$10	$30	$20	$60
None	none	None	None	$7	$35	$14	$70
none	none	None	None	$7	$35	$14	$70
None	None	None	None	$7	$35	$14	$70
None	None	None	None	$7	$35	$14	$70
None	None	None	None	$7	$35	$14	$70

Cost Sharing for National Plans		Savings account for self	Savings account for family	Deductibles			Extra for 2-day hospital stay
Plan code	Plan name (listed in alphabetical order within group)			Single	Family	Extra for drugs (self)	
National Plans When You Use Preferred Providers							
Z24-6	Aetna Advantage	None	None	$2,000	$4,000	None	None
N61-3	Aetna Direct CDHP	$900	$1,800	$1,600	$3,200	None	None
224-6	Aetna HealthFund HDHP	$800	$1,600	$1,800	$3,600	None	None
474-6	APWU CDHP	$1,200	$2,400	$2,200	$4,400	None	None
471-3	APWU-Hi	None	None	$450	$800	None	None
111-3	Blue Cross Basic	None	None	None	None	None	$350
131-3	Blue Cross FEP Blue Focus	None	None	$500	$1,000	None	None
104-6	Blue Cross-Std	None	None	$350	$700	None	$350
421-3	Compass Rose	None	None	$350	$700	None	$200
401-3	Foreign Service	None	None	$300	$600	None	None
254-6	GEHA Elevate	None	None	$500	$1,000	None	None
251-3	GEHA Elevate Plus	None	None	None	None	None	$500
341-3	GEHA HDHP	$900	$1,800	$1,500	$3,000	None	None
311-3	GEHA-Hi	None	None	$350	$700	None	$100
314-6	GEHA-Std	None	None	$350	$700	None	None
481-3	MHBP HDHP	$1,200	$2,400	$2,000	$4,000	None	$150
414-6	MHBP Value Plan	None	None	$600	$1,200	None	None
454-6	MHBP-Std	None	None	$350	$700	None	$200
324-6	NALC CDHP	$1,200	$2,400	$2,000	$4,000	None	None
KM1-3	NALC Value Plan	$100	$200	$2,000	$4,000	None	None
321-3	NALC-Hi	None	None	$300	$600	None	$350
381-3	Rural Carrier	None	None	$350	$700	$200	$200
441-3	SAMBA-Hi	None	None	$300	$600	None	$200
444-6	SAMBA-Std	None	None	$350	$900	None	$200
National Medicare Advantage Plans							
Z24-6R[1]	Aetna Advantage (Medicare Adv.)	None	None	None	None	None	None
471-3R[1]	APWU-Hi (Medicare Advantage)	None	None	None	None	None	None
421-3R[1]	Compass Rose (Medicare Advantage)	None	None	None	None	None	None
454-6R[1]	MHBP - Std (Medicare Advantage)	None	None	None	None	None	None
381-3R[1]	Rural Carrier (Medicare Advantage)	None	None	None	None	None	None

[1] This Medicare Advantage plan has special enrollment procedures.

				You pay after deductible and after using savings account:			
Hospital room & board (%)	Other hospital inpatient (%)	Visit to primary care ($ or %)	Visit to specialist ($ or %)	Prescription drugs ($) or (%)			
				Generic local pharmacy	Name brand local pharmacy	Generic mail order 90 day	Name brand mail order 90 day
30%	30%	30%	30%	$10	45%	$20	45%
20%	20%	20%	20%	$6	30%	$2	30%
15%	15%	15%	15%	$10	50%	$20	50%
15%	None	15%	15%	25%	25%	25%	25%
15%	None	$25	$25	$10	25%	$20	25%
None	None	$30	$40	$10	$55	None	None
30%	30%	$10	$10	$5	40%	None	None
None	None	$25	$35	$8	30%	$15	$90
None	None	$15	$25	$5	$45	$10	$90
None	None	10%	10%	$10	25%	$15	$60
25%	25%	$10	$25	$4	50%	None	None
None	None	$25	$40	$10	$80	$20	$200
5%	5%	5%	5%	25%	25%	25%	25%
10%	None	$20	$20	$10	25%	$20	25%
15%	15%	$15	$30	$10	50%	$20	50%
None	None	$15	$15	$10	30%	$20	$80
20%	20%	$30	$50	$10	45%	$30	45%
None	10%	$20	$30	$5	30%	$10	$80
20%	None	20%	20%	$10	$40	$20	$90
20%	None	20%	20%	$10	$40	$20	$90
None	None	$20	$20	20%	30%	$15	$90
None	None	$20	$35	30%	30%	$10	$50
None	15%	$15	$25	$10	30%	$15	30%
None	20%	$20	$30	$12	35%	$20	35%
None	None	None	None	$2	$40	$4	$80
None	None	None	None	$7	$35	$14	$70
None	None	None	None	$1	$25	$2	$50
None	None	None	None	None	$40	None	$60
None	None	None	None	$5	$40	$10	$40

Each of the table entries for costs of various types shows the dollar copayment or coinsurance percentage you must pay for bills of each type. In some cases, a plan uses both methods of payment for the same benefit, or a different amount depending on which type of provider or prescription drug is involved. These amounts and percentages do not take into account deductibles and can be very misleading. A plan that pays all expenses in excess of a deductible of $300 pays none of your bills in a year when your costs are less than $300, and only half in a year in which your costs reach $600.

In most cases, our entries are the same as those given in the plan brochures. Unfortunately, the reimbursement structure for many plans is so complicated that there is no simple way to present or compare these payments, even organized by type of expense. For example, some plans vary your hospital copayment based on how many days you stay as a patient, and while some use dollar copayments others use percentage coinsurance. Unless you are confident as to a high level of spending in a particular category, and are willing to compare several plan brochures carefully, do not rely on cost sharing details to inform your decision.

The High Deductible and Consumer-Driven plans' copayments are particularly subject to confusion because they change by expenditure level. You start the year with a savings account you can use for any physician, dental, drug, or other expense. In addition, just as in all other plans you get complete coverage of a physical exam that will cost hundreds of dollars. Your copayment for these expenses is zero. If and when you exhaust the savings account, you pay a substantial deductible. After that, you pay a small proportion of hospital and physician costs until you reach the catastrophic limit. Your coinsurance ranges from zero, to 100 percent, to 10 or 15 percent and, once you reach the catastrophic limit, back to zero. The purpose of this is to give you incentives for careful decisions on medical spending. However, these plans' designs make it very difficult to estimate your costs.

We recommend great caution in comparing the details of these plans' deductibles with each other or with traditional insurance plans. HDHP plans show as a deductible the entire amount that must be spent before regular insurance cost sharing kicks in, regardless of whether the enrollee chooses to spend the Health Savings Account, since whether or not that Account is spent is an enrollee decision. In contrast, CDHP plans require that their accounts be spent on medical expense and used up before the deductible starts, and show as a deductible the amount between that spending level and where insurance cost sharing kicks in. As a result, a CDHP plan will invariably show a much smaller deductible than an HDHP plan even if the spending level at which the insurance coverage kicks in is the same. Our estimates of out-of-pocket costs take these variations into account, but the calculations can be complex.

> ### *Dealing with a Known High Expense*
>
> There is an exception to our general advice about focusing on overall plan costs, not just one benefit category. If you know for sure that you will need a particular expensive service, you should look for the answer to "Which plans pay best?" If several plans pay equally well, then you can choose whichever of these is an overall better buy.

Non-Preferred Providers

You face far higher costs if you use non-preferred providers. Plans not only charge you more for deductibles, copayments, and coinsurance, but also require you to pay the entire cost above the rate the plan sets as its allowance used in its network for a particular procedure. That rate is bargained with health care providers and usually varies by zip code and is not available to the public or to plan enrollees in advance. In general, we advise you to stay with preferred providers whenever possible. Remember that out-of-network cost-sharing percentages are valid ONLY if the non-preferred provider accepts the plan's allowance (or, in the case of those over age 65, accepts the Medicare "limiting charge"). In most cases you may need to bargain, and the plan will likely pay less than half the bill. Half is better than nothing, but you should plan your health care to stay in network wherever possible. There is almost always a wide range of high-quality preferred providers in network.

Chapter 6

Coverage Features

Using the *Guide*'s cost comparisons, you should first select several plans for which your costs are likely to be relatively low. The second step in selecting a plan is to focus on any special needs or circumstances that the cost tables do not fully reflect. The third step is to consider how important it is to you to retain a particular doctor(s) and, if necessary, to find out whether your doctor belongs to particular plans. The best way to do this is simply to call the doctor's office and ask. You can also go to the plan's website. You can reverse the order of these steps, but it never makes sense to pay an extra $1,000 in premium if the most you will spend on a particular physician or service is a few hundred dollars. You should save the "for sure" premium cost and if necessary pay for a particular visit directly, without using your insurance.

Even if you know you are going to use a particular service, you can enroll in a plan that costs less overall but doesn't necessarily have a particularly good benefit in that area. You can use the savings to establish a Flexible Spending Account and focus that spending on that special need. Flexible Spending Accounts give employees (but not retirees) a way to reduce foreseeable costs substantially. If you anticipate, for example, having substantial dental or speech therapy expenses even after your coverage by health or dental insurance, in 2022 you could set aside up to $2,750 in a health care FSA account ($5,500 for a couple) and that income will not be subject of Federal and State income taxes, or to Social Security taxes. For most, this has the effect of reducing the amount you actually pay by about one third. You estimate your likely spending and set up this account during the same Open Season used for selecting health plans. An FSA is perfect way to get about a one-third discount on a benefit for which your plan restricts coverage. FSA accounts are no longer "use or lose" and you can carry over up to $500 into the next without penalty.

Still, it is best to choose the low-cost plan that best covers an expense you can predict. Our Coverage Features analysis and tables focus on benefit categories that vary widely across plans, such as non-network psychiatric care. Online our tables show Coverage Features for all plans in the program, nationwide. In the printed *Guide,* we present these detailed tables only for national plans and DC area local plans, and very selectively for plans in other States in the "Cost and Coverage Features of Local Plans" table at the end of the "Key Tips and Final Plan Selection" section.

We have worded the comparison headings to allow standard entries, such as "Yes," "Some," or "No." A "Yes" always means broader coverage and a "No" always means narrower coverage. However, even though a number of plans are rated "Yes," this does not mean that the benefits are identical. You need to compare brochures.

Very importantly, if you know that you will need some specific and expensive type of care, whether or not it is in our tables, and whether or not the brochure seems clear, it is always a sensible strategy to talk to at least one potential provider and ask the simple question "Which plans pay best for the care I need?" You can also talk to a plan representative, but the information you get is not always reliable and carries no guarantee. The actual providers (or their office staff) know which plans pay best in the real world. Explore especially carefully if the service is near some boundary of coverage. For example, some hospitals provide regular hospital care, skilled nursing care, and custodial care in the same facility. You need to be sure that whichever level of service you get will be billed and paid under a category paid by your plan.

Nursing Care

There are four kinds of nursing care: skilled care while in a hospital, skilled care in a special "extended" or "skilled" care facility, care in your own home provided by visiting nurses, and "custodial" care either in your own home or in a "nursing home." No health insurance plan will pay for custodial care, the kind where your principal needs are to be fed, bathed, and clothed and where you need help with ordinary life tasks rather than to recover. At the other extreme, all plans pay for necessary care by nurses while you are in the hospital. Similarly, all plans cover some form of home health care, usually with at least 90 days or visits.

Plans differ in their coverage of care in an "extended" or "skilled" nursing care facility. Most national plans offer no coverage; but a few cover 60 or 90 days per confinement, usually at the same cost to you as hospital treatment. Most HMOs, however, cover skilled nursing care, usually 90 or 100 days.

We did not reflect the value of skilled care in a facility in our cost tables. Since very few younger persons ever need such care, the plan rankings would not have changed much if we had taken into account the statistical probabilities. Virtually all retirees over age 65 have a substantial Medicare Part A benefit for skilled nursing care. Accordingly, they will rarely if ever need any FEHB plan benefit for this care.

Nonetheless, stays in skilled nursing care facilities cost about half as much as in hospitals. This is one of the potentially substantial expenses to which some plans leave you exposed. If you think you are likely to need more than a month of this care, we recommend careful attention to brochure language in relation to your particular needs. Remember, moreover, that these stays are subject to plan approval and must involve rehabilitative needs, not simply help with daily living.

For custodial care, either in your own home or a nursing home, OPM sponsors a Long-Term Care insurance program, separate from the FEHB program. This program pays for long term care services if you can't take care of yourself because of an extended illness, such as Alzheimer's disease. The program covers both institutional and home care. Premiums are substantial, and there is no government contribution. You can find out more about it at *opm. gov/insure/ltc*. Similar insurance can be purchased individually from the same companies that underwrite the OPM program. If your retirement income and assets are relatively low, and you otherwise cannot afford needed custodial care, you can ultimately rely on the Federal/ State Medicaid program.

Value of Outpatient Mental Benefits

OPM has long required that plans pay the same benefits for physician visits or hospital stays whether due to either physical or mental illness. This requirement is called "parity," and, at face value, seems to eliminate any distinction between physical and mental health benefits. It represented a significant advance in covering clinically necessary hospital stays for mental illness. In 2010 the government issued regulations requiring all employer-sponsored health plans to meet an even stricter version of parity. Under these regulations, plans are no longer allowed even to charge separate deductibles for physical and mental health or substance abuse services. In theory, all FEHB plans will now pay for unlimited mental health services without even such a small difference in cost sharing.

The catch is that all plans select the providers for their networks and will rarely if ever use providers whose practices emphasize weekly sessions of "talk therapy." Nor will plans reimburse full costs for services provided by a psychiatrist of your choosing. Instead, they provide a limited number of plan-affiliated psychiatrists, and often rely mainly on the services of clinical psychologists, clinical social workers, and other non-M.D. staff.

Few of the HMO plans offer any mental health services outside of the plan network, or outside of pre-approved treatment plans. The major exceptions are the HMOs with an Opt-Out or "Point of Service" provision. In contrast, all of the national fee-for-service plans except Blue Cross Basic offer a relatively unconstrained out-of-network benefit, as do Consumer-Driven and High Deductible plans. If you expect to use an out of network provider, consider setting up a Flexible Spending Account during Open Season.

Other Coverage Features

Most plans limit reimbursement for most of the following services. Current employees can cover any of them through a Flexible Spending Account.

- *Dental care*—We indicate which health insurance plans pay for routine and accidental dental expenses and show the better benefits with a "Yes." Our separate chapter on "Dental, Vision and Hearing" provides dollar ratings of these plans along with the standalone dental plans (we have even more detailed comparisons online). Those standalone plans charge a premium but offer stronger benefits. Nonetheless, our ratings show that for most people joining an FEHB plan with modest dental benefits is a low-cost option.

- *Vision care*—All plans pay for medically necessary care of your eyes, such as cataract surgery. No national plans pay for eyeglasses or contact lenses, although several of them have arranged for discounts at some chains. A few pay for examinations to determine the prescription you need. Among HMOs, many pay just for an "Exam," and some for most of the cost of glasses or contact lenses ("Yes" in our tables). You may want to join one of the vision plans described in our chapter on "Dental, Vision and Hearing," but a combination of prudent shopping and Flexible Spending Account will often match the value of the standalone vision plans.

- *Chiropractic services*—Most plans reimburse some chiropractic services. The medical establishment has traditionally viewed chiropractors unfavorably because chiropractors are not trained as medical doctors. However, chiropractic services have been proven useful in treating some problems of the muscles, back, and joints. We label "Yes" plans that pay for 20 or more visits at a cost of no more than $20 a visit.

- *Acupuncture*—Another non-traditional treatment that an increasing number of plans reimburse, often for a dozen or more visits.

- *Hearing aids*—Most plans pay for diagnostic hearing tests performed by a physician or audiologist, and all pay for medically necessary treatment for hearing problems. At OPM urging, most plans now pay for hearing aids for both adults and children, and others for hearing aids for children only. In our table, a "Yes" indicates both a relatively generous allowance, and coverage of both children and adults. The "Dental, Vision and Hearing" chapter provides detailed comparisons.

- *Infertility treatment*—Very few plans pay for the costs of in vitro fertilization or for the most advanced and expensive infertility treatments such as assisted reproductive technology procedures. Few plans pay for fertility drugs or for treatments such as artificial insemination. Generosity varies so you should compare brochures or consult providers before choosing a plan. Fertility physicians and clinics are likely to know which plans best cover their services.

- *Diabetic supplies*—Some plans cover drugs but do not cover the cost of syringes and/or special testing supplies and kits needed by diabetics. Even for the plans listed as "Yes," a diabetic should check brochures to determine the precise coverage the plans provide.

- *Durable medical equipment*—All national plans pay for prostheses, or artificial limbs. Some plans limit such coverage. Some plans also fail to pay for the purchase or rental costs of hospital beds, walkers, and other equipment you may need while recuperating from surgery or illness. Others pay only a limited benefit, such as 50 percent of the cost. This is another area to compare brochures and consult providers.

- *Nurse advice*—Most plans let you call a service to discuss medical problems that confuse you. Nurse advisors can greatly assist you in deciding, for example, whether to call a doctor and, if so, which specialty you need. Nurses can also advise you on handling minor medical problems of all kinds, on compliance with your medication needs, and diet and health, and on other issues. For plans that offer this, we enter the telephone number of the advisory service.

Coverage Features of D.C. Area Plans

Plan code	Plan name (listed in alphabetical order within group)	Pays for (in most cases only if medically necessary):				
		Day limit in skilled nursing facility	Maximum non-network mental outpatient	Routine dental care	Dental accident	Adult vision care
D.C. Area Plans When You Use Preferred Providers						
F51-3	Aetna HealthFund CDHP	60	Unlim	Some	Some	Exam
JN4-6	Aetna Open Access Basic	60	None	Yes	Some	Yes
JN1-3	Aetna Open Access-Hi	60	None	Yes	Some	Yes
QQ4-6	Aetna Saver	60	None	None	Some	Exam
F54-6	Aetna Value Plan	60	Unlim	None	Some	Exam
B64-6	CareFirst Blue Value Plus	Unlim	Unlim	Yes	Yes	Exam
B61-3	CareFirst HDHP	Unlim	Unlim	Yes	Yes	Exam
2G4-6	CareFirst-Std	Unlim	Unlim	Yes	Yes	Exam
T71-3	Kaiser Prosper	100	None	None	Yes	Some
E31-3	Kaiser-Hi	100	None	Some	Yes	Yes
E34-6	Kaiser-Std	100	None	Some	Yes	Yes
JP1-3	MD-IPA	60	None	Yes	Yes	Exam
LR1-3	United Choice Open Access	60	None	Some	Yes	Exam
L91-3	United Choice Plus Advanced	60	Unlim	Some	Yes	Exam
AS1-3	United Choice Plus Primary	60	Unlim	Some	Yes	Exam
Y81-3	United Choice Primary	60	None	Some	Yes	Exam
V41-3	United HDHP	60	Unlim	Some	Yes	Exam
D.C. Area Medicare Advantage Plans						
T71-3R[1]	Kaiser Prosper (Medicare Advantage)	100	Yes	None	Yes	Some
E31-3R1[1]	Kaiser-Hi (Medicare Advantage 1)	100	Yes	Yes	Yes	Yes
E31-3R2[1]	Kaiser-Hi (Medicare Advantage 2)	100	Yes	Yes	Yes	Some
E34-6R[1]	Kaiser-Std (Medicare Advantage)	100	Yes	Yes	Yes	Some
JP1-3R[1]	MD-IPA (Retiree Adv.)	100	None	Yes	Yes	Exam
LR1-3R[1]	United Choice Open Access (Ret Adv)	100	Unlim	Yes	Yes	Exam
L91-3R[1]	United Choice Plus Advanced (Ret Adv)	60	Unlim	Some	Yes	Exam
AS1-3R[1]	United Choice Plus Primary (Ret Adv)	100	Unlim	Some	Yes	Exam
Y81-3R[1]	United Choice Primary (Retiree Adv)	100	None	Some	Yes	Exam

[1] This Medicare Advantage plan has special enrollment procedures.

Pays for (in most cases only if medically necessary):							
Chiropractic	Acupuncture	Hearing aids	Infertility treatment	Prostheses (artificial limbs)	Diabetic supplies	Durable medical equipment	Nurse advice by phone
Yes	Little	None	Some	Yes	Some	Yes	800-556-1555
Some	Little	Some	Little	Yes	Yes	Yes	800-556-1555
Some	Little	Some	Little	Yes	Yes	Yes	800-556-1555
Yes	Little	None	Little	Some	Some	Some	800-556-1555
Yes	Little	None	Some	Yes	Some	Yes	800-556-1555
Some	Some	Yes	Little	Some	Yes	Yes	800-535-9700
Yes	Yes	Yes	Some	Yes	Yes	Yes	800-535-9700
Some	Some	Yes	Little	Some	Yes	Yes	800-535-9700
Some	Some	Child	Little	Yes	Yes	Yes	703-359-7878
Yes	Yes	Child	Little	Yes	Yes	Yes	703-359-7878
Some	Some	Child	Little	Yes	Yes	Yes	703-359-7878
Some	Some	Child	Little	Yes	Yes	Yes	877-835-9861
Some	Some	None	Little	Some	Some	Some	877-835-9861
Some	Some	Yes	Little	Some	Some	Some	877-835-9861
Some	Some	Yes	Little	Some	Some	Yes	877-835-9861
Yes	Yes	Yes	Little	Yes	Yes	Yes	877-835-9861
Yes	Some	Yes	Little	Yes	Yes	Yes	877-835-9861
Yes	Yes	Child	NA	Yes	Yes	Yes	703-359-7878
Yes	Yes	Yes	NA	Yes	Yes	Yes	703-359-7878
Yes	Yes	Child	NA	Yes	Yes	Yes	703-359-7878
Yes	Yes	Yes	NA	Yes	Yes	Yes	703-359-7878
Yes	Yes	Some	NA	Yes	Yes	Yes	877-835-9861
Some	Some	Some	NA	Some	Some	Some	877-835-9861
Some	Some	Yes	NA	Some	Some	Some	877-835-9861
Yes	Yes	Yes	NA	Yes	Yes	Yes	877-835-9861
Yes	Yes	Yes	NA	Yes	Yes	Yes	877-835-9861

Note: Your savings accounts in CDHP and HDHP plans, or your FSA account, pay for ALL of these benefits, in addition to what the plans pay.

Coverage Features of National Plans

Plan code	Plan name (listed in alphabetical order within group)	Pays for (in most cases only if medically necessary):				
		Day limit in skilled nursing facility	Maximum non-network mental outpatient	Routine dental care	Dental accident	Adult vision care
National Plans When You Use Preferred Providers						
Z24-6	Aetna Advantage	60	Unlim	None	Yes	Exam
N61-3	Aetna Direct CDHP	60	Unlim	None	Yes	None
224-6	Aetna HealthFund HDHP	60	Unlim	Some	Some	Yes
474-6	APWU CDHP	30	Unlim	None	None	None
471-3	APWU-Hi	30	Unlim	Yes	Yes	None
111-3	Blue Cross Basic	0	None	Some	Yes	None
131-3	Blue Cross FEP Blue Focus	0	None	None	Yes	Exam
104-6	Blue Cross-Std	30	Unlim	Some	Yes	Exam
421-3	Compass Rose	90	Unlim	Yes	Yes	None
401-3	Foreign Service	90	Unlim	Some	Yes	None
254-6	GEHA Elevate	0	Unlim	Some	Yes	None
251-3	GEHA Elevate Plus	21	Unlim	Some	Yes	None
341-3	GEHA HDHP	21	Unlim	Yes	Yes	None
311-3	GEHA-Hi	21	Unlim	Yes	Yes	None
314-6	GEHA-Std	21	Unlim	Some	Yes	None
481-3	MHBP HDHP	28	Unlim	None	Yes	None
414-6	MHBP Value Plan	40	Unlim	None	Yes	None
454-6	MHBP-Std	40	Unlim	None	Yes	None
324-6	NALC CDHP	0	Unlim	None	None	None
KM1-3	NALC Value Plan	0	Unlim	None	Yes	None
321-3	NALC-Hi	21	Unlim	None	Yes	None
381-3	Rural Carrier	60	Unlim	Yes	Yes	Exam
441-3	SAMBA-Hi	45	Unlim	None	Yes	None
444-6	SAMBA-Std	30	Unlim	None	Yes	None
National Medicare Advantage Plans						
Z24-6R[1]	Aetna Advantage (Medicare Advantage)	100[1]	Unlim	None	Yes	Exam
471-3R[1]	APWU-Hi (Medicare Advantage)	60	Yes	Yes	Yes	Exam
421-3R[1]	Compass Rose (Medicare Advantage)	100	Unlim	Yes	Yes	Yes
454-6V[1]	MHBP-Std (Medicare Advantage)	100	Unlim	None	Yes	Some
381-3R[1]	Rural Carrier (Medicare Advantage)	100	Unlim	Yes	Yes	Yes

[1] This Medicare Advantage plan has special enrollment procedures.

	Pays for (in most cases only if medically necessary):							
Chiropractic	Acupuncture	Hearing aids	Infertility treatment	Prostheses (artificial limbs)	Diabetic supplies	Durable medical equipment	Nurse advice by phone
None	None	None	Little	Some	Some	Some	800-556-1555
None	Little	Yes	Little	Yes	Yes	Yes	Many Areas
None	Little	None	Yes	Yes	Some	Yes	800-556-1555
Yes	Yes	Some	Yes	Yes	Yes	Yes	800-718-1299
Yes	Yes	Some	Yes	Yes	Yes	Yes	800-582-1314
Some	Some	Yes	Little	Some	Yes	Yes	888-258-3432
Some	Some	None	Little	Yes	Yes	Yes	888-258-3432
Some	Yes	Yes	Little	Yes	Yes	Yes	888-258-3432
Yes	Some	Some	Some	Yes	Yes	Yes	None
Yes	Yes	Yes	Yes	Yes	Yes	Yes	855-482-5750
Some	Yes	None	Little	Yes	Yes	Yes	888-257-4342
Some	Some	Some	Little	Yes	Yes	Yes	888-257-4342
Some	Yes	None	Little	Yes	Some	Some	888-257-4342
Some	Yes	Yes	Yes	Yes	Yes	Yes	888-257-4342
Some	Yes	Yes	Little	Yes	Yes	Yes	888-257-4342
Yes	Yes	Some	Little	Yes	Yes	Yes	800-694-9901
Yes	Yes	Some	Little	Yes	Yes	Yes	800-410-7778
Yes	Yes	Yes	Yes	Yes	Yes	Yes	800-410-7778
Some	Some	Yes	Little	Yes	Yes	Yes	877-220-6252
Some	Some	Some	Little	Yes	Yes	Yes	877-220-6252
Some	Some	Yes	Little	Yes	Yes	Yes	877-220-6252
Yes	Yes	Yes	Little	Yes	Yes	Yes	800-638-8432
Yes	Some	Yes	Little	Yes	Yes	Yes	800-887-9735
Some	Yes	Yes	Yes	Yes	Yes	Yes	800-887-9735
Yes	Yes	Yes	NA	Yes	Yes	Yes	800-556-1555
Yes	Yes	Yes	NA	Yes	Yes	Yes	800-582-1314
Yes	Yes	Yes	NA	Yes	Yes	Yes	None
Yes	Yes	Yes	NA	Yes	Yes	Yes	800-410-7778
Yes	Yes	Yes	NA	Yes	Yes	Yes	800-638-8432

Note: Your savings accounts in CDHP and HDHP plans, or your FSA account, pay for ALL of these benefits, in addition to what the plans pay.

Chapter 7

Dental, Vision and Hearing

The Federal government offers standalone "FEDVIP" dental and vision plans, separate and distinct from the FEHB program. These plans share the same Open Season dates as the health insurance plans, but you join them separately. To enroll, you can use the special OPM website at *www.benefeds.com*, or call 1-877-888-3337. In sharp contrast to regular health insurance benefits, there is no direct Federal government contribution to the cost of the premium. You pay it all, though with substantial tax savings to employees (but not annuitants).

While these plans do have an element of insurance, in that they protect you against some unforeseen dental or vision expenses, they are best thought of as primarily pre-paid care. Most people enroll in these kinds of plans because they know roughly what kinds of expenses to expect, and plan to do a little better than breaking even. In effect, you pay for those new contact lenses or your recurring dental expenses on the biweekly or monthly installment plan, with protection against some unanticipated expense.

The dental and vision plans save you money in two ways. First, they use affiliated providers who provide discounts because of the increased business the plans attract. Second, because employees (but not retirees) pay the premiums with "pre-tax" dollars, you save approximately one-third of the premium cost. As explained in our analysis of "Premiums and Taxes" almost all Federal employees face a marginal tax rate close to 33 percent, taking into account Federal income tax, State income tax, the Medicare tax and the Social Security tax. Any money an employee spends on dental or vision insurance is not subject to these taxes and employees get what amounts to a one-third discount on the premium, depending on their tax bracket.

On the other hand, these plans charge a premium, ranging from about $200 to $400 a year for self-only dental and about $80 to $150 a year for self-only vision, with family premiums about three times as high. Also, the companies that underwrite these plans know that they will attract persons who are heavy users of these services. This means that the premiums have to be higher than would otherwise be the case.

Virtually all FEHB health insurance plans provide insurance coverage for accidental dental or vision injuries. Typical brochure language says, "We cover services and supplies necessary to promptly repair sound natural teeth" when services are needed due to an "accidental injury." For vision services, typical brochure language says the plan will cover testing and evaluation and fitting for implanted ocular lenses or contact lenses when the impairment is "caused by accident or illness." Most FEHB plans also have some routine dental and vision benefits. These are often substantial benefits (though never as good as in FEDVIP plans). By joining a health insurance plan with better than average dental or vision benefits, you can eliminate much of the need for a supplemental plan. As an example, the Aetna Consumer-Driven plan offers a special $300 fund for self-only enrollees (and double that for families) that covers dental costs.

You can also use a Flexible Spending Account to provide prepaid dental or vision care. By earmarking several hundred or even several thousand dollars of your salary, you avoid paying taxes on that income and effectively gain the same one-third discount that the FEDVIP plans provide. To set up an FSA, you estimate your likely spending for dental, vision, or other anticipated out of pocket expenses. You create an FSA during the same Open Season used for selecting health plans and FEDVIP plans.

You can use all three approaches simultaneously. For example, suppose you enroll in a health insurance plan that pays for preventive dental care and an annual eye exam. You can also enroll in a supplemental vision or dental plan, or both. The health insurance plan will be "primary" and pay first, and the FEDVIP plan pay second. You can then use your FSA account to pay the residual that the first two sources do not cover. This three-part approach may, of course, require more planning and more paperwork than you are willing to tolerate. There is the further complication that your favorite provider may not be a plan participant under either the FEHB or FEDVIP plan. But it does give you maximum wrap-around coverage.

Annuitants do not get the same tax advantages as employees. They may sign up for supplemental dental or vision plans, but do not get the pre-tax "discount." They are not allowed to create FSAs. However, annuitants do get the government contribution towards their FEHB plans, which averages about 70 percent. A health insurance plan with a good dental benefit may be an excellent choice for retirees with low to moderate dental or vision expenses, and with heavy anticipated expenses a FEDVIP plan is a sensible choice even without the taxpayer subsidy.

Consumer-Driven and High Deductible health plans are particularly flexible and comprehensive options for funding dental and vision expenses. These plans allow you to shelter from taxes a personal savings account that you can use for dental and vision expenses and carry over from year to year. Several of them have special dental funds, and high deductible plans allow employees (but not annuitants) to augment savings accounts during the year if unanticipated expenses arise. These accounts may be used for dental or vision expenses quite apart from those expenses that the plan normally covers, and without restrictions on provider choice (though you may lose discounts if you use non-plan providers). If you already know your dental expenses will be high next year, you can even set up a special account called a Limited Expense Health Care FSA (LEX HCFSA) during Open Season. This will provide dental and vision funding over and above the normal limits on your tax-free contributions to personal savings accounts.

Dental and vision benefits are areas in which you can plan, and in which it pays to plan. Unlike true insurance, where your main need is to guard against large and unpredictable expenses, you probably have a pretty good idea what you are likely to spend on dental and eye care expenses. You can structure your decision around those predictable costs, keeping in mind of course that a tooth, crown, or bridge can break unexpectedly, or some other dental emergency arise. Be careful to read the fine print of the plan brochures carefully, however. The plan may be unlikely to pay for a denture if the need arose before you joined the plan, for example.

The dental and vision plans offer a three-part premium structure—self only, self plus one, and family of three or more. The premiums for families of two or three are almost always about double or triple the self-only premium. If you have a family of three (or more) you may enroll as self plus one and designate which two persons will be eligible for benefits.

Dental Care

Plans' dental benefits differ widely in details, and many of the brochures use technical terminology such as "gingival" (gum, in English), "alveolar" (the part of the jawbone that holds teeth in place), and "amalgam restorations" (filling cavities). Moreover, many plans use schedules of allowances so you don't know if the full charge will be paid (usually not). Since most of the plans limit coverage to the items listed in the schedule of allowances, the particular problem you have may not be covered at all. Worst of all, no plans offer a catastrophic dental benefit that would cover you if, for example, you developed a chronic infection of the jaw and required dental procedures costing thousands of dollars. If you are not sure that a plan adequately covers the particular dental problems of your family, or to be sure you get the network discount, you should talk to your dentist before choosing that plan. For example, most dental plans now cover dental implants, a very expensive procedure. But exactly which parts of the procedure are covered for sure, which options are best, which of these parts or options require plan approval, and how likely a case like yours is to get plan approval, varies from plan to plan. You can call the plan to discuss your case, but the best way to find out which dental plan will cover your implant at least cost to you is to ask your dental surgeon what his patients' experience has been.

In recent years OPM has not allowed most health plans to expand dental benefits. However, OPM has allowed plans to offer "non-FEHB" benefits to plan members, as shown on a special page in brochures. In many cases, extra dental benefits are offered, usually through a network of dentists who provide discounts for the extra business the plan brings. When these do not involve an extra premium

Dental Plan Ratings for Employees—Single Person*

Plan code	Plan name	Plan type	Extra yearly premium	Approximate yearly cost to you if your dental usage is:			Maximum benefit per person
				Low	Average	High	
D.C. Area Plans When You Use Preferred Providers							
2G4	CareFirst-Std	Unofficial	$0	$120	$400	$1,200	None
B64	CareFirst Blue Value Plus	Unofficial	$0	$120	$400	$1,200	None
B61	CareFirst HDHP	Unofficial	$0	$120	$400	$1,200	None
E31	Kaiser-Hi	Both	$0	$90	$400	$1,400	None
E34	Kaiser-Std	Both	$0	$90	$400	$1,400	None
F51	Aetna HealthFund CDHP	Official	$0	$120	$600	$2,200	$300+prev
JN1	Aetna Open Access-Hi	Official	$0	$120	$600	$2,200	None
JN4	Aetna Open Access Basic	Official	$0	$120	$600	$2,200	None
JP1	MD-IPA	Both	$0	$120	$600	$2,200	$500
AS1	United Choice Plus Primary	Unofficial	$0	$150	$750	$2,750	$500
Y81	United Choice Primary	Unofficial	$0	$150	$750	$2,750	$500
LR1	United Choice Open Access	Unofficial	$0	$150	$750	$2,750	$500
L91	United Choice Plus Advanced	Unofficial	$0	$150	$750	$2,750	$500
V41	UnitedHealthcare HDHP	Unofficial	$0	$150	$750	$2,750	$500
QQ4	Aetna Saver	Official	$0	$300	$1,000	$3,000	None
National Plans When You Use Preferred Providers							
471	APWU-Hi	Both	$0	$140	$530	$1,730	None
421	Compass Rose	Unofficial	$0	$170	$580	$1,780	None
341	GEHA HDHP	Both	$0	$140	$680	$2,480	None
321	NALC-Hi	Unofficial	$0	$210	$700	$2,100	None
KM1	NALC Value Plan	Unofficial	$0	$210	$700	$2,100	None
324	NALC CDHP	Unofficial	$0	$210	$700	$2,100	None
224	Aetna HealthFund HDHP	Official	$0	$150	$750	$2,750	None
111	Blue Cross Basic	Official	$0	$170	$780	$2,780	None
254	GEHA Elevate	Both	$0	$210	$800	$2,600	None
251	GEHA Elevate Plus	Both	$0	$210	$800	$2,600	None
314	GEHA-Std	Both	$0	$210	$800	$2,600	None
311	GEHA-Hi	Both	$0	$260	$880	$2,680	None
401	Foreign Service	Official	$0	$270	$900	$2,700	None
381	Rural Carrier	Official	$0	$310	$930	$2,730	None
104	Blue Cross-Std	Official	$0	$270	$950	$2,950	None
Supplemental Dental Plans When You Use Preferred Providers							
	Dominion Dental High	FEDVIP	$180	$220	$380	$920	Unlim
	Dominion Dental Std	FEDVIP	$120	$170	$390	$1,110	Unlim
	Humana Dental Std EPO	FEDVIP	$230	$270	$430	$970	$15,000
	Aetna Dental Std	FEDVIP	$170	$250	$580	$1,660	$1,500
	United Concordia Dental Std	FEDVIP	$180	$260	$590	$1,670	$1,500
	Blue Cross FEP Dental Std	FEDVIP	$200	$280	$610	$1,690	$1,500
	United Dental Std	FEDVIP	$210	$290	$620	$1,700	$1,500
	Delta Dental Std	FEDVIP	$230	$310	$640	$1,720	$1,500
	GEHA Dental Std	FEDVIP	$230	$310	$640	$1,720	$2,500
	Metlife Dental Std	FEDVIP	$230	$310	$640	$1,720	$1,500
	United Concordia Dental High	FEDVIP	$370	$420	$640	$1,360	Unlim
	Aetna Dental High	FEDVIP	$310	$380	$650	$1,550	Unlim
	United Concordia Dental Std	FEDVIP	$250	$330	$660	$1,740	$1,500
	Humana Dental High PPO	FEDVIP	$350	$420	$690	$1,590	Unlim
	Blue Cross FEP Dental High	FEDVIP	$380	$450	$720	$1,620	Unlim
	GEHA Dental High	FEDVIP	$410	$480	$750	$1,650	Unlim
	Metlife Dental High	FEDVIP	$420	$480	$750	$1,650	Unlim
	United Dental High	FEDVIP	$410	$480	$750	$1,650	Unlim
	Delta Dental High	FEDVIP	$460	$530	$800	$1,700	Unlim

* Plans are listed in order of lowest cost to you for an average cost year for self only in each group of plans. Plans with no dental benefits are not listed.

Dental Plan Ratings for Employees—Family of Three or More*

Plan code	Plan name	Extra yearly premium	Approximate yearly cost to you if your dental usage is:			Maximum benefit per person	Child orth-odontic
			Low	Average	High		
D.C. Area Plans When You Use Preferred Providers							
2G5	CareFirst-Std	$0	$320	$1,200	$2,800	None	Some
B65	CareFirst Blue Value Plus	$0	$320	$1,200	$2,800	None	Some
B62	CareFirst HDHP	$0	$320	$1,200	$2,800	None	No
E32	Kaiser-Hi	$0	$220	$1,220	$3,220	None	No
E35	Kaiser-Std	$0	$220	$1,220	$3,220	None	No
F52	Aetna HealthFund CDHP	$0	$280	$1,680	$4,880	$300+prev	No
JN2	Aetna Open Access-Hi	$0	$280	$1,720	$4,920	None	No
JN5	Aetna Open Access Basic	$0	$280	$1,720	$4,920	None	Some
JP2	MD-IPA	$0	$280	$1,840	$5,040	$500	Some
AS2	United Choice Plus Primary	$0	$350	$2,300	$6,300	$500	Some
Y82	United Choice Primary	$0	$350	$2,300	$6,300	$500	No
LR2	United Choice Open Access	$0	$350	$2,300	$6,300	$500	No
L92	United Choice Plus Advanced	$0	$350	$2,300	$6,300	$500	No
V42	UnitedHealthcare HDHP	$0	$350	$2,300	$6,300	$500	No
QQ5	Aetna Saver	$0	$800	$3,000	$7,000	None	No
National Plans When You Use Preferred Providers							
472	APWU-Hi	$0	$350	$1,530	$3,930	None	No
422	Compass Rose	$0	$440	$1,730	$4,130	None	No
342	GEHA HDHP	$0	$320	$2,070	$5,670	None	No
322	NALC-Hi	$0	$560	$2,100	$4,900	None	No
KM2	NALC Value Plan	$0	$560	$2,100	$4,900	None	No
325	NALC CDHP	$0	$560	$2,100	$4,900	None	No
225	Aetna HealthFund HDHP	$0	$350	$2,300	$6,300	None	No
112	Blue Cross Basic	$0	$400	$2,370	$6,370	None	No
255	GEHA Elevate	$0	$540	$2,420	$6,020	None	No
252	GEHA Elevate Plus	$0	$540	$2,420	$6,020	None	No
315	GEHA-Std	$0	$540	$2,420	$6,020	None	Yes
312	GEHA-Hi	$0	$680	$2,630	$6,230	None	No
402	Foreign Service	$0	$710	$2,700	$6,300	None	No
382	Rural Carrier	$0	$830	$2,780	$6,380	None	No
105	Blue Cross-Std	$0	$700	$2,840	$6,840	None	No
Supplemental Dental Plans When You Use Preferred Providers							
	Dominion Dental High	$540	$630	$1,130	$2,210	Unlim	Yes
	Dominion Dental Std	$370	$500	$1,180	$2,620	Unlim	Yes
	Humana Dental Std EPO	$680	$770	$1,280	$2,360	Unlim	Yes
	Aetna Dental Std	$510	$700	$1,730	$3,890	$1,500	Wait
	United Concordia Dental Std	$540	$730	$1,760	$3,920	$1,500	Yes
	Blue Cross FEP Dental Std	$600	$780	$1,720	$3,880	$1,500	Yes
	United Dental Std	$640	$840	$1,870	$4,030	$1,500	Yes
	Delta Dental Std	$680	$870	$1,900	$4,060	$1,500	Yes
	GEHA Dental Std	$680	$870	$1,900	$4,060	$2,500	Yes
	Metlife Dental Std	$700	$890	$1,920	$4,080	$1,500	Wait
	United Concordia Dental High	$1,120	$1,260	$1,920	$3,360	Unlim	Wait
	Aetna Dental High	$920	$1,080	$1,920	$3,720	Unlim	Yes
	United Concordia Dental Std	$740	$920	$1,950	$4,110	$1,500	Wait
	Humana Dental High PPO	$1,040	$1,200	$2,060	$3,860	Unlim	Yes
	Blue Cross FEP Dental High	$1,150	$1,310	$2,150	$3,950	Unlim	Yes
	GEHA Dental High	$1,230	$1,390	$2,210	$4,010	Unlim	Yes
	Metlife Dental High	$1,250	$1,410	$2,250	$4,050	Unlim	Wait
	United Dental High	$1,240	$1,400	$2,240	$4,040	Unlim	Wait
	Delta Dental High	$1,370	$1,530	$2,370	$4,170	Unlim	Wait

* Plans are listed in order of lowest cost to you for an average cost year for self only in each group of plans. Plans with no dental benefits are not listed.

Dental Plan Ratings for Annuitants—Single Person*

Plan code	Plan name	Plan type	Extra yearly premium	Approximate yearly cost to you if your dental usage is:			Maximum benefit per person
				Low	Average	High	
D.C. Area Plans When You Use Preferred Providers							
2G4	CareFirst-Std	Unofficial	$0	$120	$400	$1,200	None
B64	CareFirst Blue Value Plus	Unofficial	$0	$120	$400	$1,200	None
B61	CareFirst HDHP	Unofficial	$0	$120	$400	$1,200	None
E31	Kaiser-Hi	Both	$0	$90	$400	$1,400	None
E34	Kaiser-Std	Both	$0	$90	$400	$1,400	None
F51	Aetna HealthFund CDHP	Official	$0	$120	$600	$2,200	$300+prev
JN1	Aetna Open Access-Hi	Official	$0	$120	$600	$2,200	None
JN4	Aetna Open Access Basic	Official	$0	$120	$600	$2,200	None
JP1	MD-IPA	Both	$0	$120	$600	$2,200	$500
AS1	United Choice Plus Primary	Unofficial	$0	$150	$750	$2,750	$500
Y81	United Choice Primary	Unofficial	$0	$150	$750	$2,750	$500
LR1	United Choice Open Access	Unofficial	$0	$150	$750	$2,750	$500
L91	United Choice Plus Advanced	Unofficial	$0	$150	$750	$2,750	$500
V41	UnitedHealthcare HDHP	Unofficial	$0	$150	$750	$2,750	$500
QQ4	Aetna Saver	Official	$0	$300	$1,000	$3,000	None
National Plans When You Use Preferred Providers							
471	APWU-Hi	Both	$0	$140	$530	$1,730	None
421	Compass Rose	Unofficial	$0	$170	$580	$1,780	None
341	GEHA HDHP	Both	$0	$140	$680	$2,480	None
321	NALC-Hi	Unofficial	$0	$210	$700	$2,100	None
KM1	NALC Value Plan	Unofficial	$0	$210	$700	$2,100	None
324	NALC CDHP	Unofficial	$0	$210	$700	$2,100	None
224	Aetna HealthFund HDHP	Official	$0	$150	$750	$2,750	None
111	Blue Cross Basic	Official	$0	$170	$780	$2,780	None
254	GEHA Elevate	Both	$0	$210	$800	$2,600	None
251	GEHA Elevate Plus	Both	$0	$210	$800	$2,600	None
314	GEHA-Std	Both	$0	$210	$800	$2,600	None
311	GEHA-Hi	Both	$0	$260	$880	$2,680	None
401	Foreign Service	Official	$0	$270	$900	$2,700	None
381	Rural Carrier	Official	$0	$310	$930	$2,730	None
104	Blue Cross-Std	Official	$0	$270	$950	$2,950	None
Supplemental Dental Plans When You Use Preferred Providers							
	Dominion Dental Std	FEDVIP	$180	$230	$450	$1,170	Unlim
	Dominion Dental High	FEDVIP	$270	$310	$470	$1,010	Unlim
	Humana Dental Std EPO	FEDVIP	$340	$380	$540	$1,080	Unlim
	Aetna Dental Std	FEDVIP	$260	$340	$670	$1,750	$1,500
	United Concordia Dental Std	FEDVIP	$270	$350	$680	$1,760	$1,500
	Blue Cross FEP Dental Std	FEDVIP	$300	$380	$710	$1,790	$1,500
	United Dental Std	FEDVIP	$320	$400	$730	$1,810	$1,500
	Delta Dental Std	FEDVIP	$340	$420	$750	$1,830	$1,500
	GEHA Dental Std	FEDVIP	$340	$420	$750	$1,830	$2,500
	Metlife Dental Std	FEDVIP	$350	$430	$760	$1,840	$1,500
	United Concordia Dental Std	FEDVIP	$370	$450	$780	$1,860	$1,500
	Aetna Dental High	FEDVIP	$460	$530	$800	$1,700	Unlim
	United Concordia Dental High	FEDVIP	$560	$610	$830	$1,550	Unlim
	Humana Dental High PPO	FEDVIP	$520	$590	$860	$1,760	Unlim
	Blue Cross FEP Dental High	FEDVIP	$570	$640	$910	$1,810	Unlim
	GEHA Dental High	FEDVIP	$620	$690	$960	$1,860	Unlim
	Metlife Dental High	FEDVIP	$620	$690	$960	$1,860	Unlim
	United Dental High	FEDVIP	$620	$690	$960	$1,860	Unlim
	Delta Dental High	FEDVIP	$690	$760	$1,030	$1,930	Unlim

* Plans are listed in order of lowest cost to you for a high cost year for self only in each group of plans.

Dental Plan Ratings for Annuitants—Self Plus One*

Plan code	Plan name	Extra yearly premium	Approximate yearly cost to you if your dental usage is:			Maximum benefit per person	Child orthodontic
			Low	Average	High		
D.C. Area Plans When You Use Preferred Providers							
2G5	CareFirst-Std	$0	$320	$1,200	$2,800	None	Some
B65	CareFirst Blue Value Plus	$0	$320	$1,200	$2,800	None	Some
B62	CareFirst HDHP	$0	$320	$1,200	$2,800	None	No
E32	Kaiser-Hi	$0	$220	$1,220	$3,220	None	No
E35	Kaiser-Std	$0	$220	$1,220	$3,220	None	No
F52	Aetna HealthFund CDHP	$0	$280	$1,680	$4,880	$300+prev	No
JN2	Aetna Open Access-Hi	$0	$280	$1,720	$4,920	None	No
JN5	Aetna Open Access Basic	$0	$280	$1,720	$4,920	None	Some
JP2	MD-IPA	$0	$280	$1,840	$5,040	$500	Some
AS2	United Choice Plus Primary	$0	$350	$2,300	$6,300	$500	Some
Y82	United Choice Primary	$0	$350	$2,300	$6,300	$500	No
LR2	United Choice Open Access	$0	$350	$2,300	$6,300	$500	No
L92	United Choice Plus Advanced	$0	$350	$2,300	$6,300	$500	No
V42	UnitedHealthcare HDHP	$0	$350	$2,300	$6,300	$500	No
QQ5	Aetna Saver	$0	$800	$3,000	$7,000	None	No
National Plans When You Use Preferred Providers							
472	APWU-Hi	$0	$350	$1,530	$3,930	None	No
422	Compass Rose	$0	$440	$1,730	$4,130	None	No
342	GEHA HDHP	$0	$320	$2,070	$5,670	None	No
322	NALC-Hi	$0	$560	$2,100	$4,900	None	No
KM2	NALC Value Plan	$0	$560	$2,100	$4,900	None	No
325	NALC CDHP	$0	$560	$2,100	$4,900	None	No
225	Aetna HealthFund HDHP	$0	$350	$2,300	$6,300	None	No
112	Blue Cross Basic	$0	$400	$2,370	$6,370	None	No
255	GEHA Elevate	$0	$540	$2,420	$6,020	None	No
252	GEHA Elevate Plus	$0	$540	$2,420	$6,020	None	No
315	GEHA-Std	$0	$540	$2,420	$6,020	None	Yes
312	GEHA-Hi	$0	$680	$2,630	$6,230	None	No
402	Foreign Service	$0	$710	$2,700	$6,300	None	No
382	Rural Carrier	$0	$830	$2,780	$6,380	None	No
105	Blue Cross-Std	$0	$700	$2,840	$6,840	None	No
Supplemental Dental Plans When You Use Preferred Providers							
	Dominion Dental Std	$550	$680	$1,360	$2,800	Unlim	Yes
	Dominion Dental High	$810	$900	$1,400	$2,480	Unlim	Yes
	Humana Dental Std EPO	$1,020	$1,110	$1,620	$2,700	Unlim	Yes
	Aetna Dental Std	$770	$960	$1,990	$4,150	$1,500	Wait
	United Concordia Dental Std	$810	$1,000	$2,030	$4,190	$1,500	Yes
	Blue Cross FEP Dental Std	$890	$1,080	$2,020	$4,180	$1,500	Yes
	United Dental Std	$970	$1,160	$2,190	$4,350	$1,500	Yes
	Delta Dental Std	$1,020	$1,210	$2,240	$4,400	$1,500	Yes
	GEHA Dental Std	$1,020	$1,210	$2,240	$4,400	$2,500	Yes
	Metlife Dental Std	$1,050	$1,240	$2,270	$4,430	$1,500	Wait
	United Concordia Dental Std	$1,100	$1,290	$2,320	$4,480	$1,500	Wait
	Aetna Dental High	$1,380	$1,540	$2,380	$4,180	Unlim	Yes
	United Concordia Dental High	$1,690	$1,820	$2,480	$3,920	Unlim	Wait
	Humana Dental High PPO	$1,560	$1,720	$2,580	$4,380	Unlim	Yes
	Blue Cross FEP Dental High	$1,720	$1,880	$2,720	$4,520	Unlim	Yes
	GEHA Dental High	$1,850	$2,010	$2,830	$4,630	Unlim	Yes
	Metlife Dental High	$1,870	$2,030	$2,870	$4,670	Unlim	Wait
	United Dental High	$1,860	$2,020	$2,860	$4,660	Unlim	Wait
	Delta Dental High	$2,060	$2,220	$3,060	$4,860	Unlim	Wait

* Plans are listed in order of lowest cost to you for a high cost year for self only in each group of plans.

and represent a significant benefit that can be determined from the brochure, we have included their value in our ratings and tables. While they are not part of the OPM contract and will not be enforced by OPM, they are nonetheless plan commitments to you. In other words, don't rely on a plan brochure saying that there is no official dental benefit—check the page or pages offering "non-FEHB" benefits, or search on the word "dental" to find that unofficial and usually free benefit.

The new standalone dental plans give you a good deal more advance assurance about what is covered and how much you are likely to pay than most of the health plans. However, how much each plan will cover depends importantly on whether your expenses are mainly for children or for adults, and whether for preventive and diagnostic services, or for more expensive restorative services (including surgical, endodontic, prosthodontic, etc.).

Is Your Dentist in the Network?

Dental plans use network rates that may reduce your costs by more than the cost saving shown in the plan. It pays to choose a dentist first, and then a plan with a network he has joined.

Our dental benefit tables help you sort this out. First, we provide estimates of the cost to you under each plan that provides dental benefits, organized by type of plan. There are no extra premiums under the health plans, but there are for the standalone dental plans, and we show the annual premium cost together with the likely out of pocket cost under low, average, and high usage scenarios. Because the premium cost is a "for sure" expense we include it in each column.

We also show which plans cover roughly how much on average for child preventive, child restorative, adult preventive, and adult restorative services. These estimates are based on a market basket of dental procedures that are among the most common in each category. For example, we assume that children receive the following preventive and diagnostic services through an annual visit: periodic examination, prophylaxis, bitewing x-rays, and fluoride treatment. For adult restorative services, our index includes fillings, extractions, crowns, root canal treatment, periodontal treatment, and dentures. Although the tables show specific percentages, these are rough estimates, based on national average prices. Your dentist may charge more or less. Also, we had to translate varied plan reimbursement approaches into the "percent you pay," and sometimes this is only an approximation. However, these data can steer you towards particular plans' brochures if there are particular benefits you want to check out in detail for the best coverage.

We also show you the maximum benefit levels (if any) of each plan. Most health plans do not have maximums because their benefits are low enough that they do not face substantial cost exposure. However, most of the standalone plans impose maximum ceilings on what they will pay. If you expect very high expenses, consider a plan with a high or even unlimited maximum, but expect to pay more in premium.

Orthodontic coverage is important to some. All of the standalone FEDVIP dental plans have a substantial orthodontic benefit, as does the Foreign Service plan. The coverage terms vary, so you should compare them carefully. Especially importantly, some dental plans try to discourage you from joining at the last minute to take advantage of these benefits, often by imposing 12 month waiting periods on eligibility. Many plans, however, impose no waiting periods. Orthodontics is the perfect dental expense for combining a dental plan with an FSA account for expenses the plan doesn't cover. It is also an area where it makes sense to talk to providers about getting the lowest cost, taking into account which networks and plans they have joined.

In sum, even if you and your family do not need substantial dental work, one of the health plans may be worth several hundred dollars per year, or more, a benefit that costs you no additional premium. The standalone dental plans provide a distinctly better benefit than almost all health plans, but at a premium cost that largely offsets their better benefits. The dental plans make the most sense for persons who are sure they will have moderately or very high dental expenses, want some protection against an unexpected expense, and like the predictability of paying a regular premium and reducing wide fluctuations from month to month in what they may pay.

National Vision Plans

Plan name	Aetna Vision		Blue Cross FEP Vision		Metlife		UnitedHealthcare		VSP	
	High	Std	High	Std	High	Std	High	Std	High	Std
Website	aetnafeds.com		bcbsfepvision.com		metlife.com/ fedvip-vision		vip.myuhcvision.com		choosevsp.com	
Telephone	855-347-6899		888-550-2583		888-865-6854		866-249-1999		800-807-0764	
Annual Cost for Employees (with tax savings of one-third)										
Self only	$100	$50	$100	$60	$100	$60	$90	$60	$120	$60
Self plus one	$200	$110	$190	$120	$190	$120	$170	$110	$230	$120
Self and family	$290	$160	$290	$190	$290	$180	$250	$170	$350	$190
Annual Cost for Annuitants (published premium without tax savings)										
Self Only	$150	$80	$140	$90	$150	$90	$130	$90	$170	$90
Self Plus One	$290	$160	$290	$180	$290	$170	$260	$170	$350	$190
Self and Family	$440	$250	$430	$280	$440	$260	$380	$260	$520	$280
Copayments										
Deductible	None	None	None	None	None	None	None	None	None	None
Annual eye exam	$0	$0	$0	$0	$0	$0	$0	$10	$0	$0
Eyeglass lenses	$0	$10	$0	$10	$0	$20	$10	$25	$0	$20
Inexpensive frames	$0	$0	$0	$0	$0	$0	$0	$0	$0	$0
Contact lenses	$0	$0	$0	$0	$0	$20	$10	$25	$0	$20
Lens and Frame Benefits										
Replace lost/broken lenses?	No	No	No	No	No	No	No	No	No	No
Frequency of lenses	Annual	Annual	Annual	Annual	Annual	Annual	Annual	Annual	Annual	Annual
Frequency of frames	Annual	Annual	Annual	Annual	Annual	Annual	Annual	Annual	Annual	Annual
Frame allowance	$300	$150	$200	$140	$150	$120	$200	$200	$200	$150
Premium frames allowance/discount	20%	20%	20%	20%	$200/ 20%	$160/ 20%	None	None	250/ 20%	$200/ 20%
Anti-reflective coating cost	$20	$45	$20	$35	$26	$41	Included	$30	$21	$41
UV coating cost	Included	$15	Included	Included	Included	Included	Included	Included	Included	Included
Progressive lens cost	$0	$75	$0	$50	$0	$0	$0	$25	$0	$0
Other Benefits										
Laser surgery discount	15%	15%	40%	40%	15%	15%	35%	35%	15%	15%
Out of network	Reduced	Reduced	Reduced	None	Reduced	Reduced	Reduced	Reduced	Reduced	Reduced
International	Reduced	Reduced	Reduced	Reduced	Reduced	Reduced	Reduced	Reduced	Reduced	Reduced

Hearing Aid Benefits for Adults—D.C. Area Plans

Plan code	Plan name	Hearing aids coverage for adults?	Frequency of replacement	Most plan will pay for one ear	Most plan will pay for two ears
D.C. Area Plans When You Use Preferred Providers					
F51-3	Aetna HealthFund CDHP	No	NA	NA	NA
JN4-6	Aetna Open Access Basic	Some	3 years	$1,400	$2,800
JN1-3	Aetna Open Access-Hi	Some	3 years	$1,400	$2,800
QQ4-6	Aetna Saver	No	NA	NA	NA
F54-6	Aetna Value Plan	No	NA	NA	NA
B64-6	CareFirst Blue Value Plus	Yes	3 years	$1,000	$2,000
B61-3	CareFirst HDHP	Yes	3 years	$1,500	$3,000
2G4-6	CareFirst-Std	Yes	3 years	$1,500	$3,000
T71-3	Kaiser Prosper	No	NA	NA	NA
E31-3	Kaiser-Hi	No	NA	NA	NA
E34-6	Kaiser-Std	No	NA	NA	NA
JP1-3	MD-IPA	No	NA	NA	NA
LR1-3	United Choice Open Access	No	NA	NA	NA
L91-3	United Choice Plus Advanced	Yes	3 years	$2,500	$5,000
AS1-3	United Choice Plus Primary	Yes	3 years	$2,500	$5,000
Y81-3	United Choice Primary	Yes	3 years	$2,500	$5,000
V41-3	United HDHP	Yes	1 year	You Pay 20%	You Pay 20%
D.C. Area Medicare Advantage Plans					
T71-3R[1]	Kaiser Prosper (Medicare Advantage)	No	NA	NA	NA
E31-3R1[1]	Kaiser-Hi (Medicare Advantage 1)	Yes	3 years	$750	$1,500
E31-3R2[1]	Kaiser-Hi (Medicare Advantage 2)	No	NA	NA	NA
E34-6R[1]	Kaiser-Std (Medicare Advantage)	Yes	3 years	$500	$1,000
JP1-3R[1]	MD-IPA (Retiree Adv.)	Some	3 years	$500	$1,000
LR1-3R[1]	United Choice Open Access (Ret Adv)	Some	3 years	$1,500	$3,000
L91-3R[1]	United Choice Plus Advanced (Ret Adv)	Yes	3 years	$1,500	$3,000
AS1-3R[1]	United Choice Plus Primary (Ret Adv)	Yes	3 years	$1,500	$3,000
Y81-3R[1]	United Choice Primary (Retiree Adv)	Yes	3 years	$1,500	$3,000

[1] This Medicare Advantage plan has special enrollment procedures.

Hearing Aid Benefits for Adults—National Plans

Plan code	Plan name	Hearing aids coverage for adults?	Frequency of replacement	Most plan will pay for one ear	Most plan will pay for two ears
National Plans When You Use Preferred Providers					
Z24-6	Aetna Advantage	No	NA	NA	NA
N61-3	Aetna Direct CDHP	Yes	3 years	$3,000	$3,000
224-6	Aetna HealthFund HDHP	No	NA	NA	NA
474-6	APWU CDHP	Some	3 years	$1,500	$1,500
471-3	APWU-Hi	Some	3 years	$1,500	$1,500
111-3	Blue Cross Basic	Yes	5 years	$2,500	$2,500
131-3	Blue Cross FEP Blue Focus	No	NA	NA	NA
104-6	Blue Cross-Std	Yes	5 years	$2,500	$2,500
421-3	Compass Rose	Some	5 years	$1,200	$2,400
401-3	Foreign Service	Yes	3 years	$4,000	$4,000
254-6	GEHA Elevate	No	NA	NA	NA
251-3	GEHA Elevate Plus	Some	3 years	$1,500	$1,500
341-3	GEHA HDHP	No	NA	NA	NA
311-3	GEHA-Hi	Yes	3 years	$2,500	$2,500
314-6	GEHA-Std	Yes	3 years	$2,500	$2,500
481-3	MHBP HDHP	Some	5 years	$1,500	$1,500
414-6	MHBP Value Plan	Some	5 years	$1,500	$1,500
454-6	MHBP-Std	Yes	5 years	$2,000	$2,000
324-6	NALC CDHP	Yes	3 years	$500	$1,000
KM1-3	NALC Value Plan	Some	3 years	$500	$1,000
321-3	NALC-Hi	Yes	3 years	$1,000	$2,000
381-3	Rural Carrier	Yes	3 years	$3,000	$3,000
441-3	SAMBA-Hi	Yes	3 years	$500	$1,000
444-6	SAMBA-Std	Yes	3 years	$500	$1,000
National Medicare Advantage Plans					
Z24-6R[1]	Aetna Advantage (Medicare Advantage)	Yes	3 years	$2,500	$2,500
471-3R[1]	APWU-Hi (Medicare Advantage)	Yes	3 years	$1,500	$3,000
421-3R[1]	Compass Rose (Medicare Advantage)	Yes	3 years	$2,400	$2,400
454-6R[1]	MHBP-Std (Medicare Advantage)	Yes	5 years	$2,000	$2,000
381-3R[1]	Rural Carrier (Medicare Advantage)	Yes	3 years	$3,000	$3,000

[1] This Medicare Advantage plan has special enrollment procedures.

Hearing Aid Benefits—Children

Plan code	Plan name	Hearing aids coverage for children?	Age limit for child	Frequency of replacement	Most plan will pay for one ear	Most plan will pay for two ears
D.C. Area Plans When You Use Preferred Providers						
F51-3	Aetna HealthFund CDHP	No	NA	NA	NA	NA
JN4-6	Aetna Open Access Basic	Some	None	3 years	$1,400	$2,800
JN1-3	Aetna Open Access-Hi	Some	None	3 years	$1,400	$2,800
QQ4-6	Aetna Saver	No	NA	NA	NA	NA
F54-6	Aetna Value Plan	No	NA	NA	NA	NA
B64-6	CareFirst Blue Value Plus	Yes	NA	3 years	$1,000	$2,000
B61-3	CareFirst HDHP	Yes	NA	3 years	$1,500	$3,000
2G4-6	CareFirst-Std	Yes	NA	3 years	$1,500	$3,000
T71-3	Kaiser Prosper	Yes	19	3 years	No Limit	No Limit
E31-3	Kaiser-Hi	Yes	19	3 years	No Limit	No Limit
E34-6	Kaiser-Std	Yes	19	3 years	No Limit	No Limit
JP1-3	MD-IPA	Yes	19	3 years	$1,400	$2,800
LR1-3	United Choice Open Access	No	NA	NA	NA	NA
L91-3	United Choice Plus Advanced	Yes	None	3 years	You pay 20%	You pay 20%
AS1-3	United Choice Plus Primary	Yes	None	3 years	$2,500	$5,000
Y81-3	United Choice Primary	Yes	None	3 years	$2,500	$5,000
V41-3	United HDHP	Yes	None	1 year	You Pay 20%	You Pay 20%
National Plans When You Use Preferred Providers						
Z24-6	Aetna Advantage	No	NA	NA	NA	NA
N61-3	Aetna Direct CDHP	Yes	None	3 years	$3,000	$3,000
224-6	Aetna HealthFund HDHP	No	NA	NA	NA	NA
474-6	APWU CDHP	Some	NA	3 years	$1,500	$1,500
471-3	APWU-Hi	Yes	NA	3 years	$1,500	$1,500
111-3	Blue Cross Basic	Yes	22	1 year	$2,500	$2,500
131-3	Blue Cross FEP Blue Focus	No	NA	NA	NA	NA
104-6	Blue Cross-Std	Yes	22	1 year	$2,500	$2,500
421-3	Compass Rose	Some	None	5 years	$1,200	$2,400
401-3	Foreign Service	Yes	None	3 years	$4,000	$4,000
254-6	GEHA Elevate	No	NA	NA	NA	NA
251-3	GEHA Elevate Plus	Some	22	per person	$1,500	$1,500
341-3	GEHA HDHP	No	NA	NA	NA	NA
311-3	GEHA-Hi	Yes	NA	1 year	$2,500	$2,500
314-6	GEHA-Std	Yes	22	1 year	$2,500	$2,500
481-3	MHBP HDHP	Some	None	5 years	$1,500	$1,500
414-6	MHBP Value Plan	Some	None	5 years	$1,500	$1,500
454-6	MHBP-Std	Yes	None	5 years	$2,000	$2,000
324-6	NALC CDHP	Yes	None	3 years	$500	$1,000
KM1-3	NALC Value Plan	Some	None	3 years	$500	$1,000
321-3	NALC-Hi	Yes	None	3 years	$1,000	$2,000
381-3	Rural Carrier	No	NA	NA	NA	NA
441-3	SAMBA-Hi	Some	18	3 years	$1,000	$2,000
444-6	SAMBA-Std	Yes	18	3 years	$1,000	$2,000
Y51-3	United Advantage	Yes	None	3 years	$2,500	$5,000

Before selecting a dental plan, be sure to check with your family dentist as to which plan(s) he or she affiliates with. Our estimates are based on the assumption that you use network providers. But plan coverage out of network loses you the network discount. These plans are good buys only when you use network providers.

Vision Care

All FEHB plans pay for medically necessary care of your eyes, such as cataract surgery. Many pay for annual refractive examinations to determine your prescription for eyeglasses or contact lens, and some pay for part of the cost for the lens and frame or arrange for a discount at plan-affiliated providers (this is often stated as an unofficial non-FEHB benefit in brochures.) Our coverage tables show which health plans pay the most toward vision services.

The nation-wide standalone FEDVIP vision plans provide tax-advantaged premiums for employees (but not retirees) and use the purchasing power of their enrollees to obtain discounts for all enrollees. They are not true insurance plans and will pay neither for lost or broken glasses nor for medical or surgical care. Instead, they are a way to prepay your anticipated and routine costs for refractive eye examination, glasses and frames, contact lenses, and related services and supplies. If you plan to purchase unusually expensive frames, or multiple pairs of glasses, you will need to rely on discounts rather than direct plan benefits.

Unfortunately, the vision plan brochures do not present benefits in a consistent format, making them very hard to compare. We have attempted to capture most of the important features of the plans in our table on national vision plans to help you decide whether, and which, plans you may want to examine in depth. In general, their benefits and premiums are similar, but most offer both high and standard options with differences in both premiums and cost sharing. If you have a preferred optician or eyewear outlet you should ask which plan(s) if any it affiliates with in order to inform your decision.

You have several alternatives to enrolling in these plans. You can simply decide to pay for your predictable dental and vision expenses without the bother of using a plan or being restricted to its providers. If you combine this with prudent shopping, you can achieve substantial savings. For example, *Washington Consumers' Checkbook* has rated dozens of DC area providers for optical services and found that prices one-fourth or more below (or above) the average for glasses or contact lenses are not uncommon. Also, most FEHB health insurance plans have unofficial plan benefits and discounts for eyewear from particular chains, without paying any extra premium.

You have two other major alternatives for vision care. As for other categories of expense, employees (but not retirees) can establish a Flexible Spending Account that covers vision along with other expenses. Or you can join a Consumer-Driven or High Deductible plan and use its savings account feature to pay for vision costs. You can even supplement a High Deductible plan's savings account with a LEX HCFSA. Either of these options gives employees the same tax advantage—about a one third saving—as a separate vision plan. If you use any FEHB plan, of course, the government pays most of the premium.

The primary advantages of joining a vision plan are that it enables you to lock in a provider discount as well as a tax saving while budgeting for your eye wear. You pay roughly $10, $20, or $30 a month (depending on your family size and which plan you select) knowing that each covered family member will be able to get a good deal on a refractive examination and one good set of eyewear equipment.

Hearing Aids

All plans cover medical problems, such as infections, that affect any part of your body, including your ears. All plans cover routine hearing testing for children. Almost all will pay most of the cost for hearing-related medical procedures, such as cochlear implants. But only in recent years have plans begun to cover the cost of hearing aids to compensate for deafness. Coverages vary widely, with some plans covering only children, ages of child coverage varying, frequency of replacement varying, and big differences in the cost amount the plan will cover. We compare these coverages in our table on hearing aid benefits. Before selecting a plan on this basis, it is worth checking with providers for special discounts, some tailored to specific plans. Publications read by Federal employees or annuitants, such as the magazine of the National Active and Retired Federal Employees Association, often carry ads that promise high quality hearing aids at no cost to enrollees in specific plans.

Chapter 8

Plan Types and Flexibility

All FEHB plans impose restraints on provider choice, using networks as a key strategy to reduce payments and hold down premium costs. The only significant exception to this pattern is for retirees with Medicare Parts A and B, who in most national plans and some HMOs can go to almost any hospital or physician at no cost. This flexibility is allowed because Medicare pays first for these enrollees, and the Federal government uses its legal power to force Medicare-participating providers to accept government fee limitations regardless of their actual costs.

Although all plans, not just HMOs, now provide significantly reduced benefits if you do not use "preferred" or "network" providers, there remain significant differences between PPO plans, PPO plans with fee-for-service (FFS) benefits for using out-of-network providers, local HMOs, and the Consumer-Driven (CDHP) and High Deductible (HDHP) plans. All national plans use PPO networks, and no HMOs are national, but each type of plan can be found in local offerings in most large cities.

Type of Plan

In national plans—whether PPO/FFS, HDHP, or CDHP—you generally get a much larger selection of preferred providers, national as well as local. In addition, in all national plans except for Blue Cross Basic you can go to virtually any doctor or hospital you choose—provided you are willing to pay much more (often half or more) of the bill. Under this FFS coverage of providers outside the network, you are covered if you choose to use a world-famous facility, such as the Mayo Clinic, even if it is not a preferred provider. This flexibility gives you maximum freedom of choice but imposes higher costs on you. The national plans offering broad PPO networks and out of network coverage usually but not always charge higher premiums than most local HMOs, although the gap has narrowed in recent years. HDHP and CDHP plans also provide this flexibility, usually at lower premiums than traditional plans.

Most HMO plans are quite different. They operate through a relatively limited group or network of physicians who share your fees, regardless of which doctor you use. Our analysis below on "Joining an HMO" presents their important advantages and disadvantages in detail. Although cost and benefit comparisons are the key considerations in assessing most plans, other factors are important in deciding whether to enroll in an HMO plan and, if so, which one. Most HMOs will not cover you at all outside of their provider network except in emergencies, but some offer fee-for-service coverage for non-network providers, similar to the national plan (see the point-of-service discussion that follows). Others offer non-emergency out of area benefits to students or, in some cases, to your whole family.

HDHP and CDHP present yet another dimension of choice. These plans provide incentives to you to hold costs down by prudent shopping. The plans provide savings accounts, which, if not fully used, roll over their balances so they can be used in future years. In fact, in some of these plans the amount in your savings account at the end of the year will exceed what you paid in premium (after Premium Conversion savings), if your usage is low. However, once the savings account is used up, you face a high deductible before complete health insurance kicks in. Thus, these plans seemingly present more risk than traditional PPO or HMO plans, as described below in "Joining a High Deductible Plan." However, they have significant tax advantages that largely negate their seemingly higher risk, and their catastrophic cost protection is generally as good or better than in other plans.

Cost Controls

Plans engage in many forms of cost control. All plans now use networks of preferred providers, who agree to accept lower fees and avoid unnecessary utilization. All plans also engage in other measures, such as second opinions before surgery, penalties for non-emergency hospital admissions without a "preadmission certification," prior approval of expensive services or products, case management, or a combination. Some cost control measures, such as second opinions before elective surgery, are good for both you and the plan since neither wants you to have an unnecessary operation. Another "win-win" measure is high discounts on generic drugs that are therapeutically equivalent to name brand drugs. Others pose problems if you are not careful.

In the national PPO and FFS plans, there is a $500 penalty for any non-emergency hospital admission without a "preadmission certification." HMOs normally refuse to pay for unauthorized non-emergency admissions. This means that **you must obtain permission from the plan, not just your doctor, before you enter a hospital**. Likewise, with the major exceptions of routine visits and emergencies, many plans do not pay for expensive care that is not approved in advance by the plan. Such requirements have often been expanded to "specialty" drugs for cancer or other diseases. Plans also use "case management" to reduce expenses in costly cases. For example, if you have a stroke, the plan may authorize extra home health benefits in lieu of prolonged hospitalization. This can benefit you as well as the plan, but you must use the procedure specified by the plan.

Preferred Providers

All national plans obtain reduced rates from "preferred providers," operating through PPO networks. You share in these savings through elimination of deductibles or lower copayments if you use one of these preferred providers. These providers also guarantee that their fee will be accepted by the plan. Such PPO plans are similar in some ways to HMOs. The main difference is that the number of preferred providers in each community is often much larger. At any time, you can switch to a provider of your choice rather than a preferred provider. However, you get the low copayments only from preferred providers, and the plans will not recognize costs above their fee schedule.

Each national plan, except Blue Cross Basic and FEP Blue Focus, allows you to use non-preferred providers on a fee-for-service basis, but limits reimbursement for doctors who are not in the network to a schedule of charges. These schedules often reflect usual rates (or less), but never allow higher rates. The problem is that your doctor may be one who charges much more than the plan will allow. Moreover, in recent years most plans have reduced the generosity of the fee schedules they use with non-participating doctors. **You should never use a non-preferred provider without first checking to be sure that the provider will accept the plan's payment level, including your coinsurance or copayment, as payment in full**. The way to find out is simple: **BEFORE** incurring an expensive procedure, ask the provider point blank if he or she will accept your plan's payment level. Do not accept an equivocal answer—they know roughly what the plans pay and can offer in advance to accept that amount. Moreover, you can bargain for a network or Medicare rate. (Retirees over age 65 face little such risk, since by law almost all physicians must give them a Medicare rate.)

For provider choice, the value of the PPO benefit depends in part on how many doctors and hospitals participate. Blue Cross has agreements with about half of all physicians and most hospitals to be preferred providers. Most other plans also offer you a wide choice. For example, GEHA, APWU, NALC, and other national plans use UnitedHealthcare, Aetna, and other insurance firms to provide an almost equally broad selection of providers. However, it is prudent to check provider lists, particularly if you live in a rural area. The best way to check for overall choices is to use plan Web sites. For a specific provider, simply call the office and check not only whether he or she is currently participating, but also whether he or she intends to continue with the plan.

Point of Service

Some HMOs provide a Point of Service (POS) option under which you may, by paying a deductible and coinsurance, use any doctor or hospital. This benefit is essentially identical to the fee-for-service benefit in national plans. In effect, these HMOs operate as dual plans, in which you can go to any doctor of your choice if you pay a deductible and coinsurance. In most cases the deductible is $250 or $300, and you pay coinsurance of 25 or 30 percent. These arrangements allow you to join an HMO, get most of your health care with little out-of-pocket cost, but preserve the ability to go out of plan "just in case" you want a doctor not participating in the plan. In other words, if you join an HMO with a POS benefit, you get essentially the same choices as if you join a national plan with both PPO and FFS benefits. Some HMOs offer this benefit limited to college students while away from home.

Joining a Traditional HMO

HMO plans provide not just insurance, but also a different approach to health care delivery from traditional fee-for-service medicine. Therefore, although cost and benefit comparisons are the key considerations in assessing most plans, other factors are important in deciding whether to enroll in an HMO plan and, if so, which one.

There are two main types of HMO plans. One is the facility-based group practice where enrollees agree to receive their health care from a group of doctors working together at the plan's facilities and at hospitals chosen by the plan. The doctors usually are on salary or in a form of partnership. They generally are paid no more if their patients receive more extensive surgery or other medical treatment, thus, their incentives are different from those of doctors working in the traditional fee-for-service system, who can increase their incomes by increasing the amount of care. The Kaiser plans are the largest of this type.

A much more common type of HMO plan is the individual practice association (IPA). In IPAs, physicians agree to share costs and premium income. Each physician continues to practice in his or her own office and continues to serve some patients who are not plan members. All IPAs have a system to assure that physicians do not give costly, excessive service. In a typical system, each physician negotiates a fee schedule with the plan. After seeing a patient, the physician bills the plan for the agreed fee, but the plan pays only part of the bill, such as 80 percent. The remaining 20 percent is kept in a reserve. If costs are held down, the plan will later distribute the reserve to the physicians. To protect against physicians who might deliver excessive services, a committee of physicians regularly reviews treatment practices of each physician. Joining an individual practice association plan is a more modest departure from the fee-for-service system than joining a group practice plan. Some have both groups and individual physicians. Each HMO brochure describes which of these models it uses, and how you get service.

Some features of HMO plans considered desirable by many consumers are:

• They generally have systems for doctors to review each other's practices.
• They eliminate the inconvenience of submitting claims for costs of services.
• They assure you access to a group of doctors.
• They prevent a doctor from charging more than the plan will reimburse.

Some features of HMO plans considered undesirable by many consumers are:

• The IPA plans often have many participating physicians and hospitals, but rarely a majority of those in the community, and rarely prestigious facilities in other states, such as the Lombardi Center or Mayo Clinic. In contrast, the preferred provider panels offered by the national plans are generally far broader and cover many facilities around the country.
• The group plans require you to go to one of their office locations except in emergencies. Some group plans have only a few locations. They limit your choice of doctor even further: to those who work for the plan. You will have to give up your existing doctors when you join a group plan. In contrast, IPA plans use doctors in private practice and your physician may well participate in one or more IPA HMOs.
• Both types of plan impose barriers to obtaining care as rapidly as you might like, such as waits for the next available appointment for "non-urgent" visits or, rarely nowadays, obtaining the approval of a "gatekeeper" primary care physician in order to see a specialist.

Some features that you may or may not like are:

- Some HMOs rely very heavily on mid-level professionals such as nurse practitioners and physician assistants.
- HMOs generally put patients in hospitals less frequently and keep them there for a shorter time than fee-for-service physicians. This is the major reason HMOs usually have lower costs. A number of studies have found no overall difference in medical outcomes between HMOs and traditional practice. On the other hand, if you want quick surgery to relieve a painful but not life-threatening problem, you may not want to wait while an HMO tries more conservative therapies.
- Few HMOs offer the extra benefits to Medicare enrollees that are found in most national plans, although the number that do so is increasing.

Joining a High Deductible Plan

Several national companies and some local HMO organizations now offer High Deductible or Consumer-Driven plans. Aetna offers such plans in almost all parts of the country, and United-Healthcare in many places. These plans differ in detail, but all share two main features. First, they provide some form of savings account for health care expenses, financed on a tax-free basis through the premium paid to the plan and, in some cases, through additional contributions by enrollees. This account is typically about $1,000 for a self-only enrollment, and twice as much for a family enrollment. During the year, you can use this account to pay for any of your qualified health care expenses, including expenses that the plan does not otherwise cover, such as a hearing aid. Second, if you use up the account on other expenses (or decide to save it rather than use it), you face a high deductible, often almost twice as much as the savings account. Thereafter, you typically pay 10 or 15 percent of expenses, up to an out-of-pocket spending limit, though some plans pay everything above the deductible. The main focus of these plans is to encourage you to be a prudent purchaser. If you are relatively healthy and spend wisely, you may avoid any out-of-pocket expenses. Furthermore, your unused account balances "roll over" and you can build up a substantial cushion that even earns interest. Your total cost under these plans can be LESS than your tax-preferred premium share.

Because of this design, there is no simple answer to "what is my copayment" or "what is my deductible." If you stay within your spending account, both are zero. After your account is used up you pay 100 percent, until you pass your deductible amount. In our tables, we provide the percentage that applies after your deductible and until you hit the catastrophic limit.

Two other important features that these plans share is that routine preventive care does not count against either the spending account or the deductible, and you have good catastrophic expense protection. Most of these plans' limits have none of the loopholes found in other plans.

The High Deductible plans offer two kinds of spending accounts. Which one you get depends on your eligibility. A "Health Savings Account" (HSA) not only lets you accumulate funds, but also lets you retain the savings account when you change plans or retire. Moreover, you can earn interest or capital gains, tax-free, for decades to come. The HSA is your property. In contrast, a "Health Reimbursement Arrangement" (HRA), or "Personal Care Account" as it is called in some plans, works almost the same but terminates when you change plans. In that case, the unspent balance remains with the plan. The Consumer-Driven plans offer only HRAs. Unlike HSAs, HRAs do not let you grow the account through interest. You can use an HRA, but not an HSA, if you are covered by other health insurance, such as TRICARE, a spouse's plan, or Medicare. In the HDHP plans, annuitants with Medicare get an HRA in the same amount as the HSA received by other enrollees. To fully understand these complex plans, you should read the explanations in their brochures carefully, and you may want to consult material on the OPM Web site.

The other important characteristic of an HSA account (in contrast to an HRA) is that you can make voluntary contributions to it during the year. This feature comes into play if your expenses are much higher than you expected, but you can make contributions regardless of your expected expenses. In an HSA you can make voluntary contributions up to the amount of the deductible, less the personal account amount funded by the plan. Your contributions are tax preferred. Thus, if you need to spend an extra thousand dollars, rather than pay it directly to providers you can contribute

Plan Flexibility: D.C. Area Plans

Plan code	Plan name (listed in alphabetical order within group)	Get regular benefits anywhere?	Payment for out of network providers (non-emergency)?		Specialist visits covered without referral?		Open formulary?	Company offers a Medicare Advantage plan?	Medicare premium rebate available?
			Without Medicare Part B?	Cost-free with Part B?	Gynecologist	Other specialists			
D.C. Area Plans When You Use Preferred Providers									
F51-3	Aetna HealthFund CDHP	Many Areas	Reduced	No	Yes	Yes	Pay More	Most Areas	No
JN4-6	Aetna Open Access Basic	Many Areas	No	No	Yes	Yes	Pay More	No	No
JN1-3	Aetna Open Access-Hi	Many Areas	No	No	Yes	Yes	Pay More	No	No
QQ4-6	Aetna Saver	Many Areas	No	No	Yes	Yes	Pay More	No	No
F54-6	Aetna Value Plan	Many Areas	Reduced	No	Yes	Yes	Pay More	Most Areas	No
B64-6	CareFirst Blue Value Plus	Some Areas	Reduced	Yes	Yes	Yes	Pay More	No	No
B61-3	CareFirst HDHP	Some Areas	Reduced	Yes	Yes	Yes	Pay More	No	No
2G4-6	CareFirst-Std	Some Areas	Reduced	Yes	Yes	Yes	Pay More	No	No
T71-3	Kaiser Prosper	Some Areas	No	No	Yes	Some	Pay More	Yes	No
E31-3	Kaiser-Hi	Some Areas	No	No	Yes	Some	Pay More	Yes	No
E34-6	Kaiser-Std	Some Areas	No	No	Yes	Some	Pay More	Yes	No
JP1-3	MD-IPA	No	No	Yes	Yes	No	Pay More	Yes	No
LR1-3	United Choice Open Access	No	No	No	Yes	Some	Pay More	Yes	No
L91-3	United Choice Plus Advanced	Some Areas	Reduced	No	Yes	Yes	Pay More	Yes	No
AS1-3	United Choice Plus Primary	Many Areas	Reduced	No	Yes	Yes	Pay More	Yes	No
Y81-3	United Choice Primary	No	No	No	Yes	Some	Pay More	Yes	No
V41-3	United HDHP	No	Reduced	No	Yes	Yes	Pay More	Yes	No
D.C. Area Medicare Advantage Plans									
T71-3R[1]	Kaiser Prosper (Med Adv.)	Some Areas	No	No	Yes	Some	Pay More	Yes	No
E31-3R1[1]	Kaiser-Hi (Medicare Adv. 1)	Some Areas	No	No	Yes	Some	Pay More	Yes	No
E31-3R2[1]	Kaiser-Hi (Medicare Adv. 2)	Some Areas	No	No	Yes	Some	Pay More	Yes	Yes
E34-6R[1]	Kaiser-Std (Medicare Adv.)	Some Areas	No	No	Yes	Some	Pay More	Yes	No
JP1-3R[1]	MD-IPA (Retiree Adv.)	Nationwide	Yes	Yes	Yes	Yes	Pay More	Yes	Yes
LR1-3R[1]	United Open Access (Ret. Adv.)	Nationwide	Yes	Yes	Yes	Yes	Pay More	Yes	Yes
L91-3R[1]	United Plus Advanced (Ret. Adv.)	Nationwide	Yes	Yes	Yes	Yes	Pay More	Yes	Yes
AS1-3R[1]	United Plus Primary (Ret.Adv.)	Nationwide	Yes	Yes	Yes	Yes	Pay More	Yes	Yes
Y81-3R[1]	United Primary (Ret. Adv.)	Nationwide	Yes	Yes	Yes	Yes	Pay More	Yes	Yes

[1] This Medicare Advantage plan has special enrollment procedures.

Plan Flexibility: National Plans

Plan code	Plan name (listed in alphabetical order within group)	Get regular benefits anywhere?	Payment for out of network providers (non-emergency)?		Specialist visits covered without referral?		Open formulary?	Company offers a Medicare Advantage plan?	Medicare premium rebate available?
			Without Medicare Part B?	Cost-free with Part B?	Gynecologist	Other specialists			
National Plans When You Use Preferred Providers									
Z24-6	Aetna Advantage	Many Areas	Reduced	Yes	Yes	Yes	Pay More	Some Areas	No
N61-3	Aetna Direct CDHP	Reduced	Many Areas	Yes	Yes	Yes	Pay More	Yes	No
224-6	Aetna HealthFund HDHP	Many Areas	Reduced	No	Yes	Yes	Pay More	Some Areas	No
474-6	APWU CDHP	Nationwide	Reduced	No	Yes	Yes	Yes	No	No
471-3	APWU-Hi	Nationwide	Reduced	Yes	Yes	Yes	Yes	Yes	No
111-3	Blue Cross Basic	Nationwide	No	Ntwk only	Yes	Yes	Pay More	Many Areas	Yes
104-6	Blue Cross-Std	Nationwide	Reduced	Yes	Yes	Yes	Pay More	Many Areas	No
421-3	Compass Rose	Nationwide	Reduced	Yes	Yes	Yes	Pay More	No	No
131-3	FEP Blue Focus	Nationwide	No	Ntwk only	Yes	Yes	No	Many Areas	No
401-3	Foreign Service	Nationwide	Reduced	Yes	Yes	Yes	Pay More	No	No
254-6	GEHA Elevate	Nationwide	Reduced	No	Yes	Yes	Yes	No	No
251-3	GEHA Elevate Plus	Nationwide	Reduced	Yes	Yes	Yes	Pay More	No	No
341-3	GEHA HDHP	Nationwide	Reduced	No	Yes	Yes	Yes	No	No
311-3	GEHA-Hi	Nationwide	Reduced	Yes	Yes	Yes	Pay More	No	Yes
314-6	GEHA-Std	Nationwide	Reduced	Yes	Yes	Yes	Yes	No	No
481-3	MHBP HDHP	Nationwide	Reduced	Yes	Yes	Yes	Pay More	Yes	No
414-6	MHBP Value Plan	Nationwide	Reduced	No	Yes	Yes	Yes	No	No
454-6	MHBP-Std	Nationwide	Reduced	Yes	Yes	Yes	Pay More	Yes	No
324-6	NALC CDHP	Nationwide	Reduced	No	Yes	Yes	Yes	No	No
KM1-3	NALC Value Plan	Nationwide	Reduced	No	Yes	Yes	Yes	No	No
321-3	NALC-Hi	Nationwide	Reduced	Yes	Yes	Yes	Yes	Yes	No
381-3	Rural Carrier	Nationwide	Reduced	Yes	Yes	Yes	Yes	Yes	No
441-3	SAMBA-Hi	Nationwide	Reduced	Yes	Yes	Yes	Pay More	No	No
444-6	SAMBA-Std	Nationwide	Reduced	Yes	Yes	Yes	Pay More	No	No
National Medicare Advantage Plans									
Z24-6R[1]	Aetna Advantage (Med. Adv.)	Many Areas	Reduced	Yes	Yes	Yes	Pay More	Yes	Yes
471-3R[1]	APWU-Hi (Medicare Adv.)	Nationwide	Reduced	Yes	Yes	Yes	Yes	Yes	Yes
421-3R[1]	Compass Rose (Med. Adv.)	Nationwide	Reduced	Yes	Yes	Yes	Pay More	Yes	Yes
454-6R[1]	MHBP-Std (Medicare Adv.)	Nationwide	Reduced	Yes	Yes	Yes	Pay More	Yes	Yes
381-3R[1]	Rural Carrier (Medicare Adv.)	Nationwide	Reduced	Yes	Yes	Yes	Yes	Yes	Yes

[1] This Medicare Advantage plan has special enrollment procedures.

it to the HSA account, lower your taxable income by a thousand dollars, and pay providers from the HSA account. If you are in a 33 percent tax bracket, this saves you over three hundred dollars compared to traditional health insurance plans. This is a better arrangement for you than under Flexible Spending Accounts, because there is no "use or lose" penalty. **HSA accounts are sometimes described as "Trifecta" benefits because the contribution is tax-free, the account grows tax-free, and disbursements from the account are tax-free when spent for health care.**

Annuitants are eligible for these plans, but most of these plans do not provide extra benefits for having Medicare Parts A and B (significant exceptions are the Aetna Direct CDHP and MHBP HDHP national plans, and in the Washington DC area the CareFirst HDHP plan). However, these spending accounts cover many expenses that Medicare does not, and Medicare protects you from substantial copayment expense. For hospital expenses, you will almost always get the zero percent Medicare rate (after deductible) rather than the plan's rate of cost sharing. Therefore, they work well for retirees with Medicare. Once you have Medicare the law allows you to contribute only to an HRA, not to an HSA, and the HDHP plans all allow for that.

Plan Flexibility

Our comparisons of flexibility capture as best as we can the features of each plan that affect your ability to select the providers of your preference. We would like to display the number of affiliated providers in each local area, but such data are not available for many plans. Of course, staff model HMOs would always show a relatively low number, because they ordinarily limit you to primary care providers on their staff.

In our comparisons, we show first which HMOs allow you to get regular plan benefits from providers located outside the plan's main service area. For example, the Kaiser plans allow you to use Kaiser facilities and providers anywhere they are located. Of course, national plans all cover the entire nation. All plans cover emergencies throughout the world (not shown). Second, we show how plans deal with providers who are not preferred. National plans and some HMOs let you use non-preferred providers with a significantly higher cost sharing. Third, we show which plans provide annuitants with Medicare Parts A and B wrap around benefits to make all hospital and doctor care cost-free, in or out of network.

We show which plans allow women to visit a gynecologist without having to be referred by a primary care provider. Almost all HMOs now allow self-referral, at least for an annual exam (those which allow only an examination without referral are marked "Exam"). Unfortunately, some HMOs do not allow self-referral to other specialists, though the number that do so is growing.

Our entry for "open formulary" indicates whether the plan will pay for any name brand drug that your physician prescribes, or just for those that are on the plan's list of approved drugs (commonly called a "formulary"). Most plans will pay for any drug but require higher copays for non-formulary drugs. We indicate these with a "Pay More" entry.

We indicate whether each company sponsors a Medicare Advantage (MA) plan, so that Medicare participants can elect to stay with their health plan while paying only one premium. However, even though we enter "Yes" you have to check further to see if the Medicare Advantage plan covers the exact area where you live. Not shown, all Medicare Parts A and B enrollees have access to at least some MA plans, and most have access to dozens.

Finally, we show which plans will reimburse much or most of your Medicare Part B premium either as a separate contribution or as an allowed use of your savings account.

Chapter 9

Quality and Service

For traditional fee-for-service insurance plans, service quality used to be a minor issue. The main service concerns were how easily you could get help from plan representatives regarding coverage questions and how fairly and promptly claims were paid.

Now even fee-for-service plans now have some involvement in the quality of your health care. All plans require you to get authorization before hospitalization or surgery. And almost all have assembled networks of preferred providers and have prescription drug formularies. Because you save money by using providers from these networks and preferred drugs in these formularies, the availability and quality of preferred providers and the lists of preferred drugs are important.

An HMO can have an even bigger impact on the quality of medical care its members receive. With an HMO, your choice of physicians, hospitals, and other healthcare providers is limited to a selected list of participating providers. It may be set up so that you primary care doctor is a "gatekeeper" who decides whether to authorize referrals to specialty care and other services.

Customer Satisfaction Ratings

The table beginning on page 99 displays plan-by-plan customer satisfaction ratings reported by OPM. These ratings come from a 2021 survey in which a standardized questionnaire was sent to a sample of each plan's members.

The table tells you how plans compare for several categories of service, based on answers given to various questions asked on the survey. OPM reports scores for "overall quality of the plan," "overall rating of personal doctors," "getting needed care," "getting care quickly," "coordination of care," and "claims processing."

For each of these aspects of care, the table reports how OPM scored the survey results for each plan. OPM used the following scale:

● = Outstanding (plan's score was in the 90th percentile)
◗ = Excellent (plan's score was in the 75th-89th percentile)
◑ = Good (plan's score was in the 50th-74th percentile)
◔ = Fair (plan's score was in the 25th to 49th percentile)
○ = Poor (plan's score was worse than the 25th percentile)
N/A = Indicates no data was reported for the measure

We advise that you keep several points in mind when using the customer ratings:

- Some of the ratings are based on opinions. Your opinions might not be the same as those of survey respondents.
- The way enrollees rate their plans can be affected by their age, education level, state of health, and other characteristics. For example, older individuals tend to rate their plans relatively high. If one plan has attracted a large proportion of members over age 65, its ratings might be high for that reason. The scores reported here have not been adjusted for member characteristics. Within the group of HMO and POS plans, it does not appear that such differences in member characteristics had much effect on scores; very few plans' overall scores would change by more than two

percentage points if the scores were adjusted for member differences. But the effects might be greater among fee-for-service plans.

- Since the survey included only a sample of plan members, it is possible that a plan's ratings were affected by "the luck of the draw": a disproportionately large number of satisfied or dissatisfied members happened to respond.

- Some enrollees did not return the questionnaire. It is possible that those who responded are more satisfied or less satisfied than those who did not. Our analysis of these and similar survey data has indicated that younger members and men are less likely to respond than women and older members. Young male members also tend to give somewhat lower ratings than older members of either gender. Fortunately, with roughly 40 percent of surveyed members responding for most plans, the respondents do at least represent a substantial portion of members.

In interpreting member ratings, also keep in mind that comparing across different *types* of plans is at best imperfect. First, it is not possible directly to compare regional plans (primarily HMO and POS plans) to national plans. For example, high or low ratings of "personal doctors" by enrollees in a national plan don't tell you how that plan's members in a particular region rate their doctors, and yet it is the national plan's doctors in that region who should be compared to the doctors of members of regional plans serving only that region. Second, for the national plans (and the ratings we report for Blue Cross and Blue Shield by state), the ratings are only from FEHBP enrollees, while the ratings for the regional HMO and POS plans include ratings from non-FEHBP enrollees.

Even among HMO and POS plans, the ratings given by non-federal members may have been given for a different variant of the plan. We have found, for example, that among members of the same plan, POS users are about two to three percentage points less likely than basic HMO users to give high ratings to the plan.

Differences in the way the survey was administered might explain small differences in plan scores. All of the plans are required to use an independent firm to conduct their surveys under the supervision of the nonprofit National Committee for Quality Assurance (NCQA) using standardized survey procedures. But there is some room for variation in procedures. For example, some plans get a relatively high percentage of their responses by phone (as opposed to mail), and phone responders tend to give higher ratings than mail responders.

Disputed Claims

Along with the customer satisfaction survey results, we have another indicator of service quality for the fee-for-service plans. We checked "disputed claims" on file at OPM. A "disputed claim" is a case in which a plan member has been denied benefits and has followed the required procedure to appeal the denial to OPM.

Disputed Claims Per 10,000 Federal Enrollees Filed with the Office of Personnel Management

Plan name	Disputed claims	Disputed claims in which plan's decision was changed or reversed
Blue Cross Blue Shield	2.13	0.52
NALC	3.14	1.02
Rural Carrier*	3.39	0.34
MHBP	4.64	2.75
APWU	5.79	2.34
SAMBA	5.85	1.95
Foreign Service*	7.52	3.9
GEHA	8.81	4.42
Aetna HealthFund	12.39	4.81
Compass Rose*	12.45	4.36

* Plans is not open to all.

Continues on page 118

Plan Quality

See chapter text for discussion of these data

	Enrollment code	Ratings from plan members					
		Overall rating of plan	Overall rating of personal doctors	Getting needed care	Getting care quickly	Coordination of care	Claims processing
National Plans							
APWU (PPO)	47	◐	◔	◐	◕	◔	◔
APWU CDHP (PPO)	47	◕	○	○	○	◔	○
Blue Cross Basic (PPO)	11	●	◔	◐	◐	◔	◐
Blue Cross FEP Blue Focus (PPO)	13	◐	○	○	○	○	◔
Blue Cross-Std (PPO)	10	◕	◐	◐	◕	◔	◐
Compass Rose (PPO)	42	◕	○	◔	◔	◐	◐
Foreign Service (PPO)	40	◕	○	○	○	○	◐
GEHA Elevate (PPO)	25	◔	○	○	○	○	○
GEHA Elevate Plus (PPO)	25	◐	○	○	○	○	○
GEHA HDHP (PPO)	34	●	◐	◐	◕	◐	◔
GEHA-Hi (PPO)	31	◐	○	○	◐	○	○
GEHA-Std (PPO)	31	◐	○	○	○	○	◔
MHBP HDHP (PPO)	48	◔	○	○	○	N/A	◐
MHBP Value Plan (PPO)	41	◐	◐	◐	◐	○	◔
MHBP-Std (PPO)	45	●	●	●	◐	●	◔
NALC CDHP (PPO)	32	●	◐	◔	◕	◕	◔
NALC Value Plan (PPO)	KM	○	○	◔	○	N/A	◔
NALC-Hi (PPO)	32	○	○	◔	○	N/A	◔
Panama Canal (POS)	43	●	◕	◕	◕	◔	○
Rural Carrier (PPO)	38	◕	◐	◐	●	◐	◐
SAMBA-Hi (PPO)	44	●	◐	◕	◐	◐	◔
SAMBA-Std (PPO)	44	●	◔	◐	◕	○	◐
Local Plans and National Plans with Scores from Members in Specific States							
Alabama							
Aetna Advantage (PPO)	Z2	◐	◐	◐	●	○	◔
Aetna Direct CDHP (PPO)	N6	◐	◐	◐	●	○	◔
Aetna HealthFund HDHP/Aetna Direct (PPO)	22	◐	◐	◐	●	○	◔

● = Outstanding (plan's score was in the 90th percentile)
◕ = Excellent (plan's score was in the 75th-89th percentile)
◐ = Good (plan's score was in the 50th-74th percentile)
◔ = Fair (plan's score was in the 25th to 49th percentile)
○ = Poor (plan's score was worse than the 25th percentile)
N/A = Blanks indicate no data was reported for the measure

Plan Quality

See chapter text for discussion of these data

Plan	Enrollment code	Ratings from plan members					
		Overall rating of plan	Overall rating of personal doctors	Getting needed care	Getting care quickly	Coordination of care	Claims processing
Aetna HealthFund HDHP/Aetna Value (PPO)	F5	◑	◑	◑	●	○	◔
Blue Cross Basic (PPO)	11	●	◔	◕	◕	○	◕
Blue Cross-Std (PPO)	10	●	◕	◑	●	○	●
United Choice Open Access (POS)	KK	◔	◔	◔	N/A	N/A	N/A
United Choice Plus Primary (POS)	AS	◔	◔	◔	N/A	N/A	N/A
United Choice Primary (POS)	Y8	◔	◔	◔	N/A	N/A	N/A
United HDHP (POS)	LS	◔	◔	◔	N/A	N/A	N/A
Alaska							
Aetna Advantage (PPO)	Z2	◔	○	◔	◑	◔	○
Aetna Direct CDHP (PPO)	N6	◔	○	◔	◑	◔	○
Aetna HealthFund CDHP/Aetna Value (PPO)	JS	◔	○	◔	◑	◔	○
Aetna HealthFund HDHP/Aetna Direct (PPO)	22	◔	○	◔	◑	◔	○
Blue Cross Basic (PPO)	11	◕	○	○	◑	◔	◑
Blue Cross-Std (PPO)	10	◕	◔	◑	◑	◑	◑
Arizona							
Aetna Advantage (PPO)	Z2	◑	○	○	N/A	N/A	N/A
Aetna Direct CDHP (PPO)	N6	◑	○	○	N/A	N/A	N/A
Aetna HealthFund CDHP/Aetna Value (PPO)	G5	◑	○	○	N/A	N/A	N/A
Aetna HealthFund HDHP/Aetna Direct (PPO)	22	◑	○	○	N/A	N/A	N/A
Aetna Open Access (HMO/POS)	WQ	◑	◑	○	○	○	N/A
Blue Cross Basic (PPO)	11	●	○	◔	◔	○	◑
Blue Cross-Std (PPO)	10	●	○	◔	○	◔	◑
GEHA-Std (PPO)	31	◕	○	◔	N/A	N/A	N/A
Humana CoverageFirst CDHP (HMO/POS) (Phoenix)	R6	◔	N/A	N/A	N/A	N/A	N/A
Humana CoverageFirst CDHP (HMO/POS) (Tuscon)	R9	◔	N/A	N/A	N/A	N/A	N/A
Humana Health (HMO/POS) (Phoenix)	BF	◔	N/A	N/A	N/A	N/A	N/A
United Choice Open Access (POS)	KT	◑	○	○	N/A	N/A	N/A
United Choice Plus Primary (POS)	WF	◑	○	○	N/A	N/A	N/A
United Choice Primary (POS)	VD	◑	○	○	N/A	N/A	N/A
United HDHP (POS)	LU	◑	○	○	N/A	N/A	N/A

Plan Quality

See chapter text for discussion of these data

	Enrollment code	Ratings from plan members					
		Overall rating of plan	Overall rating of personal doctors	Getting needed care	Getting care quickly	Coordination of care	Claims processing
Arkansas							
Aetna Advantage (PPO)	Z2	◕	◔	◑	◕	◑	◑
Aetna Direct CDHP (PPO)	N6	◕	◔	◑	◕	◑	◑
Aetna HealthFund CDHP/Aetna Value (PPO)	F5	◕	◔	◑	◕	◑	◑
Aetna HealthFund HDHP/Aetna Direct (PPO)	22	◕	◔	◑	◕	◑	◑
Blue Cross Basic (PPO)	11	●	◑	●	◑	◔	●
Blue Cross-Std (PPO)	10	●	◑	◑	◑	◑	◕
QualChoice (HMO/POS)	DH	◔	◕	◔	◑	◔	◕
United Choice Open Access (POS)	KK	○	◕	◔	N/A	N/A	N/A
United Choice Plus Primary (POS)	AS	○	◕	◔	N/A	N/A	N/A
United Choice Primary (POS)	Y8	○	◕	◔	N/A	N/A	N/A
United HDHP (POS)	LS	○	◕	◔	N/A	N/A	N/A
California							
Aetna Advantage (PPO)	Z2	◑	◕	◔	○	◔	N/A
Aetna Direct CDHP (PPO)	N6	◑	◕	◔	○	◔	N/A
Aetna HealthFund CDHP/Aetna Value (PPO)	JS	◑	◕	◔	○	◔	N/A
Aetna HealthFund HDHP/Aetna Direct (PPO)	22	◑	◕	◔	○	◔	N/A
Aetna Open Access (HMO/POS)	2X	◔	○	○	○	N/A	N/A
Anthem Blue Cross (HMO/POS)	B3	◑	○	○	N/A	N/A	N/A
Blue Cross Basic (PPO)	11	◕	○	○	◔	○	◑
Blue Cross-Std (PPO)	10	◕	◔	◔	◔	◔	◑
Blue Shield of California (HMO/POS)	SI	◕	○	○	◔	◔	◑
GEHA-Std (PPO)	31	◕	○	◔	N/A	N/A	N/A
Health Net-Basic (HMO/POS) (Northern Calif)	T4	◑	○	○	○	◔	○
Health Net-Basic (HMO/POS) (Southern Calif)	P6	◑	○	○	○	◔	○
Health Net-Hi (HMO/POS) (Southern Calif)	LP	◑	○	○	○	◔	○
Kaiser (HMO) (Fresno)	NZ	◑	○	◔	◔	◔	N/A
Kaiser (HMO) (Southern Calif)	62	◕	○	◔	○	○	N/A

● = Outstanding (plan's score was in the 90th percentile)
◕ = Excellent (plan's score was in the 75th-89th percentile)
◑ = Good (plan's score was in the 50th-74th percentile)
◔ = Fair (plan's score was in the 25th to 49th percentile)
○ = Poor (plan's score was worse than the 25th percentile)
N/A = Blanks indicate no data was reported for the measure

Plan Quality See chapter text for discussion of these data	Enrollment code	Ratings from plan members					
		Overall rating of plan	Overall rating of personal doctors	Getting needed care	Getting care quickly	Coordination of care	Claims processing
Kaiser Prosper (HMO) (Northern Calif)	KC	◑	○	◕	◕	◕	N/A
Kaiser-Hi (HMO) (Northern Calif)	59	◑	○	◕	◕	◕	N/A
Colorado							
Aetna Advantage (PPO)	Z2	○	○	◑	○	N/A	N/A
Aetna Direct CDHP (PPO)	N6	○	○	◑	○	N/A	N/A
Aetna HealthFund CDHP/Aetna Value (PPO)	G5	○	○	◑	○	N/A	N/A
Aetna HealthFund HDHP/Aetna Direct (PPO)	22	○	○	◑	○	N/A	N/A
Blue Cross Basic (PPO)	11	●	◑	◑	◕	○	●
Blue Cross-Std (PPO)	10	●	○	◕	◑	◔	◑
BlueAdvantage (HMO)	WW	○	◑	◕	N/A	N/A	N/A
Kaiser Prosper (HMO)	N4	◔	◔	◕	○	◔	○
Kaiser-Hi (HMO)	65	◔	◔	◕	○	◔	○
United Choice Open Access (POS)	KT	◔	○	◕	N/A	N/A	N/A
United HDHP (POS)	LU	◔	○	◕	N/A	N/A	N/A
Connecticut							
Aetna Advantage (PPO)	Z2	○	●	◕	◑	●	N/A
Aetna Direct CDHP (PPO)	N6	○	●	◕	◑	●	N/A
Aetna HealthFund CDHP/Aetna Value (PPO)	EP	○	●	◕	◑	●	N/A
Aetna HealthFund HDHP/Aetna Direct (PPO)	22	○	●	◕	◑	●	N/A
Blue Cross Basic (PPO)	11	●	◕	◑	◕	◑	◕
Delaware							
Aetna Open Access (PPO)	P3	◕	○	◑	◕	◑	◑
District of Columbia							
Aetna Advantage (PPO)	Z2	◕	◑	◑	◕	○	N/A
Aetna Direct CDHP (PPO)	N6	◕	◑	◑	◕	○	N/A
Aetna HealthFund CDHP/Aetna Value (PPO)	F5	◕	◑	◑	◕	○	N/A
Aetna HealthFund HDHP/Aetna Direct (PPO)	22	◕	◑	◑	◑	○	N/A
Aetna Open Access (HMO/POS)	JN	◑	●	◑	◔	◑	N/A
Aetna Saver (HMO/POS)	QQ	◑	●	◑	◔	◑	N/A

Plan Quality

See chapter text for discussion of these data

	Enrollment code	Ratings from plan members					
		Overall rating of plan	Overall rating of personal doctors	Getting needed care	Getting care quickly	Coordination of care	Claims processing
Blue Cross Basic (PPO)	11	◐	○	○	○	○	◐
Blue Cross-Std (PPO)	10	◐	○	◔	◐	○	○
CareFirst (HMO/POS)	B6	●	◔	◕	◐	○	◐
CareFirst-Std (HMO/POS)	2G	●	◔	◕	◐	○	◐
GEHA-Std (PPO)	31	◐	○	○	N/A	N/A	◔
Kaiser (HMO)	E3	◕	◔	◐	◐	◕	N/A
Kaiser Prosper (HMO)	T7	◕	◔	◐	◐	◕	N/A
MD-IPA (HMO/POS)	JP	◕	◕	●	◔	◐	◕
United Choice Open Access (POS)	LR	◔	◐	◔	N/A	N/A	N/A
United Choice Plus Advanced (POS)	L9	◔	◐	◔	N/A	N/A	N/A
United Choice Plus Primary (POS)	AS	◔	◐	◔	N/A	N/A	N/A
United Choice Primary (POS)	Y8	◔	◐	◔	N/A	N/A	N/A
United HDHP (POS)	V4	◔	◐	◔	N/A	N/A	N/A
Florida							
Aetna Advantage (PPO)	Z2	◕	◔	◔	○	○	◔
Aetna Direct CDHP (PPO)	N6	◕	◔	◔	○	○	◔
Aetna HealthFund CDHP/Aetna Value (PPO)	F5	◕	◔	◔	○	○	◔
Aetna HealthFund HDHP/Aetna Direct (PPO)	22	◕	◔	◔	○	○	◔
AvMed HDHP (HMO/POS)	WZ	●	◕	◔	◔	N/A	N/A
AvMed-Std (HMO/POS)	ML	●	◕	◔	◔	N/A	N/A
Blue Cross Basic (PPO)	11	●	◕	◕	◐	◔	◐
Blue Cross-Std (PPO)	10	●	◔	●	◕	○	◐
Capital Health (HMO)	EA	●	◕	◔	◕	◔	◕
GEHA-Std (PPO)	31	◕	◐	○	◐	○	◔
Humana CoverageFirst (HMO/POS) (Daytona)	W9	◔	◔	◐	○	◐	◔
Humana CoverageFirst (HMO/POS) (Orlando)	X2	◔	◔	◐	○	◐	◔
Humana CoverageFirst (HMO/POS) (South Fla)	QP	◔	◔	◐	○	◐	◐
Humana CoverageFirst (HMO/POS) (Tampa)	MJ	◔	◔	◐	○	◐	◔

● = Outstanding (plan's score was in the 90th percentile)
◕ = Excellent (plan's score was in the 75th-89th percentile)
◐ = Good (plan's score was in the 50th-74th percentile)
◔ = Fair (plan's score was in the 25th to 49th percentile)
○ = Poor (plan's score was worse than the 25th percentile)
N/A = Blanks indicate no data was reported for the measure

Plan Quality

See chapter text for discussion of these data

Plan Quality	Enrollment code	Ratings from plan members					
		Overall rating of plan	Overall rating of personal doctors	Getting needed care	Getting care quickly	Coordination of care	Claims processing
Humana Medical (HMO/POS) (Daytona)	EX	◔	◔	◑	○	◑	◔
Humana Medical (HMO/POS) (Orlando)	E2	◔	◔	◑	○	◑	◔
Humana Medical (HMO/POS) (South Fla)	EE	◔	◔	◑	○	◑	◔
Humana Medical (HMO/POS) (Tampa)	LL	◔	◔	◑	○	◑	◔
United Choice Open Access (POS)	KK	◑	◑	◔	N/A	N/A	N/A
United Choice Plus Advanced (POS)	LV	◑	◑	◔	N/A	N/A	N/A
United Choice Plus Primary (POS)	AS	◑	◑	◔	N/A	N/A	N/A
United Choice Primary (POS)	Y8	◑	◑	◔	N/A	N/A	N/A
United HDHP (POS)	LS	◑	◑	◔	N/A	N/A	N/A
Georgia							
Aetna Advantage (PPO)	Z2	◕	◑	◑	◑	N/A	◑
Aetna Direct CDHP (PPO)	N6	◕	◑	◑	◑	N/A	◑
Aetna HealthFund CDHP/Aetna Value (PPO)	F5	◕	◑	◑	◑	N/A	◑
Aetna HealthFund HDHP/Aetna Direct (PPO)	22	◕	◑	◑	◑	N/A	◑
Aetna Open Access (HMO/POS)	2U	○	◑	N/A	N/A	N/A	N/A
Blue Cross Basic (PPO)	11	●	◔	○	◑	○	●
Blue Cross-Std (PPO)	10	●	●	●	◑	◕	◕
Blue Open Access (HMO/POS)	QM	◑	◑	◑	◑	○	N/A
GEHA-Std (PPO)	31	◕	◑	○	◑	○	◔
Humana CoverageFirst CDHP (HMO/POS)	AD	◔	◑	◔	◔	○	◔
Humana CoverageFirst CDHP (HMO/POS)	S9	◔	◑	◔	◔	○	◔
Humana Employers-Basic (HMO/POS) (Atlanta)	Q7	◔	◑	◔	◔	○	◔
Humana Employers-Basic (HMO/POS) (Columbus)	RM	◔	◑	◔	◔	○	◔
Humana Employers-Basic (HMO/POS) (Macon)	RJ	◔	◑	◔	◔	○	◔
Humana Value Plan (HMO/POS)	LM	◔	◑	◔	◔	○	◔
Kaiser (HMO)	F8	◑	◑	○	○	◔	N/A
Kaiser Prosper (HMO)	LA	◑	◑	○	○	◔	N/A
United Choice Plus Advance (POS)	LV	◕	◑	N/A	N/A	N/A	N/A
United Choice Plus Primary (POS)	AS	◕	◑	N/A	N/A	N/A	N/A
United Choice Primary (POS)	Y8	◕	◑	N/A	N/A	N/A	N/A

Plan Quality

See chapter text for discussion of these data

Plan Quality	Enrollment code	Ratings from plan members					
		Overall rating of plan	Overall rating of personal doctors	Getting needed care	Getting care quickly	Coordination of care	Claims processing
Guam							
Calvo's Selectcare (HMO)	B4	◔	○	○	◔	N/A	N/A
TakeCare (HMO)	JK	○	○	○	N/A	N/A	N/A
TakeCare HDHP (HMO)	KX	○	○	○	N/A	N/A	N/A
Hawaii							
HMSA Plan (HMO/POS)	87	●	◕	◕	◕	●	◕
Kaiser (HMO)	63	◕	○	◔	◔	○	N/A
Idaho							
Aetna Advantage (PPO)	Z2	◐	◐	◐	◐	◔	◐
Aetna Direct CDHP (PPO)	N6	◐	◐	◐	◐	◔	◐
Aetna Health/Altius-Hi (HMO/POS)	9K	◔	◕	●	◐	◔	◔
Aetna Health/Altius-Std (HMO/POS)	DK	◔	◕	●	◐	◔	◔
Aetna HealthFund CDHP/Aetna Value (PPO)	H4	◐	◐	◐	◐	◔	◐
Aetna HealthFund HDHP/Aetna Direct (PPO)	22	◐	◐	◐	◐	◔	◐
Blue Cross Basic (PPO)	11	●	◔	◔	●	◔	◕
Kaiser (HMO)	54	◔	◔	○	○	○	N/A
Kaiser Prosper (HMO)	PT	◔	◔	○	○	○	N/A
Illinois							
Aetna Advantage (PPO)	Z2	◐	●	◔	◕	●	N/A
Aetna Direct CDHP (PPO)	N6	◐	●	◔	◕	●	N/A
Aetna HealthFund CDHP/Aetna Value (PPO)	H4	◐	●	◔	◕	●	N/A
Aetna HealthFund HDHP/Aetna Direct (PPO)	22	◐	●	◔	◕	●	N/A
Blue Cross Basic (PPO)	11	●	◐	●	◔	◐	●
Blue Cross-Std (PPO)	10	●	◐	◔	◐	◐	◕
Blue Preferred (HMO)	9G	◐	◐	◐	●	◕	◐
Health Alliance (HMO/POS)	K8	●	◕	◕	◐	◐	N/A
Humana CoverageFirst CDHP (HMO/POS) (Central IL)	GB	◔	●	●	N/A	N/A	N/A
Humana CoverageFirst CDHP (HMO/POS) (Chicago)	MW	◔	●	●	N/A	N/A	N/A

● = Outstanding (plan's score was in the 90th percentile)
◕ = Excellent (plan's score was in the 75th-89th percentile)
◐ = Good (plan's score was in the 50th-74th percentile)
◔ = Fair (plan's score was in the 25th to 49th percentile)
○ = Poor (plan's score was worse than the 25th percentile)
N/A = Blanks indicate no data was reported for the measure

Plan Quality See chapter text for discussion of these data	Enrollment code	Ratings from plan members					
		Overall rating of plan	Overall rating of personal doctors	Getting needed care	Getting care quickly	Coordination of care	Claims processing
Humana Health (HMO/POS) (Chicago area)	75	◔	●	●	N/A	N/A	N/A
Humana Health (HMO/POS) (Rockford/NW IL)	9F	◔	●	●	N/A	N/A	N/A
Humana Health (HMO/POS) (Rockford/NW)	AB	◔	●	●	N/A	N/A	N/A
Humana Health-Basic (HMO/POS) (Chicago area)	RW	◔	●	●	N/A	N/A	N/A
United Choice Plus Advanced (POS)	L9	◔	○	N/A	N/A	N/A	N/A
United Choice Plus Primary (POS)	AS	◔	○	N/A	N/A	N/A	N/A
United Choice Primary (POS)	Y8	◔	○	N/A	N/A	N/A	N/A
Indiana							
Aetna Advantage (PPO)	Z2	◕	◑	◕	◕	◑	◑
Aetna Direct CDHP (PPO)	N6	◕	◑	◕	◕	◑	◑
Aetna HealthFund CDHP/Aetna Value (PPO)	JS	◕	◑	◕	◕	◑	◑
Aetna HealthFund HDHP/Aetna Direct (PPO)	22	◕	◑	◕	◕	◑	◑
Blue Cross Basic (PPO)	11	●	◔	◕	◕	◑	●
Blue Cross-Std (PPO)	10	●	◕	●	●	◕	●
Health Alliance (HMO/POS)	K8	●	◕	◕	◑	◑	N/A
Humana CoverageFirst/Humana Value (HMO/POS)	MW	◔	●	●	N/A	N/A	N/A
Humana Health (HMO/POS) (Chicago area)	75	◔	●	●	N/A	N/A	N/A
Humana Health (HMO/POS) (Cincinnati)	A6	○	◑	◑	◔	●	○
Humana Health (HMO/POS) (Southern IN)	MH	◔	●	◕	N/A	N/A	N/A
Humana Health-Basic (HMO/POS) (Chicago area)	RW	◔	●	●	N/A	N/A	N/A
Iowa							
Aetna Advantage (PPO)	Z2	◔	◕	●	●	●	◔
Aetna Direct CDHP (PPO)	N6	◔	◕	●	●	●	◔
Aetna HealthFund CDHP/Aetna Value (PPO)	H4	◔	◕	●	●	●	◔
Aetna HealthFund HDHP/Aetna Direct (PPO)	22	◔	◕	●	●	●	◔
Blue Cross Basic (PPO)	11	●	●	●	●	◑	◕
Blue Cross-Std (PPO)	10	●	◑	●	●	◑	◕
Health Alliance (HMO/POS)	K8	●	◕	◕	◑	◑	N/A
HealthPartners (HMO/POS)	V3	◑	◑	○	◔	◔	●
United Choice Open Access (POS)	LJ	◑	●	◕	◔	N/A	N/A

Plan Quality

See chapter text for discussion of these data

Plan	Enrollment code	Ratings from plan members					
		Overall rating of plan	Overall rating of personal doctors	Getting needed care	Getting care quickly	Coordination of care	Claims processing
United Choice Plus Primary (POS)	AS	◐	●	◕	◔	N/A	N/A
United Choice Primary (POS)	Y8	◐	●	◕	◔	N/A	N/A
United HDHP (POS)	N7	◐	●	◕	◔	N/A	N/A
Kansas							
Aetna Advantage (PPO)	Z2	○	◕	◕	◔	N/A	N/A
Aetna Direct CDHP (PPO)	N6	○	◕	◕	◔	N/A	N/A
Aetna HealthFund CDHP/Aetna Value (PPO)	G5	○	◕	◕	◔	N/A	N/A
Aetna HealthFund HDHP/Aetna Direct (PPO)	22	○	◕	◕	◔	N/A	N/A
Aetna Open Access (HMO/POS)	HA	◐	●	●	◕	◔	◔
Blue Cross Basic (PPO)	11	●	◔	●	●	◐	◕
Blue Cross-Std (PPO)	10	●	◐	◐	◕	◔	◕
Humana CoverageFirst CDHP (HMO/POS)	PH	◐	◐	●	●	◕	N/A
Humana Health (HMO/POS)	MS	◐	◐	●	●	◕	N/A
Kentucky							
Aetna Advantage (PPO)	Z2	◕	◕	◐	◐	●	◔
Aetna Direct CDHP (PPO)	N6	◕	◕	◐	◐	●	◔
Aetna HealthFund CDHP/Aetna Value (PPO)	H4	◕	◕	◐	◐	●	◔
Aetna HealthFund HDHP/Aetna Direct (PPO)	22	◕	◕	◐	◐	●	◔
Blue Cross Basic (PPO)	11	●	●	◐	◕	◐	◕
Blue Cross-Std (PPO)	10	●	◐	◐	◔	◔	●
Humana CoverageFirst CDHP (HMO/POS) (Lexington)	6N	◔	●	◕	N/A	N/A	N/A
Humana CoverageFirst CDHP (HMO/POS) (Louisville)	TC	◔	●	◕	N/A	N/A	N/A
Humana Health (HMO/POS) (Cincinnati)	A6	○	◐	◐	◔	●	○
Humana Health (HMO/POS) (Lexington/Central)	MI	◔	●	◕	N/A	N/A	N/A
Humana Health (HMO/POS) (Louisville)	MH	◔	●	◕	N/A	N/A	N/A
Humana Health Basic (HMO/POS) (Cincinnati)	W6	○	◐	◐	◔	●	○
United Choice Open Access (POS)	LJ	◐	◐	◐	N/A	N/A	N/A
United Choice Plus Primary (POS)	AS	◐	◐	◐	N/A	N/A	N/A

● = Outstanding (plan's score was in the 90th percentile)
◕ = Excellent (plan's score was in the 75th-89th percentile)
◐ = Good (plan's score was in the 50th-74th percentile)
◔ = Fair (plan's score was in the 25th to 49th percentile)
○ = Poor (plan's score was worse than the 25th percentile)
N/A = Blanks indicate no data was reported for the measure

Plan Quality See chapter text for discussion of these data	Enrollment code	Ratings from plan members					
		Overall rating of plan	Overall rating of personal doctors	Getting needed care	Getting care quickly	Coordination of care	Claims processing
United Choice Primary (POS)	Y8	◑	◑	◑	N/A	N/A	N/A
United HDHP (POS)	N7	◑	◑	◑	N/A	N/A	N/A
Louisiana							
Blue Cross Basic (PPO)	11	●	●	◕	◔	◔	◕
Blue Cross-Std (PPO)	10	●	◕	●	◑	◔	●
Humana Health (HMO/POS) (Baton Rouge)	AE	◕	N/A	N/A	N/A	N/A	N/A
Humana Health (HMO/POS) (New Orleans)	BC	◕	N/A	N/A	N/A	N/A	N/A
United Choice Open Access (POS)	KK	◕	◑	◑	N/A	N/A	N/A
United Choice Plus Primary (POS)	AS	◕	◑	◑	N/A	N/A	N/A
United Choice Primary (POS)	Y8	◕	◑	◑	N/A	N/A	N/A
United HDHP (POS)	LS	◕	◑	◑	N/A	N/A	N/A
Maine							
Blue Cross Basic (PPO)	11	◕	○	◔	○	◑	◑
Maryland							
Aetna Advantage (PPO)	Z2	◕	◑	◑	◕	○	N/A
Aetna Direct CDHP (PPO)	N6	◕	◑	◑	◕	○	N/A
Aetna HealthFund CDHP/Aetna Value (PPO)	F5	◕	◑	◑	◕	○	N/A
Aetna HealthFund HDHP (PPO)	22	◕	◑	◑	◕	○	N/A
Aetna Open Access (HMO/POS)	JN	◑	●	◑	◔	◑	N/A
Aetna Saver (HMO/POS)	QQ	◑	●	◑	◔	◑	N/A
Blue Cross Basic (PPO)	11	◕	○	◔	○	◔	◕
Blue Cross-Std (PPO)	10	●	◑	◕	◕	◑	◑
CareFirst (HMO/POS)	B6	●	◔	◕	◑	○	◑
CareFirst-Std (HMO/POS)	2G	●	◔	◕	◑	○	◑
GEHA-Std (PPO)	31	◑	○	○	N/A	N/A	◔
Kaiser (HMO)	E3	◕	◔	◑	◑	◕	N/A
Kaiser Prosper (HMO)	T7	◕	◔	◑	◑	◕	N/A
MD-IPA (HMO/POS)	JP	◕	◕	●	◔	◑	◕
United Choice Open Access (POS)	LR	◕	◕	◑	N/A	N/A	N/A

Plan Quality

See chapter text for discussion of these data

	Enrollment code	Ratings from plan members					
		Overall rating of plan	Overall rating of personal doctors	Getting needed care	Getting care quickly	Coordination of care	Claims processing
United Choice Plus Advanced (POS)	L9	◕	◕	◑	N/A	N/A	N/A
United Choice Plus Primary (POS)	AS	◕	◕	◑	N/A	N/A	N/A
United Choice Primary (POS)	Y8	◕	◕	◑	N/A	N/A	N/A
United HDHP (POS)	V4	◕	◕	◑	N/A	N/A	N/A
Massachusetts							
Aetna Advantage (PPO)	Z2	○	◔	○	◔	◔	○
Aetna Direct CDHP (PPO)	N6	○	◔	○	◔	◔	○
Aetna HealthFund CDHP/Aetna Value (PPO)	EP	○	◔	○	◔	◔	○
Aetna HealthFund HDHP/Aetna Direct (PPO)	22	○	◔	○	◔	◔	○
Blue Cross Basic (PPO)	11	●	○	◔	◔	○	◑
Blue Cross-Std (PPO)	10	●	◑	◑	◔	◔	◔
Michigan							
Blue Care Network (HMO) (Detroit)	LX	◔	◔	◑	◑	◑	◕
Blue Care Network (HMO) (Flint/Saginaw)	K5	◔	◔	◑	◑	◑	◕
Blue Cross Basic (PPO)	11	◕	◑	◑	◔	◑	●
Blue Cross-Std (PPO)	10	◕	◑	◕	◔	◔	●
Health Alliance-Hi (HMO/POS) (Detroit/Flint/Saginaw)	52	◕	◑	◔	◔	◑	◑
Health Alliance-Std (HMO/POS) (Detroit/Flint/Saginaw)	GY	◕	◑	◔	◔	◑	◑
Priority Health (HMO/POS)	LE	○	◑	◕	◑	●	◔
Priority Health Value (HMO/POS)	Y4	○	◑	◕	◑	●	◔
Minnesota							
Blue Cross Basic (PPO)	11	●	◑	◔	◑	◕	●
Blue Cross-Std (PPO)	10	◕	◕	●	◔	◑	◕
HealthPartners (HMO/POS)	V3	◑	◑	○	◔	◔	●
Mississippi							
Blue Cross Basic (PPO)	11	●	●	◑	◕	◑	●
Blue Cross-Std (PPO)	10	●	◑	●	●	○	◑
United Choice Open Access (POS)	KK	◑	●	◕	N/A	N/A	N/A

● = Outstanding (plan's score was in the 90th percentile)
◕ = Excellent (plan's score was in the 75th-89th percentile)
◑ = Good (plan's score was in the 50th-74th percentile)
◔ = Fair (plan's score was in the 25th to 49th percentile)
○ = Poor (plan's score was worse than the 25th percentile)
N/A = Blanks indicate no data was reported for the measure

Plan Quality

See chapter text for discussion of these data

Legend for rating symbols: ○ = empty, ◔ = one-quarter, ◑ = half, ◕ = three-quarters, ● = full

	Enrollment code	Ratings from plan members					
		Overall rating of plan	Overall rating of personal doctors	Getting needed care	Getting care quickly	Coordination of care	Claims processing
United Choice Plus Primary (POS)	AS	◑	●	◕	N/A	N/A	N/A
United Choice Primary (POS)	Y8	◑	●	◕	N/A	N/A	N/A
United HDHP (POS)	LS	◑	●	◕	N/A	N/A	N/A
Missouri							
Aetna Advantage (PPO)	Z2	◔	◔	◔	◑	◑	N/A
Aetna Direct CDHP (PPO)	N6	◔	◔	◔	◑	◑	N/A
Aetna HealthFund CDHP/Aetna Value (PPO)	G5	◔	◔	◔	◑	◑	N/A
Aetna HealthFund HDHP/Aetna Direct (PPO)	22	◔	◔	◔	◑	◑	N/A
Aetna Open Access (HMO/POS)	HA	◑	●	●	◕	◔	◔
Blue Cross Basic (PPO)	11	●	◔	◔	◔	◔	◑
Blue Cross-Std (PPO)	10	●	◕	●	◔	◑	●
Blue Preferred (HMO/POS)	9G	◑	◑	◑	●	◕	◑
GEHA-Std (PPO)	31	●	◑	◔	○	○	◑
Humana CoverageFirst CDHP (HMO/POS)	PH	◑	◑	●	●	◕	N/A
Humana Health (HMO/POS)	MS	◑	◑	●	●	◕	N/A
United Choice Plus Primary (POS)	AS	◑	○	N/A	N/A	N/A	N/A
United Choice Primary (POS)	Y8	◑	○	N/A	N/A	N/A	N/A
Montana							
Blue Cross Basic (PPO)	11	◕	◔	○	◑	○	◑
Nebraska							
Blue Cross Basic (PPO)	11	●	◑	●	●	◔	◑
Nevada							
Aetna Advantage (PPO)	Z2	◑	○	○	N/A	N/A	N/A
Aetna Direct CDHP (PPO)	N6	◑	○	○	N/A	N/A	N/A
Aetna HealthFund CDHP/Aetna Value (PPO)	G5	◑	○	○	N/A	N/A	N/A
Aetna HealthFund HDHP/Aetna Direct (PPO)	22	◑	○	○	N/A	N/A	N/A
Blue Cross Basic (PPO)	11	◕	◔	○	○	○	◑
Health Plan of Nevada (HMO/POS)	NM	◑	◔	○	○	○	◔
United Choice Open Access (POS)	KT	◑	○	○	N/A	N/A	N/A

Plan Quality

See chapter text for discussion of these data

Legend: ● = Outstanding · ◕ = Excellent · ◑ = Good · ◔ = Fair · ○ = Poor · N/A

Plan	Enrollment code	Overall rating of plan	Overall rating of personal doctors	Getting needed care	Getting care quickly	Coordination of care	Claims processing
United Choice Plus Primary (POS)	WF	◑	○	○	N/A	N/A	N/A
United Choice Primary (POS)	VD	◑	○	○	N/A	N/A	N/A
United HDHP (POS)	LU	◑	○	○	N/A	N/A	N/A
New Hampshire							
Blue Cross Basic (PPO)	11	●	◔	◕	●	◕	●
New Jersey							
Aetna Advantage (PPO)	Z2	◔	○	○	○	N/A	N/A
Aetna Direct CDHP (PPO)	N6	◔	○	○	○	N/A	N/A
Aetna HealthFund CDHP/Aetna Value (PPO)	EP	◔	○	○	○	N/A	N/A
Aetna HealthFund HDHP/Aetna Direct (PPO)	22	◔	○	○	○	N/A	N/A
Aetna Open Access (PPO) (Northern NJ)	JR	●	◑	◑	◔	◕	N/A
Aetna Open Access (PPO) (Southern NJ)	P3	●	◑	◑	◔	◕	N/A
Blue Cross Basic (PPO)	11	◕	◔	◑	○	○	◕
Blue Cross-Std (PPO)	10	●	◔	◑	◑	○	◔
GHI Health (PPO)	80	◑	◕	○	◑	◕	N/A
HIP (HMO)	51	◔	○	○	N/A	N/A	N/A
HIP (HMO/POS)	YL	◔	○	○	N/A	N/A	N/A
New Mexico							
Aetna Advantage (PPO)	Z2	○	○	○	○	N/A	○
Aetna Direct CDHP (PPO)	N6	○	○	○	○	N/A	○
Aetna HealthFund CDHP/Aetna Value (PPO)	G5	○	○	○	○	N/A	○
Aetna HealthFund HDHP/Aetna Direct (PPO)	22	○	○	○	○	N/A	○
Blue Cross Basic (PPO)	11	●	○	◔	◑	○	◕
Blue Cross-Std (PPO)	10	●	◑	◑	○	◔	◕
Presbyterian (HMO/POS)	P2	◔	○	○	○	○	○
Presbyterian Wellness (HMO/POS)	PS	◔	○	○	○	○	○

● = Outstanding (plan's score was in the 90th percentile)
◕ = Excellent (plan's score was in the 75th-89th percentile)
◑ = Good (plan's score was in the 50th-74th percentile)
◔ = Fair (plan's score was in the 25th to 49th percentile)
○ = Poor (plan's score was worse than the 25th percentile)
N/A = Blanks indicate no data was reported for the measure

Plan Quality

See chapter text for discussion of these data

	Enrollment code	Ratings from plan members					
		Overall rating of plan	Overall rating of personal doctors	Getting needed care	Getting care quickly	Coordination of care	Claims processing
New York							
Aetna Advantage (PPO)	Z2	◔	◔	◔	○	◔	N/A
Aetna Direct CDHP (PPO)	N6	◔	◔	◔	○	◔	N/A
Aetna HealthFund CDHP/Aetna Value (PPO)	EP	◔	◔	◔	○	◔	N/A
Aetna HealthFund HDHP/Aetna Direct (PPO)	22	◔	◔	◔	○	◔	N/A
Aetna Open Access (PPO)	JC	◔	◔	◔	○	◔	N/A
Blue Cross Basic (PPO)	11	●	○	◔	◔	◔	◕
Blue Cross-Std (PPO)	10	◕	◔	◑	◔	◔	◔
CDPHP (PPO)	SG	●	◔	◕	◑	◕	N/A
GHI Health (PPO)	80	◑	◕	○	◑	◕	N/A
HIP-Hi (HMO/POS)	51	◔	○	○	N/A	N/A	N/A
HIP-Std (HMO/POS)	YL	◔	○	○	N/A	N/A	N/A
Independent Health-Hi (HMO/POS)	QA	●	◑	◕	●	●	●
Independent Health-Std (HMO/POS)	C5	●	◑	◕	●	●	●
North Carolina							
Blue Cross Basic (PPO)	11	●	◔	◕	◕	●	◑
Blue Cross-Std (PPO)	10	●	◑	◑	●	◔	◑
United Choice Open Access (POS)	KK	●	◕	◑	N/A	N/A	N/A
United Choice Plus Primary (POS)	AS	●	◕	◑	N/A	N/A	N/A
United Choice Primary (POS)	Y8	●	◕	◑	N/A	N/A	N/A
United HDHP (POS)	LS	●	◕	◑	N/A	N/A	N/A
North Dakota							
HealthPartners (HMO/POS)	V3	◑	◑	○	◔	◔	●
Ohio							
Aetna Advantage (PPO)	Z2	◔	◑	◔	◔	●	N/A
Aetna Direct CDHP (PPO)	N6	◔	◑	◔	◔	●	N/A
Aetna HealthFund CDHP/Aetna Value (PPO)	JS	◔	◑	◔	◔	●	N/A
Aetna HealthFund HDHP/Aetna Direct (PPO)	22	◔	◑	◔	◔	●	N/A
AultCare (HMO)	3A	◑	◔	●	N/A	N/A	N/A
Blue Cross Basic (PPO)	11	●	○	●	●	◔	●

Plan Quality

See chapter text for discussion of these data

	Enrollment code	Ratings from plan members					
		Overall rating of plan	Overall rating of personal doctors	Getting needed care	Getting care quickly	Coordination of care	Claims processing
Blue Cross-Std (PPO)	10	●	◔	●	◑	◑	●
GEHA-Std (PPO)	31	●	●	◕	●	◔	◑
Humana CoverageFirst/Humana Value (HMO/POS)	X3	○	◑	◑	◔	●	○
Humana Health Basic (HMO/POS) (Cincinnati)	W6	○	◑	◑	◔	●	○
Medical Mutual (HMO/POS) (Dayton)	YF	◑	◑	◑	◑	◔	●
Medical Mutual (HMO/POS) (Toledo)	X6	◑	◑	◑	◑	◔	●
Medical Mutual-Basic (HMO/POS) (Cleveland/Akron)	UX	◑	◑	◑	◑	◔	●
Medical Mutual-Std (HMO/POS) (Cleveland/Akron)	64	◑	◑	◑	◑	◔	●
Oklahoma							
Blue Cross Basic (PPO)	11	●	◑	◔	●	○	◕
Blue Cross-Std (PPO)	10	●	◑	◑	◑	◑	●
Oregon							
Blue Cross Basic (PPO)	11	◕	○	○	○	○	◕
Blue Cross-Std (PPO)	10	◕	○	◔	◑	◔	◑
Kaiser Northwest (HMO)	57	◑	○	○	○	◑	N/A
Kaiser Northwest Prosper (HMO)	AM	◑	○	○	○	◑	N/A
United Choice Open Access (POS)	KT	○	○	○	○	N/A	○
United Choice Plus Primary (POS)	WF	○	○	○	○	N/A	○
United Choice Primary (POS)	VD	○	○	○	○	N/A	○
United HDHP (POS)	LU	○	○	○	○	N/A	○
Pennsylvania							
Aetna Advantage (PPO)	Z2	◔	◑	◑	◔	◑	N/A
Aetna Direct CDHP (PPO)	N6	◔	◑	◑	◔	◑	N/A
Aetna HealthFund CDHP/Aetna Value (PPO)	H4	◔	◑	◑	◔	◑	N/A
Aetna HealthFund HDHP/Aetna Direct (PPO)	22	◔	◑	◑	◔	◑	N/A
Aetna Open Access (HMO/POS)	YE	◔	○	◔	○	◔	N/A
Aetna Open Access (PPO)	P3	◔	○	◔	○	◔	N/A
Blue Cross Basic (PPO)	11	●	◑	◔	◕	◑	◕

● = Outstanding (plan's score was in the 90th percentile)
◕ = Excellent (plan's score was in the 75th-89th percentile)
◑ = Good (plan's score was in the 50th-74th percentile)
◔ = Fair (plan's score was in the 25th to 49th percentile)
○ = Poor (plan's score was worse than the 25th percentile)
N/A = Blanks indicate no data was reported for the measure

Plan Quality

See chapter text for discussion of these data

Plan	Enrollment code	Ratings from plan members					
		Overall rating of plan	Overall rating of personal doctors	Getting needed care	Getting care quickly	Coordination of care	Claims processing
Blue Cross-Std (PPO)	10	◕	◑	◕	◑	◑	◕
Geisinger (HMO/POS)	GG	◔	◕	◑	◑	◑	N/A
Geisinger Health Plan (HMO/POS)	AJ	◔	◕	◑	◑	◑	N/A
United Choice Open Access (POS)	LR	◑	◔	◔	N/A	N/A	N/A
United Choice Plus Primary (POS)	AS	◑	◔	◔	N/A	N/A	N/A
United Choice Primary (POS)	Y8	◑	◔	◔	N/A	N/A	N/A
United HDHP (POS)	V4	◑	◔	◔	N/A	N/A	N/A
UPMC (PPO) (Western)	8W	○	◑	◑	◔	◑	●
UPMC HDHP (HMO) (Western)	8W	◕	●	◕	◑	◕	◕
UPMC-Std (HMO) (Western)	UW	◕	●	◕	◑	◕	◕
Puerto Rico							
Humana Health (HMO)	ZJ	◕	◕	◔	○	N/A	N/A
Triple-S Salud (PPO)	89	●	◑	○	○	○	N/A
Rhode Island							
Blue Cross Basic (PPO)	11	◕	◔	◑	●	◔	◔
South Carolina							
Blue Cross Basic (PPO)	11	●	○	◑	◑	◑	◕
Blue Cross-Std (PPO)	10	●	◑	◕	●	◑	◑
South Dakota							
Blue Cross Basic (PPO)	11	●	◕	◕	●	◑	◕
HealthPartners (HMO/POS)	V3	◑	◑	○	◔	◔	●
Tennessee							
Blue Cross Basic (PPO)	11	●	●	◕	●	◔	●
Blue Cross-Std (PPO)	10	●	●	◑	●	◑	●
Humana CoverageFirst CDHP (HMO/POS)	TT	◕	●	N/A	N/A	N/A	N/A
Humana Health (HMO/POS) (Knoxville)	GJ	◕	●	N/A	N/A	N/A	N/A
United Choice Open Access (POS)	KK	◑	○	●	N/A	N/A	N/A
United Choice Plus Primary (POS)	AS	◑	○	●	N/A	N/A	N/A
United Choice Primary (POS)	Y8	◑	○	●	N/A	N/A	N/A
United HDHP (POS)	LS	◑	○	●	N/A	N/A	N/A

Plan Quality

See chapter text for discussion of these data

	Enrollment code	Ratings from plan members					
		Overall rating of plan	Overall rating of personal doctors	Getting needed care	Getting care quickly	Coordination of care	Claims processing
Texas							
Aetna Advantage (PPO)	Z2	◐	◔	◐	N/A	N/A	N/A
Aetna Direct CDHP (PPO)	N6	◐	◔	◐	N/A	N/A	N/A
Aetna HealthFund CDHP/Aetna Value (PPO)	JS	◐	◔	◐	N/A	N/A	N/A
Aetna HealthFund HDHP/Aetna Direct (PPO)	22	◐	◔	◐	N/A	N/A	N/A
Blue Cross Basic (PPO)	11	●	◐	◔	◔	◔	◕
Blue Cross-Std (PPO)	10	●	◐	◕	◐	◔	◕
GEHA-Std (PPO)	31	●	◔	◕	N/A	N/A	N/A
Humana CoverageFirst/Value (HMO/POS) (Austin)	TV	◔	◔	●	◕	○	○
Humana CoverageFirst/Value (HMO/POS) (Crp Chsti)	TP	◕	◔	○	◔	○	●
Humana CoverageFirst/Value (HMO/POS) (Houston)	T3	◔	◕	◐	○	N/A	N/A
Humana CoverageFirst/Value (HMO/POS) (San Ant)	TU	◐	○	◐	○	○	◕
Humana Health-Basic (HMO/POS) (Austin)	QY	◔	◔	●	◕	○	○
Humana Health-Basic (HMO/POS) (Corpus Christi)	Q2	◕	◔	○	◔	○	●
Humana Health-Basic (HMO/POS) (Houston)	Q6	◔	◕	◐	○	N/A	N/A
Humana Health-Basic (HMO/POS) (San Antonio)	QX	◐	○	◐	○	○	◕
Scott & White-Basic (HMO/POS)	P8	◕	●	◕	◐	◐	N/A
Scott & White-Std (HMO/POS)	A8	◕	●	◕	◐	◐	N/A
United Choice Plus Advanced (POS)	L9	◕	●	◐	◕	N/A	N/A
United Choice Plus Primary (POS)	AS	◕	●	◐	◕	N/A	N/A
United Choice Primary (POS)	Y8	◕	●	◐	◕	N/A	N/A
Utah							
Aetna Health/Altius-Hi (HMO/POS)	9K	◔	◕	●	◐	◔	◔
Aetna Health/Altius-Std (HMO/POS)	DK	◔	◕	●	◐	◔	◔
Blue Cross Basic (PPO)	11	●	◐	◕	◐	○	◐
Blue Cross-Std (PPO)	10	●	◐	◔	○	◔	◐
SelectHealth HDHP (HMO/POS)	WX	◐	◐	◔	N/A	N/A	N/A
SelectHealth-Std (HMO/POS)	SF	◐	◐	◔	N/A	N/A	N/A

● = Outstanding (plan's score was in the 90th percentile)
◕ = Excellent (plan's score was in the 75th-89th percentile)
◐ = Good (plan's score was in the 50th-74th percentile)
◔ = Fair (plan's score was in the 25th to 49th percentile)
○ = Poor (plan's score was worse than the 25th percentile)
N/A = Blanks indicate no data was reported for the measure

Plan Quality	Enrollment code	Ratings from plan members					
		Overall rating of plan	Overall rating of personal doctors	Getting needed care	Getting care quickly	Coordination of care	Claims processing
Virgin Islands							
Triple-S Salud (PPO)	85	●	◐	○	○	○	N/A
Virginia							
Aetna Advantage (PPO)	Z2	◐	◐	◕	◐	◕	N/A
Aetna Direct CDHP (PPO)	N6	◐	◐	◕	◐	◕	N/A
Aetna HealthFund CDHP/Aetna Value (PPO)	F5	◐	◐	◕	◐	◕	N/A
Aetna HealthFund HDHP/Aetna Direct (PPO)	22	◐	◐	◕	◐	◕	N/A
Aetna Open Access (HMO/POS)	JN	◐	●	◐	◕	◐	N/A
Aetna Saver (HMO/POS)	QQ	◐	●	◐	◕	◐	N/A
Blue Cross Basic (PPO)	11	◕	◔	◔	◕	◔	◐
Blue Cross-Std (PPO)	10	◕	◔	◔	◔	○	◐
CareFirst (HMO/POS)	B6	●	◔	◕	◐	○	◐
CareFirst-Std (HMO/POS)	2G	●	◔	◕	◐	○	◐
GEHA-Std (PPO)	31	◐	○	○	N/A	N/A	◕
Kaiser (HMO)	E3	◕	◔	◐	◐	◕	N/A
Kaiser Prosper (HMO)	T7	◕	◔	◐	◐	◕	N/A
MD-IPA (HMO/POS)	JP	◕	◕	●	◔	◐	◕
Optima Health (HMO/POS)	PG	◐	◔	○	○	◔	◐
United Choice Open Access (POS)	LR	◐	◕	○	N/A	N/A	N/A
United Choice Plus Advanced (POS)	L9	◐	◕	○	N/A	N/A	N/A
United Choice Plus Primary (POS)	AS	◐	◕	○	N/A	N/A	N/A
United Choice Primary (POS)	Y8	◐	◕	○	N/A	N/A	N/A
United HDHP (POS)	V4	◐	◕	○	N/A	N/A	N/A
Washington							
Aetna Advantage (PPO)	Z2	◔	○	◔	◔	N/A	N/A
Aetna Direct CDHP (PPO)	N6	◔	○	◔	◔	N/A	N/A
Aetna HealthFund CDHP/Aetna Value (PPO)	G5	◔	○	◔	◔	N/A	N/A
Aetna HealthFund HDHP/Aetna Direct (PPO)	22	◔	○	◔	◔	N/A	N/A
Blue Cross Basic (PPO)	11	◐	○	○	◐	◕	◐
Blue Cross-Std (PPO)	10	◕	○	◔	◕	◕	◕

Plan Quality — See chapter text for discussion of these data	Enrollment code	Ratings from plan members					
		Overall rating of plan	Overall rating of personal doctors	Getting needed care	Getting care quickly	Coordination of care	Claims processing
GEHA-Std (PPO)	31	◐	○	○	N/A	N/A	N/A
Kaiser Northwest (HMO)	57	◐	○	○	○	◐	N/A
Kaiser Northwest Prosper (HMO)	AM	◐	○	○	○	◐	N/A
Kaiser Options (PPO)	L1	○	○	○	○	○	N/A
Kaiser Washington (HMO)	54	◔	◔	○	○	○	N/A
Kaiser Washington Prosper (HMO)	PT	◔	◔	○	○	○	N/A
United Choice Open Access (POS)	KT	○	○	○	N/A	N/A	N/A
United Choice Plus Primary (POS)	WF	○	○	○	N/A	N/A	N/A
United Choice Primary (POS)	VD	○	○	○	N/A	N/A	N/A
United HDHP (POS)	LU	○	○	○	N/A	N/A	N/A
West Virginia							
Blue Cross Basic (PPO)	11	◕	○	◕	◕	○	●
Blue Cross-Std (PPO)	10	◕	◔	◐	◐	○	●
Wisconsin							
Aetna Advantage (PPO)	Z2	◔	◐	◐	●	●	◔
Aetna Direct CDHP (PPO)	N6	◔	◐	◐	●	●	◔
Aetna HealthFund CDHP/Aetna Value (PPO)	JS	◔	◐	◐	●	●	◔
Aetna HealthFund HDHP/Aetna Direct (PPO)	22	◔	◐	◐	●	●	◔
Blue Cross Basic (PPO)	11	●	◔	◕	●	◕	●
Blue Cross-Std (PPO)	10	●	●	◐	◕	●	◕
Dean Health (HMO)	AG	◔	◕	◐	◐	●	◔
Dean Health-Std (HMO)	WD	◔	◕	◐	◐	●	◔
Group Health (HMO)	WJ	◐	◐	◐	◕	●	N/A
HealthPartners (HMO/POS)	V3	◐	◐	○	◔	◔	●
Wyoming							
Aetna Health/Altius-Hi (HMO/POS)	9K	◔	◕	●	◐	◔	◔
Aetna Health/Altius-Std (HMO/POS)	DK	◔	◕	●	◐	◔	◔

● = Outstanding (plan's score was in the 90th percentile)
◕ = Excellent (plan's score was in the 75th-89th percentile)
◐ = Good (plan's score was in the 50th-74th percentile)
◔ = Fair (plan's score was in the 25th to 49th percentile)
○ = Poor (plan's score was worse than the 25th percentile)
N/A = Blanks indicate no data was reported for the measure

Continued from page 98

The Disputed Claims table on page 98 shows for national plans disputed claims per 10,000 Federal enrollees for the period from October 2020 through September 2021. The table also shows in how many cases per 10,000 enrollees a plan's initial decision in a disputed claim was changed or reversed.

There are several possible explanations for differences in incidence of disputed claims. For example, some plans may have an unusually large share of hypercritical members, be more aggressive than others in enforcing their policy limitations to prevent benefit abuses, or have benefit limits that enrollees tend not to notice or not to understand. Most of the disputed claims are resolved in favor of the plans on the grounds that they involve matters that are not within the plans' coverage. But do you want to be in a plan where you will feel the need to file a disputed claim? Everything else equal, it seems preferable to join a plan where the coverage limits are easily understood, communication is good, benefit limitations are interpreted broadly—and disputed claims are rare.

Clinical Quality of Care

At GuideToHealthPlans.org, we report additional ratings from OPM on how plans compared for clinical quality of care. These ratings indicate how well plans performed for prevention measures (immunizations, breast cancer screenings, etc.) and how well plans performed for treating chronic conditions (asthma, diabetes, etc.). OPM used the same scale to report these results as it did for the customer satisfaction survey results.

Accreditation

At GuideToHealthPlans.org, we also report whether or not plans are accredited by NCQA or by URAC or AAAHC, two smaller accrediting organizations. These organizations have procedures to determine whether plans meet the organization's accreditation standards. The standards cover many areas of performance, such as whether the plan takes appropriate steps to check the credentials of its physicians, whether the plan has appropriate health promotion and disease prevention programs, and whether the plan has appropriate protections of patients' rights. NCQA includes in its accreditation process assessments of plan performance on member satisfaction survey measures and effectiveness of care measures, such as the percentage of two-year-olds who have had all recommended immunizations and the percentage of heart attack patients who are given a specific type of recommended medication.

Chapter 10

Premiums and Taxes

There are major tax advantages for health insurance. The "employer share" of health insurance—paid by agencies for employees and by OPM for annuitants—is part of employee compensation but by law is exempted from being counted as taxable income. For Federal employees and annuitants, the non-taxable premium share paid by employing agencies and OPM averages over $6,000 for self-only enrollments, over $13,000 for self plus one, and over $14,000 for families. The tax laws also allow employers to make the "employee share" of the premium tax-free to employees, and to set up tax advantaged Flexible Spending Accounts for employees. The average tax-sheltered employee share of premium for Federal self-only enrollees is about $2,000 and for families about $5,000. In total, employees in family plans shelter about $20,000 in employee compensation for health insurance from Federal, State, and local income taxes, as well as from OASDI taxes. This saves employees a tidy sum, about $6,000 per family on average. By law, only the tax benefits for the employer share, but not the annuitant share, are available to retirees in either the public or private sectors. But annuitants in Medicare Parts A and B also get over $9,000 per person of untaxed insurance benefits on top of their FEHB savings, paid by taxpayers, for a total tax shelter of about $22,000 for a retired couple.

Tax Savings for Employee Premium Share

Federal employees shelter their share of the FEHB plan premium from income taxes through what is called "Premium Conversion." Employees have the right to opt out of this program. This increases very slightly future Social Security benefits. However, that offsetting amount is a very small fraction—a few pennies on the dollar—of the gains from the Premium Conversion program. We strongly advise all employees NOT to opt out of Premium Conversion tax savings.

How much employees gain from this tax subsidy varies depending on employee salary, spousal salary, other income, state income tax rate, number of dependents, amount of deductions, whether or not they file jointly, and whether or not they are in FERS (and hence paying Social Security taxes). The overall marginal tax rate can often reach 40 percent, or even more in some high tax states.

At income ranges typical of Federal employees, whether in single- or dual-earner families, and whether in the FERS or CSRS retirement systems, almost everyone will save at least 25 percent, and very few will save much more than 40 percent, from tax-sheltered health care premiums or other expenses.

How Much Tax-Sheltered Premiums Are Reduced

Because the effects of different marginal tax rates are relatively small in comparing plans, and never change our relative rankings or the general magnitude of plan-to-plan differences, we use a 33 percent premium savings estimate in all Guide tables for employees, who are eligible for Premium Conversion. This simplifies presentation and gives you the essential information you need to compare plans. You can, of course, make your own calculation of marginal tax rate, but this is complicated and will not affect most plan comparisons substantially.

Flexible Spending Accounts

Health Care Flexible Spending Accounts (FSAs) provide a way to shelter even more health care spending from taxes. FSAs allow you to shelter the out-of-pocket costs that you incur for copayments, coinsurance, deductibles, charges above customary and reasonable, and uncovered health care expenses. Under health reform, you can no longer use an FSA account to pay for over-the-counter drugs without a physician prescription (insulin is an exception) but all other categories of expense are unchanged. For most people, the favored categories for using FSAs are dental expenses, vision expenses, and your share of costs for services covered by the plan—for example, the coinsurance you pay for mental health services, or the annual deductible.

Under IRS rules, you have to set up your FSA account and amount in advance. OPM allows you to use the regular Open Season period for setting up your account. For health care, in 2022 you can elect to choose any amount from a minimum of $100 to a maximum of $2,750. (You can also elect to set aside additional amounts for "Dependent Care.") You establish the account by enrolling online at *www.fsafeds.com* or by calling 1-877-372-3337. Unlike Premium Conversion, you have to elect this benefit and will NOT be enrolled automatically. Until recently, enrollees in Consumer-Driven and High Deductible plans were not allowed to create FSAs. However, they may now set up "Limited Expense" FSAs that cover only dental and vision expenses that are not reimbursed by insurance.

You can carry up to $500 in unused FSA accounts into the next year. But any amount over $500 that you elect to set aside for an FSA must be spent by the end of the year, or it will be forfeited (a "grace period" of 2½ months is no longer allowed). You should plan carefully based on your best "guesstimate" as to health care expenses that you are virtually certain to incur, such as maintenance prescription drugs, routine dental care, and routine eye care or any services for which you make multiple and foreseeable provider visits.

Only about one in five Federal employees are signing up each year for FSA accounts. This means that about four out of five employees are leaving money on the table each year. Almost everyone has at least a few hundred dollars in foreseeable out-of-pocket health care expenses. Those who don't sign up are throwing away a one-third discount on these costs. We recommend that ALL employees who are not in High Deductible plans establish an FSA if they have foreseeable expenses.

Health Savings Accounts

Both Health Reimbursement Arrangements (HRAs) and Health Savings Accounts (HSAs) provide significant tax advantages, beyond those available through Premium Conversion and FSAs. The simpler case involves HRAs, where your savings account can grow as long as you stay with the same plan (if you change plans the entire amount is lost), and you can also use an FSA to supplement the HRA amount set aside by the plan. For example, if you expect out of pocket drug and dental expenses of five hundred dollars next year, you could place that amount in an FSA in the expectation that the HRA amount paid through your premiums would remain available for unforeseen expenses next year or in future years. Unfortunately, retirees cannot use the FSA method of supplementing HRAs.

HSAs convey far larger advantages. First, you can add to your HSA account by advance planning, just as if it were an FSA. Second, while you can only establish an FSA account in advance, you can add to your HSA account at any time during the year. Thus, if you have unanticipated expenses late in the year of an extra thousand dollars, in most High Deductible plans you can have a thousand dollars transferred from your pay to your HSA, lower your taxable income by a thousand dollars, pay the bill through the HSA, and obtain what amounts to a one-third discount on your unplanned expenses. Or you can transfer the extra thousand dollars even if you don't have any unexpected expenses, saving one third in taxes, and build up your account for future years. Since you retain the HSA account for life, regardless of Open Season plan changes or retirement, and it can accumulate tax-free earnings, it can become a very substantial lifelong protection against health care expense.

This account augmentation advantage is dramatic if you consider the catastrophic guarantee provided by most FEHB plans. Consider a traditional plan, national or local, that holds self-only total out-of-pocket cost to $6,000, without significant loopholes. Compare that to a High Deductible plan, with a guarantee of $7,000 for a self-only enrollment, also without significant loopholes. The traditional plan seems better. However, under the High Deductible plan your plan-paid HSA account of $1,000 (a typical amount) can be used to defray large expenses, thereby reducing your potential loss to $6,000. Beyond that, you are allowed to make tax advantaged voluntary contributions of over $2,000 and pay your bills through your augmented account. This lets you save approximately $700 through lower tax payments if you face catastrophic expense. Hence, your total cost exposure is only about $5,300, lower than that claimed by the traditional plan, and reversing the conclusion as to which plan has a better guarantee. Most HDHP plans, evaluated this way, offer catastrophic expense protection as good as or better than most traditional plans.

While retirees over the age of 65 cannot establish HSAs, those nearing retirement not only can take advantage of HSAs, but also are eligible for "catch up" contributions after age 55, until enrolled in Medicare. These contributions can reduce after-tax expenses by hundreds of dollars a year more, or simply be added to the growing HSA balance. After retirement, the HSA balance remains available for the rest of your life and continues to earn tax-free returns. After death, it is part of your estate and passes to your heirs.

Chapter 11

Key Tips and Final Plan Selection

The data we have presented should help you to narrow your choice quickly and easily to two or three of the plans, out of the dozens you are offered. At this point, compare the brochures of these carefully. Underline key points, or parts of the plans that confuse you, and compare these points among the plans. It is very easy to use our online website, or OPMs, to find copies of plan brochures for your area. Then you can search on a word such as "maternity," "surgery," or "chiropractor" in the brochure for each plan and find the benefit details in seconds. Probably the plans will be similar on most things, so concentrate on differences that are important to you.

When you have figured out the major differences among the best plans, you are ready to make your final decision. One way to do this is to write out the most important ways in which the plans differ. These differences may not be strictly financial. For example, suppose it turns out that your choice is between a national plan and an HMO. Let's say that our ratings show that the HMO costs $1,000 dollars a year less on average and has slightly better coverage for a benefit you need. But you are unwilling to give up a particular doctor you have been using for years. This seems to be an impasse, but there are several possible ways to resolve it. Perhaps your doctor is affiliated with the HMO—why not ask? Or consider using part of the money you will save by joining the HMO to continue going to your doctor and paying out-of-pocket (using a Flexible Spending Account will cut this cost by a third). Or you may have more than one doctor you want to keep and conclude that the national plan is well worth the higher cost.

Throughout this *Guide* we have argued that your best strategy is to make the primary factor in your plan selection the predicted cost of the plan for families like yours. This takes into account that none of us can predict whether or not we may have a heart attack, a stroke, a cancer, or other costly condition that strikes unexpectedly. You should use your known, predictable routine expenses to calculate how much to put in a Flexible Spending Account, not to choose an insurance plan whose main purpose is to protect you against unexpected and high expenses. There is an important exception to this general strategy. If you know that you will need some particular service next year, and it is very expensive (for example, hip surgery or maternity) and likely to cost you tens of thousands of dollars, it makes sense to select the physician you would like to use (or several you are considering) and ask two simple questions: "What plan networks are you in?" and "In your experience, which Federal employee health plan or plans pay best for the care I need?" Sometimes the answer will be that all of them pay well. But sometimes the answer will be that only a few plans pay well. Whatever you find, complete your detective work by checking the plan brochure on your procedure. But do not forget that some other disease may strike, so factor in both known problems and overall ratings in choosing among these few plans.

Whatever your personal decision turns on, you may be overwhelmed by details and confused by the choices you face. Here are some concluding thoughts based on some of the most common questions we have heard. Try to focus your decision on several key questions. Are you willing to join an HMO or a High Deductible plan? Do you expect big bills for a particular event such as surgery? Do you really "have to have" doctor sawbones in the plan network? (Hint: in the DC metro area, we have a "doc find" feature that tells you which plan networks include doctor sawbones.) If you can't afford a high premium to get the benefits you want, pick a plan that at least gives you good catastrophic protection.

Tips

Throughout the *Guide* we have provided vital tips. We repeat some here:

- **Getting "Free" Health Insurance**—Some Consumer-Driven and High Deductible FEHB plans provide you a savings account larger than your actual premium cost after taxes. You can end the year with more money than you started if your medical costs are low.

- **Avoid a Big Risk**—Many people who are covered by their spouse's insurance drop FEHB insurance. This saves premium costs. However, if you are not enrolled and die suddenly, your spouse cannot ever enroll again. Your best option is to carry an FEHB family policy and drop the spousal insurance.

- **Protect Your Retirement**—Your spouse's free insurance may cover you both. Do not drop out of the FEHBP. It is not expensive to enroll in an FEHB plan for the five years before retirement. Several plans have annual premiums that are about $1,500. These plans cost about $1,000 after tax savings. Some plans give you savings accounts higher than the tax advantaged premium cost.

- **Be Sure to Elect a Survivor Annuity for Your Spouse**—If you die and your spouse receives no Federal pension, your spouse will lose FEHB health insurance coverage forever. If you die while enrolled as self-only, your spouse will also lose coverage.

- **Bargain with Out of Network Providers**—Most plans have very low payments for non-preferred providers. Negotiate with these doctors before any expensive procedure. One good tactic is to ask for their "preferred" or Medicare rate.

- **Check Your Brochure**—Do not stay in the same plan without reading at least "How We Change" for next year or join a new plan without checking any benefits of particular importance to your health care.

- **Flexible Spending Account**—You can only establish your FSA during Open Season. Be sure to carefully consider this important option to reduce your health costs. Almost all employees should set up an FSA.

- **Medicare Flexibility at a Low or High Price**—The best two arguments for paying the Medicare Part B premium are to preserve your choices over time, as both the FEHB and Medicare programs evolve, and to get you low costs for providers who are not in your plan network. This choice is costly in most but not all plans. Check out the plans we rate as lowest cost with Medicare Part B.

- **Huge Annuitant Cost Saving**—Annuitants with Medicare Parts A and B can suspend their FEHB enrollment, join a Medicare Advantage plan, and pay only the Medicare premium. They can reenroll in an FEHB plan in the future without penalty, and in the meantime, enjoy good catastrophic protection, have low copays, and save thousands in premium costs. In some plans they can enroll in both programs but collect a reimbursement for most of the Part B premium while also enjoying good catastrophic protection and low copays, and saving the cost of a second premium. Or these same annuitants can join an FEHB plan with a good Part B premium rebate and a special Medicare Advantage plan with zero copays. One way or the other, these are excellent choices for most annuitants.

- **Dealing with a Known High Expense**—There is an exception to our general advice about focusing on overall plan costs, not just one benefit category. If you know for sure that you will need an expensive service, you should look for the answer to "Which plans pay best?" If several plans pay equally well, then you can choose whichever of these is an overall better buy.

Questions and Answers

Here is a short list of frequent questions and their answers (we provide a far longer list in the online Guide):

- **What if I expect to have a baby?** What plan offers the best maternity benefits? Most plans offer low or no cost maternity coverage. Check brochures for this and check network lists online to make sure you will have a good selection of obstetricians. Or select an obstetrician and then use her experience to steer you towards a few plans from which to choose.

- **What if I am going to have a major operation?** Pay particular attention to catastrophic limits. If you know for sure that you are going to face bills of $25,000 or more, then pick a plan with a tight limit on your costs. In comparing catastrophic expense limits, use *Guide* figures. Our estimates include the "for sure" premium expense and adjust for inconsistencies among stated catastrophic limits, such as failing to include deductibles in the stated limit. If you are not sure what plans will work best in your case, check brochures and consult your surgeon to discuss which plans work best. Be sure your surgeon is in your plan network or will give you a network rate.

- **My two doctors aren't preferred providers for any plan. What should I do?** Set up an FSA account for about half the amount you expect to spend on those doctors. Then pick one of the top ranked plans that includes a fee-for-service benefit, use that benefit for whatever it will pay (which will probably be about half), and use the FSA to cover the rest. Or change doctors.

- **I need over 30 psychiatric visits. What plan is best?** The mental health parity requirement—which theoretically allows unlimited visits at a low cost—might arguably make all plans meet your needs. But plans require using preferred providers to get network rates. First, talk to your provider and see if he or she is "preferred" under any plan. If so, this plan is likely to be your best choice. Alternatively, most plans will pay sixty or seventy percent of the "plan allowance" for out of network visits. Since that is well below what most providers charge, you will likely pay half or more of the cost of each visit. Try making an arithmetic calculation. Estimate the number of visits you are likely to make and how much each of several plans will pay for these visits. Then add the annual premium cost to the amount that you will pay the doctor under each of those plans. If one of them stands out, you have an answer. If they are all about the same, choose on some other basis (like our overall ratings). Finally, you are a perfect candidate for a Flexible Spending Account, and your FSA tax savings will reduce your cost by about a third.

- **I really like the service from plan X. But it is rated halfway down your cost table. Would I be a sucker to stay with it?** No. Differences of several hundred dollars in estimated costs can move a plan up or down the table a long way. Our methods of estimating average costs are only approximations. Differences of $100 or less are not significant, and a national plan even halfway down the table is a perfectly acceptable deal. Furthermore, staying with the same plan will eliminate the hassle of changing doctors and of dealing with a plan bureaucracy that may not be as customer friendly as the one you have now.

- **You rated the plan I am in highly last year, but this year it has moved way down. Why did this happen, and should I switch?** Premium differences are the biggest factor in our cost rankings, and premiums can swing widely from year to year. That is probably why your plan moved so far—but check the brochure's change page for a benefit cutback that could have affected our ratings. Or other plans could have improved their benefits. One of the big change factors, for example, is the catastrophic limit promised to you by the plan: these often move up or down by thousands of dollars and are big factors in our ratings. You can stick with your plan if it has not become unreasonably costly and has given you good service. But consider the possible savings from the plans we rank higher.

- **I don't have much money and can't afford an expensive premium. Is it safe to join one of the plans with a really low premium?** All plans are reputable, and all will pay the benefits they promise. Every plan, not just the ones with the lowest premiums, has gaps or loopholes of one kind or another. But the lower-premium national plans generally expose you to higher copayments and deductibles, so they may not save you as much money as you think. Look at our ratings tables and several brochures carefully, and then decide. A lower premium does not mean a worse plan, or a higher premium a better plan. Our estimates of average costs are a far better guide to likely costs than premiums alone.

- **I'm not very healthy and could easily have expenses of many thousands of dollars next year. I don't think that your rankings based on average costs are what I should use. What should I do?** A good method is to skip the average column and look at the column for high expenses of $30,000. Within that column, choose among several plans that our comparisons indicate are relatively low-cost. Another approach is to compare catastrophic limits. But keep in mind that our "average" columns include some very expensive years. Most people, in most years, will be out-of-pocket far less.

- **I can't decide whether I should get Medicare Part B and join a plan that guarantees I won't pay anything at all for medical bills, or plan to drop Medicare Part B and save about $1,800 a year in premium cost.** If your doctors are mostly preferred providers, consider dropping Part B. You won't save the entire amount of the Part B premium, but you will save most of it in most years. The main two arguments for getting Part B are that you have complete flexibility to use any doctor who accepts new Medicare patients, even if he is not preferred, and in the many plans with wraparound benefits you will pay nothing for hospital or doctor costs. But these savings and this flexibility costs you over a thousand dollars a year in most plans. Check out the plans we rate as costing you almost nothing, or even saving you money, when you are covered by Part B. Whatever you do, do not drop out of the FEHB program. If you decide to keep Part B, move to a low premium plan that waives cost sharing for those with Medicare Parts A and B, such as Aetna Direct, Blue Cross Basic, MHBP High Deductible, or in the DC area CareFirst High Deductible. Some plans not only provide a Medicare wraparound, but also pay part of the Part B premium.

- **My spouse has excellent family coverage from his or her employer and pays no premium. Is there any reason why I should not drop out of the Federal program?** If you are within five years of retirement, do not even consider dropping out. That private plan will go away sooner or later, and you and your spouse will be stuck. You are not allowed to remain in the FEHB program after retirement without five years of continuous prior enrollment immediately preceding retirement (there are some narrow exceptions, such as layoffs). A good move would be to join a High Deductible plan, rely mainly on your spouse's coverage for medical care, and save the Health Savings Account money as your "IRA on steroids".

- **I read that High Deductible plans are bad buys for older and less healthy individuals.** Nonsense. These plans are among the best deals in the program. Taking into account their tax advantages and savings accounts, they rival or beat many other plans. If you know that your routine physician and drug expenses, priced at retail, will be three or four thousand dollars or more next year, you will probably do better in an HMO or national plan with low copayments. But high expense, in and of itself, is not an argument against High Deductible plans. They have some of the best catastrophic limit guarantees.

- **Some expensive plans have higher quality scores than some less expensive plans. How much weight should I put on quality?** The quality scores are driven by survey results from enrollees in each plan. Our ratings also show some of the particular factors those enrollees most like or dislike. Only you can judge how important these are to you. It may help to consider two things: most enrollees in just about all plans rate the plans quite favorably; and ultimately it is the doctors you choose, not the plan, that drives the quality of medical care you get. That said, the anecdotal evidence we get tells us that these scores measure things that are important and real.

- **I have an expensive condition that I am not sure is covered by several plans that you rank high. What should I do?** The first step is to get those plan brochures and compare them side-by-side. OPM's policy for standard brochure formats and clear English is immensely helpful. If you read and compare the specific language you may find the answer. If you do not, call at least one plan, and preferably several plans, and call again to protect yourself against mistakes that plan representatives sometimes make. If you are still not sure, consult providers who deal with your condition, or other patients with your condition, or both. Sometimes there is no way around doing your homework.

- **Skip all the details. What is the best plan?** There is no one best plan. Every plan is best for at least some people. Our rankings give you a good starting point, but only a starting point. If you don't want to be bothered with details, then check out only one or two plans carefully. But whatever else you do, read the "how we change" pages of the brochure, along with the "summary of benefits" near the end of the brochure, before you stay in the plan you are in or sign up for a new plan.

Cost & Special Features of All Plans			Average yearly cost in dollars (premiums and out-of-pocket costs)					
Plan code	Plan name (primary service area)	Phone number	General Schedule			Annuitants 55 to 64		
			Self only	Self plus one	Family	Self only	Self plus one	Family of two
National Plans								
Z24-6R	Aetna Advantage	888-238-6240	3070	6270	6720	4580	9490	10160
Z24-6R	Aetna Advantage (Medicare Advantage)	888-238-6240	NA	NA	NA	NA	NA	NA
N61-3	Aetna Direct CDHP	888-238-6240	2140	**4350**	4760	3590	7370	7990
224-6	Aetna HealthFund HDHP	888-238-6240	3410	7130	6560	5520	11550	10690
474-6	APWU CDHP	800-222-2798	**1890**	**3950**	**4180**	3380	**7080**	**7440**
471-3	APWU-Hi	800-222-2798	3090	5930	6900	4610	8980	10430
471-3R	APWU-Hi (Medicare Advantage)	800-222-2798	NA	NA	NA	NA	NA	NA
111-3	Blue Cross Basic	800-411-2583	2240	4900	5180	3470	7550	7970
131-3	Blue Cross FEP Blue Focus	800-411-2583	2350	**4220**	**4420**	3520	**6430**	**6730**
104-6	Blue Cross-Std	800-411-2583	3430	7190	7620	5150	10910	11540
421-3	Compass Rose	888-438-9135	2520	5470	5830	3840	8350	8890
421-3R	Compass Rose (Medicare Advantage)	888-438-9135	NA	NA	NA	NA	NA	NA
401-3	Foreign Service	202-833-4910	2120	4750	**4680**	3220	**7190**	**7070**
254-6	GEHA Elevate	800-821-6136	**1860**	**3530**	**3960**	2940	**5610**	**6240**
251-3	GEHA Elevate Plus	800-821-6136	2430	5060	5200	3740	7820	8030
341-3	GEHA HDHP	800-821-6136	**1660**	**3440**	**3980**	2870	**5880**	**6690**
311-3	GEHA-Hi	800-821-6136	3100	6640	7630	4600	10020	11510
314-6	GEHA-Std	800-821-6136	2570	5020	5550	3870	7730	8510
454-6R	MHBP - Std (Medicare Advantage)	800-410-7778	NA	NA	NA	NA	NA	NA
481-3	MHBP HDHP	800-694-9901	**1890**	**3950**	**4090**	3340	**6910**	**7130**
414-6	MHBP Value Plan	800-410-7778	3090	6660	6710	4650	10110	10170
454-6	MHBP-Std	800-410-7778	2640	5580	5330	3990	8490	8130
324-6	NALC CDHP	888-636-6252	**1610**	**3380**	**3510**	2960	**6250**	**6440**
KM1-3	NALC Value Plan	888-636-6252	2500	5190	5300	3720	7830	7990
321-3	NALC-Hi	888-636-6252	2860	6110	5540	4290	9190	8340
381-3	Rural Carrier	800-638-8432	3210	6020	5830	4860	9110	8830
381-3R	Rural Carrier (Medicare Advantage)	800-638-8432	NA	NA	NA	NA	NA	NA
441-3	SAMBA-Hi	800-638-6589	4010	8520	9070	5980	12830	13650
444-6	SAMBA-Std	800-638-6589	2880	5720	5850	4320	8690	8890

Lowest costs in bold type. Family costs are lower than self-plus-one in some plans. Medicare Advantage plans have special enrollment procedures.

Average yearly cost (continued)			Medicare wrap-around	Day limit in skilled nursing facility	Pays for...					
Annuitants 65 or older with Medicare Parts A & B					Routine dental	Chiro-practic	Acupunc-ture	Hearing aids	Adult vision care	Non network providers
Self only	Self plus one	Family								
6870	14150	14830	Yes	60	None	None	None	None	Exam	Reduced
3520	**6890**	**7570**	Yes	100	None	Yes	Yes	Yes	Exam	Reduced
4040	7960	8580	Yes	60	None	None	Little	Yes	None	Reduced
7820	16100	15240	No	60	Some	None	Little	None	Yes	Reduced
5730	11540	11900	No	30	None	Yes	Yes	Some	None	Reduced
6310	12160	13610	Yes	30	Yes	Yes	Yes	Some	None	No
4970	9610	11060	Yes	60	Yes	Yes	Yes	Yes	Exam	No
4260	9040	9460	Network only	0	Some	Some	Some	Yes	None	Reduced
4480	8670	8970	Network only	0	None	Some	Some	None	Exam	Reduced
6360	13120	13760	Yes	30	Some	Some	Yes	Yes	Exam	Reduced
5290	11240	11780	Yes	90	Yes	Yes	Some	Some	None	Reduced
3920	8600	9140	Yes	100	Yes	Yes	Yes	Yes	Yes	Reduced
4860	10260	10140	Yes	90	Some	Yes	Yes	Yes	None	Reduced
4810	9540	10170	No	0	Some	Some	Yes	None	None	Reduced
5270	10680	10890	Yes	21	Some	Some	Some	Some	None	Reduced
5060	10190	11000	No	21	Yes	Some	Yes	None	None	Reduced
5540	11440	12930	Yes	21	Yes	Some	Yes	Yes	None	Reduced
5640	10910	11690	Yes	21	Some	Some	Yes	Yes	None	Reduced
3910	8410	8040	Yes	100	Yes	Yes	Yes	Yes	Yes	Reduced
4610	9150	9370	Yes	28	None	Yes	Yes	Some	None	Reduced
7060	15200	15270	No	40	None	Yes	Yes	Some	None	Reduced
4960	10470	10100	Yes	40	None	Yes	Yes	Yes	None	Reduced
5290	10640	10840	No	0	None	Some	Some	Yes	None	Reduced
6090	12280	12440	No	0	None	Some	Some	Some	None	Reduced
5750	12070	11230	Yes	21	None	Some	Some	Yes	None	Reduced
6410	12040	11760	Yes	60	Yes	Yes	Yes	Yes	Exam	Reduced
4880	9180	8900	Yes	100	Yes	Yes	Yes	Yes	Yes	Reduced
7280	15240	16050	Yes	45	None	Yes	Some	Yes	None	Reduced
5510	10890	11090	Yes	30	None	Some	Yes	Yes	None	Reduced

Cost & Special Features of All Plans			Average yearly cost in dollars (premiums and out-of-pocket costs)					
Plan code	Plan name (primary service area)	Phone number	General Schedule			Annuitants 55 to 64		
			Self only	Self plus one	Family	Self only	Self plus one	Family of two
Local Plans								
Alabama								
F51-3	Aetna HealthFund CDHP	888-238-6240	3200	7530	6820	5250	12280	11230
F54-6	Aetna Value Plan	888-238-6240	4450	9750	9210	6620	14660	13850
KK1-3	United Choice Open Access	877-835-9861	3460	7150	8660	5260	10910	13180
KK1-3R	United Choice Open Access (Retiree Adv.)	844-481-8821	NA	NA	NA	NA	NA	NA
AS1-3	United Choice Plus Primary	877-835-9861	2640	5150	5430	4020	7920	8340
AS1-3R	United Choice Plus Primary (Retiree Adv.)	844-481-8821	NA	NA	NA	NA	NA	NA
Y81-3	United Choice Primary	877-835-9861	2500	4850	5100	3810	7480	7850
Y81-3R	United Choice Primary (Retiree Adv.)	844-481-8821	NA	NA	NA	NA	NA	NA
LS1-3	United HDHP	877-835-9861	**1990**	**4350**	**4530**	**3280**	**7160**	**7440**
Alaska								
JS1-3	Aetna HealthFund CDHP	888-238-6240	4530	10530	9860	7250	16790	15790
JS4-6	Aetna Value Plan	888-238-6240	6050	13450	12790	9000	20220	19230
Arizona								
G51-3	Aetna HealthFund CDHP	888-238-6240	5320	12310	11660	8420	19460	18480
WQ1-3	Aetna Open Access	800-537-9384	8020	19940	19350	12120	30090	29220
G54-6	Aetna Value Plan	888-238-6240	3960	8650	8090	5880	13020	12180
R61-3	Humana CoverageFirst CDHP (Ph'nix)	800-448-6262	3610	7340	7180	5920	12140	11900
R91-3	Humana CoverageFirst CDHP (Tuc'n)	800-448-6262	2730	5460	5210	4610	9320	8950
BV1-3	Humana HDHP (Phoenix)	1-800-4HUMA	2300	4780	5050	3700	7680	8080
BY1-3	Humana HDHP (Tucson)	1-800-4HUMA	2190	4530	4770	3530	7310	7670
BF4-6	Humana Health-Std (Phoenix)	800-448-6262	6970	14540	14680	10580	22080	22290
C74-6	Humana Health-Std (Tuc'n)	800-448-6262	4330	8860	8730	6620	13550	13370
R64-6R	Humana Value Medicare Advantage (Ph'nix)	800-448-6262	NA	NA	NA	NA	NA	NA
R94-6R	Humana Value Medicare Advantage (Tuc'n)	800-448-6262	NA	NA	NA	NA	NA	NA
R64-6	Humana Value Plan (Ph'nix)	800-448-6262	3260	6530	6660	4890	9960	10160
R94-6	Humana Value Plan(Tuc'n)	800-448-6262	3100	6180	6290	4650	9450	9620
KT1-3	United Choice Open Access	877-835-9861	3600	7450	9010	5470	11360	13710
KT1-3R	United Choice Open Access (Retiree Adv.)	844-481-8821	NA	NA	NA	NA	NA	NA
WF1-3	United Choice Plus Primary	877-835-9861	2670	5230	5510	4070	8040	8470

Lowest costs in bold type. Family costs are lower than self-plus-one in some plans. Medicare Advantage plans have special enrollment procedures.

Average yearly cost (continued) Annuitants 65 or older with Medicare Parts A & B			Medicare wrap-around	Day limit in skilled nursing facility	Pays for...					
Self only	Self plus one	Family			Routine dental	Chiro-practic	Acupuncture	Hearing aids	Adult vision care	Non network providers
7480	16760	15710	No	60	Some	Yes	Little	None	Exam	Reduced
8830	19000	18190	No	60	None	Yes	Little	None	Exam	Reduced
7500	15150	17430	No	60	Some	Some	Some	None	Exam	No
4820	9930	12200	Yes	100	Yes	Some	Some	Some	Exam	Reduced
6110	12220	12640	No	60	Some	Some	Some	Yes	Exam	Reduced
2970	**5910**	**6330**	Yes	100	Some	Yes	Yes	Yes	Exam	Reduced
5910	11770	12150	No	60	Some	Yes	Yes	Yes	Exam	No
2760	**5460**	**5830**	Yes	100	Some	Yes	Yes	Yes	Exam	Reduced
5570	11770	12050	No	60	Some	Yes	Some	Yes	Exam	Reduced
9480	21270	20260	No	60	Some	Yes	Little	None	Exam	Reduced
11220	24560	23570	No	60	None	Yes	Little	None	Exam	Reduced
10660	23940	22960	No	60	Some	Yes	Little	None	Exam	Reduced
14340	34350	33480	No	60	Yes	Yes	Some	None	Yes	No
8100	17360	16520	No	60	None	Yes	Little	None	Exam	Reduced
8240	16790	16550	Yes	60	None	Some	Some	None	None	Reduced
6930	13970	13600	Yes	60	None	Some	Some	None	None	Reduced
5940	12250	12650	No	60	None	Some	Some	Yes	None	Reduced
5780	11880	12240	No	60	None	Some	Some	Yes	None	Reduced
13000	26720	26920	Yes	100	Yes	Some	Some	None	Exam	No
9040	18190	18000	Yes	100	Yes	Some	Some	None	Exam	No
4130	7960	8160	Yes	100	Yes	Yes	Yes	Yes	Yes	No
3890	**7440**	**7610**	Yes	100	Yes	Yes	Yes	Yes	Yes	No
7280	14690	14890	Yes	60	None	Some	Some	None	None	No
7040	14170	14340	Yes	60	None	Some	Some	None	None	No
7710	15610	17950	No	60	Some	Some	Some	None	Exam	No
5030	10380	12730	Yes	100	Yes	Some	Some	Some	Exam	Reduced
6170	12340	12770	No	60	Some	Yes	Some	Yes	Exam	Reduced

Cost & Special Features of All Plans			Average yearly cost in dollars (premiums and out-of-pocket costs)					
Plan code	Plan name (primary service area)	Phone number	General Schedule			Annuitants 55 to 64		
			Self only	Self plus one	Family	Self only	Self plus one	Family of two
WF1-3R	United Choice Plus Primary (Retiree Adv)	844-481-8821	NA	NA	NA	NA	NA	NA
VD1-3	United Choice Primary	877-835-9861	2650	5180	5460	4040	7970	8390
VD1-3R	United Choice Primary (Retiree Adv.)	844-481-8821	NA	NA	NA	NA	NA	NA
LU1-3	United HDHP	877-835-9861	**2090**	4550	4750	**3420**	7460	7760
Arkansas								
F51-3	Aetna HealthFund CDHP	888-238-6240	3200	7530	6820	5250	12280	11230
F54-6	Aetna Value Plan	888-238-6240	4450	9750	9210	6620	14660	13850
DH1-3	QualChoice-Hi (Statewide)	800-235-7111	2530	**4440**	6870	3850	**6790**	10420
DH4-6	QualChoice-Std (Statewide)	800-235-7111	2120	**3920**	**4680**	3260	**6030**	**7170**
KK1-3	United Choice Open Access	877-835-9861	3460	7150	8660	5260	10910	13180
KK1-3R	United Choice Open Access (Retiree Adv.)	844-481-8821	NA	NA	NA	NA	NA	NA
AS1-3	United Choice Plus Primary	877-835-9861	2640	5150	5430	4020	7920	8340
AS1-3R	United Choice Plus Primary (Retiree Adv.)	844-481-8821	NA	NA	NA	NA	NA	NA
Y81-3	United Choice Primary	877-835-9861	2500	4850	5100	3810	7480	7850
Y81-3R	United Choice Primary (Retiree Adv.)	844-481-8821	NA	NA	NA	NA	NA	NA
LS1-3	United HDHP	877-835-9861	**1990**	**4350**	**4530**	**3280**	**7160**	**7440**
California								
JS1-3	Aetna HealthFund CDHP	888-238-6240	4530	10530	9860	7250	16790	15790
2X1-3	Aetna Open Access (LA/Bakersfield)	800-537-9384	4830	11400	10920	7330	17300	16580
JS4-6	Aetna Value Plan	888-238-6240	6050	13450	12790	9000	20220	19230
B31-3	Anthem Blue Cross (Southern)	800-235-8631	2890	5890	6130	4340	8910	9270
SI1-3	Blue Shield Access-Hi (Southern)	800-880-8086	3730	8260	8110	5620	12480	12260
T41-3	Health Net Basic (Northern)	800-522-0088	4480	9680	10340	6780	14710	15710
P61-3	Health Net Basic (Southern)	800-522-0088	**1960**	**3800**	**3960**	**3020**	**5900**	**6150**
LB1-3	Health Net-Hi (Northern)	800-522-0088	9600	20930	22660	14440	31480	34080
LP1-3	Health Net-Hi (Southern)	800-522-0088	5260	11390	12260	7940	17190	18490
KC1-3	Kaiser Prosper (Northern)	800-464-4000	2690	5710	5560	4000	8650	8430
KC1-3R	Kaiser Prosper No CA (Senior Advantage)	800-464-4000	NA	NA	NA	NA	NA	NA
NZ1-3	Kaiser-Hi (Fresno)	800-464-4000	2900	7240	6380	4360	10940	9650
591-3	Kaiser-Hi (Northern)	800-464-4000	4430	11370	10510	6650	17130	15840
621-3R	Kaiser-Hi (Senior Advantage 1)	800-443-0815	NA	NA	NA	NA	NA	NA

Lowest costs in bold type. Family costs are lower than self-plus-one in some plans. Medicare Advantage plans have special enrollment procedures.

Average yearly cost (continued)			Medicare wrap-around	Day limit in skilled nursing facility	Pays for...					
Annuitants 65 or older with Medicare Parts A & B					Routine dental	Chiro-practic	Acupunc-ture	Hearing aids	Adult vision care	Non network providers
Self only	Self plus one	Family								
3030	**6020**	**6450**	Yes	60	Yes	Yes	Yes	Yes	Exam	Reduced
6130	12270	12690	No	60	Yes	Some	Some	Yes	Exam	No
2990	**5950**	**6380**	Yes	100	Some	Some	Some	Yes	Exam	Reduced
5710	12080	12380	No	60	Some	Yes	Some	Yes	Exam	Reduced
7480	16760	15710	No	60	Some	Yes	Little	None	Exam	Reduced
8830	19000	18190	No	60	None	Yes	Little	None	Exam	Reduced
5490	9960	13600	Yes	60	None	Yes	None	Yes	Exam	Reduced
4800	8980	10120	Yes	60	None	Some	None	Yes	Exam	No
7500	15150	17430	No	60	Some	Some	Some	None	Exam	No
4820	9930	12200	Yes	100	Yes	Some	Some	Some	Exam	Reduced
6110	12220	12640	No	60	Some	Some	Some	Yes	Exam	Reduced
2970	**5910**	**6330**	Yes	100	Some	Yes	Yes	Yes	Exam	Reduced
5910	11770	12150	No	60	Some	Yes	Yes	Yes	Exam	No
2760	**5460**	**5830**	Yes	100	Some	Yes	Yes	Yes	Exam	Reduced
5570	11770	12050*	No	60	Some	Yes	Some	Yes	Exam	Reduced
9480	21270	20260	No	60	Some	Yes	Little	None	Exam	Reduced
9550	21560	20850	No	60	Yes	Yes	Some	None	Yes	No
11220	24560	23570	No	60	None	Yes	Little	None	Exam	Reduced
6080	11870	12220	Yes	150	None	Yes	Yes	Yes	None	No
7790	16890	16660	No	100	None	Yes	None	Some	Exam	No
8140	17150	18150	Yes	100	None	Yes	Yes	Yes	Exam	No
4320	8350	8600	Yes	100	None	Yes	Yes	Some	Yes	No
16670	35780	38370	No	100	None	Yes	Yes	Some	Exam	No
10170	21490	22780	No	100	None	Yes	Yes	Yes	Yes	No
6180	12990	12760	Yes	100	None	Yes	Yes	Child	Exam	No
5670	11570	11340	Yes	100	None	Yes	Yes	None	Some	No
6460	15160	13880	Yes	100	None	Yes	Yes	Child	Exam	No
8680	21030	19750	Yes	100	None	Yes	Yes	Child	Exam	No
8170	15720	14430	Yes	60	None	Some	Yes	Child	Yes	No

Cost & Special Features of All Plans			Average yearly cost in dollars (premiums and out-of-pocket costs)					
			General Schedule			Annuitants 55 to 64		
Plan code	Plan name (primary service area)	Phone number	Self only	Self plus one	Family	Self only	Self plus one	Family of two
621-3	Kaiser-Hi (Southern/Bakersfield)	800-464-4000	2470	6260	5400	3730	9470	8180
NZ1-3R	Kaiser-Hi Fresno (Senior Advantage 1)	800-464-4000	NA	NA	NA	NA	NA	NA
591-3R	Kaiser-Hi No CA (Senior Advantage 1)	800-443-0815	NA	NA	NA	NA	NA	NA
591-3R	Kaiser-Hi No CA (Senior Advantage 2)	800-443-0815	NA	NA	NA	NA	NA	NA
621-3R	Kaiser-Hi So CA (Senior Advantage 2)	800-443-0815	NA	NA	NA	NA	NA	NA
FL1-3	Kaiser-Prosper So CA	800-464-4000	**1800**	**3650**	**4020**	**2780**	**5720**	**6260**
NZ4-6	Kaiser-Std (Fresno)	800-464-4000	**2070**	4520	**4520**	**3130**	**6910**	**6910**
594-6	Kaiser-Std (Northern)	800-464-4000	3160	7950	7100	4770	12060	10770
624-6	Kaiser-Std (Southern/Bakersfield)	800-464-4000	**1860**	**4040**	**4050**	**2820**	**6200**	**6200**
NZ4-6R	Kaiser-Std Fresno (Senior Advantage)	800-464-4000	NA	NA	NA	NA	NA	NA
594-6R	Kaiser-Std No CA (Senior Advantage 1)	800-443-0815	NA	NA	NA	NA	NA	NA
594-6R	Kaiser-Std No CA (Senior Advantage 2)	800-443-0815	NA	NA	NA	NA	NA	NA
624-6R	Kaiser-Std So CA (Senior Advantage 1)	800-464-4000	NA	NA	NA	NA	NA	NA
624-6R	Kaiser-Std So CA (Senior Advantage 2)	800-464-4000	NA	NA	NA	NA	NA	NA
Colorado								
G51-3	Aetna HealthFund CDHP	888-238-6240	5320	12310	11660	8420	19460	18480
G54-6	Aetna Value Plan	888-238-6240	3960	8650	8090	5880	13020	12180
WW4-6	BlueAdvantage HDHP	833-611-6919	**2080**	**4430**	**4640**	3480	7460	7770
WW1-3	BlueAdvantage-HMO	833-611-6919	2370	5150	5380	3650	7930	8270
R21-3	Humana Health Basic (Col Springs)	800-448-6262	2620	5210	5330	4070	8200	8390
RZ1-3	Humana Health Basic (Denv/Boulder)	800-448-6262	2450	4840	4940	3810	7640	7800
NR1-3	Humana Health-Hi (Col Springs)	800-448-6262	4580	9430	9360	6970	14330	14210
NT1-3	Humana Health-Hi (Denv/Boulder)	800-448-6262	3820	7790	7640	5830	11870	11630
NR4-6	Humana Health-Std (Col Springs)	800-448-6262	2550	4970	5110	3940	7700	7900
NT4-6	Humana Health-Std (Denv/Boulder)	800-448-6262	2390	4650	4770	3710	7220	**7390**
N41-3	Kaiser Prosper (Most of St)	800-632-9700	2150	**3970**	**4130**	3240	6080	6310
N41-3R	Kaiser Prosper (Senior Advantage)	800-632-9700	NA	NA	NA	NA	NA	NA
651-3	Kaiser-Hi (Most of St)	800-632-9700	2880	6640	5780	4340	10100	8810
651-3R	Kaiser-Hi (Senior Advantage 1)	800-476-2167	NA	NA	NA	NA	NA	NA
651-3R	Kaiser-Hi (Senior Advantage 2)	800-476-2167	NA	NA	NA	NA	NA	NA
654-6	Kaiser-Std (Most of St)	800-632-9700	2450	4990	4990	3730	7680	7680

Lowest costs in bold type. Family costs are lower than self-plus-one in some plans. Medicare Advantage plans have special enrollment procedures.

| Average yearly cost (continued) | | | Medicare wrap-around | Day limit in skilled nursing facility | Pays for... | | | | | |
| Annuitants 65 or older with Medicare Parts A & B | | | | | Routine dental | Chiro-practic | Acupunc-ture | Hearing aids | Adult vision care | Non network providers |
Self only	Self plus one	Family								
5820	13700	12410	Yes	100	None	Yes	Yes	Child	Exam	No
7100	15210	13930	Yes	100	None	Yes	Yes	Child	Alot	No
11090	23360	22080	Yes	120	None	Yes	Yes	Child	Some	No
7050	17290	16000	Yes	100	None	Yes	Yes	Some	Exam	No
4170	9720	8430	Yes	100	None	Yes	Yes	Some	Exam	No
5090	10260	10810	Yes	100	Yes	None	Yes	Child	Exam	No
5150	10780	10780	Yes	100	None	Some	Some	Child	Exam	No
6950	16490	15200	Yes	100	None	Yes	Little	Child	Exam	No
5010	10630	10630	Yes	100	None	Yes	Yes	Child	Exam	No
5870	11120	11120	Yes	100	None	Some	Some	Child	Yes	No
9200	18190	16900	Yes	120	None	Yes	Yes	Child	Some	No
5280	12320	11030	Yes	100	None	Yes	Yes	Child	Exam	No
7280	12380	12380	Yes	100	None	Yes	Yes	Child	Exam	No
3380	**6500**	**6500**	Yes	100	None	Yes	Yes	Child	Exam	No
10660	23940	22960	No	60	Some	Yes	Little	None	Exam	Reduced
8100	17360	16520	No	60	None	Yes	Little	None	Exam	Reduced
5690	11840	12150	No	150	Yes	Yes	Yes	Yes	Yes	Reduced
5970	12400	12740	No	100	None	Yes	Yes	Child	Exam	No
6570	13050	13230	Yes	100	None	Some	Some	None	Exam	No
6310	12490	12650	Yes	100	None	Some	Some	None	Exam	No
9310	18800	18680	Yes	100	None	Some	Some	None	Exam	No
8160	16340	16100	Yes	100	None	Some	Some	None	Exam	No
6330	12270	12470	Yes	100	None	Some	Some	None	Exam	No
6100	11780	11960	Yes	100	None	Some	Some	None	Exam	No
5250	10180	10410	No	100	None	Yes	None	Child	Exam	No
5060	9730	9960	No	100	None	Yes	Yes	None	Exam	No
6570	14520	13240	No	100	None	Some	None	Child	Exam	No
6100	13160	11880	Yes	100	None	Yes	Yes	Yes	Yes	No
4620	10110	8820	Yes	100	None	Some	Yes	Child	Some	No
6060	12170	12170	No	100	None	Yes	None	Child	Exam	No

Cost & Special Features of All Plans			Average yearly cost in dollars (premiums and out-of-pocket costs)					
			General Schedule			Annuitants 55 to 64		
Plan code	Plan name (primary service area)	Phone number	Self only	Self plus one	Family	Self only	Self plus one	Family of two
654-6R	Kaiser-Std (Senior Advantage 1)	800-632-9700	NA	NA	NA	NA	NA	NA
654-6R	Kaiser-Std (Senior Advantage 2)	800-476-2167	NA	NA	NA	NA	NA	NA
KT1-3	United Choice Open Access	877-835-9861	3600	7450	9010	5470	11360	13710
KT1-3R	United Choice Open Access (Retiree Adv.)	844-481-8821	NA	NA	NA	NA	NA	NA
LU1-3	United HDHP	877-835-9861	**2090**	4550	4750	**3420**	7460	7760
Connecticut								
EP1-3	Aetna HealthFund CDHP	888-238-6240	5490	12690	12040	8680	20030	19060
EP4-6	Aetna Value Plan	888-238-6240	4710	10320	9800	7000	15530	14740
Delaware								
EP1-3	Aetna HealthFund CDHP	888-238-6240	5490	12690	12040	8680	20030	19060
P34-6	Aetna Open Access Basic (Phil)	800-537-9384	10390	23910	23370	15730	36140	35330
P31-3	Aetna Open Access-Hi (Philadelphia)	800-537-9384	10620	26120	25600	16010	39350	38570
EP4-6	Aetna Value Plan	888-238-6240	4710	10320	9800	7000	15530	14740
District of Columbia								
F51-3	Aetna HealthFund CDHP	888-238-6240	3200	7530	6820	5250	12280	11230
JN4-6	Aetna Open Access Basic	800-537-9384	2990	5770	6020	4590	8930	9300
JN1-3	Aetna Open Access-Hi	800-537-9384	6400	14310	13670	9690	21620	20670
QQ4-6	Aetna Saver	800-537-9384	3010	6050	6280	4450	9110	9440
F54-6	Aetna Value Plan	888-238-6240	4450	9750	9210	6620	14660	13850
B64-6	CareFirst Blue Value Plus	888-789-9065	2780	5010	5920	4220	7690	9060
B61-3	CareFirst HDHP	888-789-9065	**1950**	**3700**	**4150**	**3280**	6310	**6990**
2G4-6	CareFirst-Std	888-789-9065	3910	6870	8730	5960	10510	13310
T71-3	Kaiser Prosper	877-574-3337	**1750**	**3700**	4060	**2670**	**5700**	6260
T71-3R	Kaiser Prosper (Medicare Advantage)	877-574-3337	NA	NA	NA	NA	NA	NA
E31-3	Kaiser-Hi	877-574-3337	2280	5690	4830	**3460**	8620	**7330**
E31-3R	Kaiser-Hi (Medicare Advantage 1)	877-574-3337	NA	NA	NA	NA	NA	NA
E31-3R	Kaiser-Hi (Medicare Advantage 2)	877-574-3337	NA	NA	NA	NA	NA	NA
E34-6	Kaiser-Std	877-574-3337	**1900**	**4080**	**4070**	**2910**	**6280**	**6280**
E34-6R	Kaiser-Std (Medicare Advantage)	877-574-3337	NA	NA	NA	NA	NA	NA
JP1-3	MD-IPA	877-835-9861	4660	8160	14200	7080	12430	21480
JP1-3R	MD-IPA (Retiree Adv.)	844-481-8821	NA	NA	NA	NA	NA	NA

Lowest costs in bold type. Family costs are lower than self-plus-one in some plans. Medicare Advantage plans have special enrollment procedures.

Average yearly cost (continued)			Medicare wrap-around	Day limit in skilled nursing facility	Pays for...					
Annuitants 65 or older with Medicare Parts A & B					Routine dental	Chiro-practic	Acupunc-ture	Hearing aids	Adult vision care	Non network providers
Self only	Self plus one	Family								
5840	11490	11490	No	100	None	Yes	Yes	None	Exam	No
4100	7960	7960	No	100	None	Yes	Yes	Child	Exam	No
7710	15610	17950	No	60	Some	Some	Some	None	Exam	No
5030	10380	12730	Yes	100	Yes	Some	Some	Some	Exam	Reduced
5710	12080	12380	No	60	Some	Yes	Some	Yes	Exam	Reduced
10910	24510	23530	No	60	Some	Yes	Little	None	Exam	Reduced
9220	19870	19080	No	60	None	Yes	Little	None	Exam	Reduced
10910	24510	23530	No	60	Some	Yes	Little	None	Exam	Reduced
17620	40060	39250	No	60	Yes	Some	Little	None	Yes	No
18240	43640	42860	No	60	Yes	Some	Little	None	Yes	No
9220	19870	19080	No	60	None	Yes	Little	None	Exam	Reduced
7480	16760	15710	No	60	Some	Yes	Little	None	Exam	Reduced
6850	13410	13780	No	60	Yes	Some	Little	Some	Yes	No
11850	25810	24860	No	60	Yes	Some	Little	Some	Yes	No
6670	13680	14010	No	60	None	Yes	Little	None	Exam	No
8830	19000	18190	No	60	None	Yes	Little	None	Exam	Reduced
5610	10400	11760	Yes	Unlimited	Yes	Some	Some	Yes	Exam	Reduced
3860	**7280**	7960	Yes	Unlimited	Yes	Yes	Yes	Yes	Exam	Reduced
7450	13550	16350	Yes	Unlimited	Yes	Some	Some	Yes	Exam	Reduced
4920	10190	10750	No	100	None	Some	Some	Child	Some	No
4780	9280	9840	No	100	None	Yes	Yes	Child	Some	No
5540	12730	11440	No	100	Some	Yes	Yes	Child	Yes	No
5140	11920	10630	No	100	Yes	Yes	Yes	Yes	Yes	No
3590	8690	**7410**	No	100	Yes	Yes	Yes	Child	Some	No
5080	10560	10560	No	100	Some	Some	Some	Child	Yes	No
4670	9580	9580	No	100	Yes	Yes	Yes	Yes	Some	No
8610	15440	24490	Yes	60	Yes	Some	Some	Child	Exam	No
6790	11710	20750	Yes	100	Yes	Yes	Yes	Some	Exam	Reduced

Cost & Special Features of All Plans			Average yearly cost in dollars (premiums and out-of-pocket costs)					
			General Schedule			Annuitants 55 to 64		
Plan code	Plan name (primary service area)	Phone number	Self only	Self plus one	Family	Self only	Self plus one	Family of two
LR1-3	United Choice Open Access	877-835-9861	3260	6710	7300	4960	10260	11150
LR1-3R	United Choice Open Access (Retiree Adv.)	844-481-8821	NA	NA	NA	NA	NA	NA
L91-3	United Choice Plus Advanced	877-835-9861	2430	4890	5400	3540	7250	8030
L91-3R	United Choice Plus Advanced (Retiree Adv.)	844-481-8821	NA	NA	NA	NA	NA	NA
AS1-3	United Choice Plus Primary	877-835-9861	2640	5150	5430	4020	7920	8340
AS1-3R	United Choice Plus Primary (Retiree Adv.)	844-481-8821	NA	NA	NA	NA	NA	NA
Y81-3	United Choice Primary	877-835-9861	2500	4850	5100	3810	7480	7850
Y81-3R	United Choice Primary (Retiree Adv.)	844-481-8821	NA	NA	NA	NA	NA	NA
V41-3	United HDHP	877-835-9861	**2070**	**4500**	**4690**	**3390**	7390	7670
Florida								
F51-3	Aetna HealthFund CDHP	888-238-6240	3200	7530	6820	5250	12280	11230
F54-6	Aetna Value Plan	888-238-6240	4450	9750	9210	6620	14660	13850
WZ1-3	AvMed HDHP (South)	800-882-8633	2520	4730	5510	4030	7650	8830
ML4-6	AvMed-Std (South)	800-882-8633	3210	6320	7610	4850	9640	11570
EA1-3	Capital Health (Tallahassee)	850-383-3311	2760	5640	5540	4230	8630	8490
W91-3	Humana CoverageFirst CDHP (D'tona)	800-448-6262	2430	4820	**4680**	4160	8360	8160
X21-3	Humana CoverageFirst CDHP (Orl)	800-448-6262	2130	**4130**	**4250**	3700	7320	7510
QP1-3	Humana CoverageFirst CDHP (South)	800-448-6262	3230	6550	6350	5360	10960	10670
MJ1-3	Humana CoverageFirst CDHP (Tampa)	800-448-6262	5140	10640	10630	8220	17090	17080
FF1-3	Humana HDHP (Daytona)	1-800-4HUMA	2200	4570	4820	3560	7370	7730
AP1-3	Humana HDHP (Orlando)	1-800-4HUMA	2360	4910	5200	3790	7870	8310
BR1-3	Humana HDHP (South Florida)	1-800-4HUMA	2240	4660	4920	3620	7500	7880
A41-3	Humana HDHP (Tampa)	1-800-4HUMA	2350	4890	5180	3770	7840	8270
EX1-3	Humana Medical-Hi (Daytona)	800-448-6262	5370	11130	11130	8160	16870	16870
E21-3	Humana Medical-Hi (Orlando)	800-448-6262	7630	15980	16210	11540	24140	24480
EE1-3	Humana Medical-Hi (South)	800-448-6262	7410	15510	15720	11210	23440	23740
LL1-3	Humana Medical-Hi (Tampa)	800-448-6262	11170	23610	24190	16860	35580	36450
ex4-6	Humana Medical-St (Daytona)	800-448-6262	4180	8530	8390	6390	13070	12860
e24-6	Humana Medical-Std (Orlando)	800-448-6262	3440	6930	6720	5280	10670	10350
ee4-6	Humana Medical-Std (South)	800-448-6262	6470	13460	13550	9830	20460	20590
ll4-6	Humana Medical-Std (Tampa)	800-448-6262	7260	15160	15330	11010	23010	23260

Lowest costs in bold type. Family costs are lower than self-plus-one in some plans. Medicare Advantage plans have special enrollment procedures.

Average yearly cost (continued) Annuitants 65 or older with Medicare Parts A & B			Medicare wrap-around	Day limit in skilled nursing facility	Pays for...					
Self only	Self plus one	Family			Routine dental	Chiro-practic	Acupunc-ture	Hearing aids	Adult vision care	Non network providers
7200	14510	15390	No	60	Some	Some	Some	None	Exam	No
4520	9280	10170	Yes	100	Yes	Some	Some	Some	Exam	Reduced
5690	11610	12380	No	60	Some	Some	Some	Yes	Exam	Reduced
3010	**5690**	**6470**	Yes	60	Some	Some	Some	Yes	Exam	Reduced
6110	12220	12640	No	60	Some	Some	Some	Yes	Exam	Reduced
2970	**5910**	**6330**	Yes	100	Some	Yes	Yes	Yes	Exam	Reduced
5910	11770	12150	No	60	Some	Yes	Yes	Yes	Exam	No
2760	**5460**	**5830**	Yes	100	Some	Yes	Yes	Yes	Exam	Reduced
5680	12010	12290	No	60	Some	Yes	Some	Yes	Exam	Reduced
7480	16760	15710	No	60	Some	Yes	Little	None	Exam	Reduced
8830	19000	18190	No	60	None	Yes	Little	None	Exam	Reduced
6270	12040	13210	No	30	None	Yes	None	Yes	None	Reduced
7110	14120	16060	Yes	30	None	Some	None	Yes	None	No
6570	13110	12970	No	60	None	Some	Yes	None	None	No
6490	13010	12810	Yes	60	None	Some	Some	None	None	Reduced
6020	11970	12160	Yes	60	None	Some	Some	None	None	Reduced
7680	15610	15310	Yes	60	None	Some	Some	None	None	Reduced
10540	21740	21730	Yes	60	None	Some	Some	None	None	Reduced
5800	11940	12300	No	60	None	Some	Some	Yes	None	Reduced
6030	12440	12880	No	60	None	Some	Some	Yes	None	Reduced
5860	12070	12450	No	60	None	Some	Some	Yes	None	Reduced
6020	12410	12840	No	60	None	Some	Some	Yes	None	Reduced
10490	21340	21340	Yes	100	None	Yes	Yes	None	Yes	No
13870	28610	28950	Yes	100	None	Yes	Yes	None	Yes	No
13540	27910	28210	Yes	100	None	Yes	Yes	None	Yes	No
19190	40050	40910	Yes	100	None	Yes	Yes	None	Yes	No
8810	17700	17490	Yes	100	None	Yes	Yes	None	Yes	No
7700	15310	14990	Yes	100	None	Yes	Yes	None	Yes	No
12250	25100	25230	Yes	100	None	Yes	Yes	None	Yes	No
13440	27650	27900	Yes	100	None	Yes	Yes	None	Yes	No

Cost & Special Features of All Plans			Average yearly cost in dollars (premiums and out-of-pocket costs)					
Plan code	Plan name (primary service area)	Phone number	General Schedule			Annuitants 55 to 64		
			Self only	Self plus one	Family	Self only	Self plus one	Family of two
W94-6	Humana Value (Daytona)	800-448-6262	3130	6250	6360	4700	9540	9720
X24-6	Humana Value (Orlando)	800-448-6262	3020	6020	6340	4540	9190	9690
MJ4-6	Humana Value (Tampa)	800-448-6262	3050	6080	6360	4580	9290	9710
W94-6R	Humana Value Medicare Adv. (Daytona)	800-448-6262	NA	NA	NA	NA	NA	NA
X24-6R	Humana Value Medicare Adv. (Orlando)	800-448-6262	NA	NA	NA	NA	NA	NA
QP4-6R	Humana Value Medicare Adv. (South)	800-448-6262	NA	NA	NA	NA	NA	NA
MJ4-6R	Humana Value Medicare Adv. (Tampa)	800-448-6262	NA	NA	NA	NA	NA	NA
QP4-6	Humana Value Plan (South)	800-448-6262	3030	6030	6140	4550	9220	9390
KK1-3	United Choice Open Access	877-835-9861	3460	7150	8660	5260	10910	13180
KK1-3R	United Choice Open Access (Retiree Adv.)	844-481-8821	NA	NA	NA	NA	NA	NA
LV1-3	United Choice Plus Advance	877-835-9861	4030	8570	13810	5940	12770	20640
LV1-3R	United Choice Plus Advanced (Retiree Adv.)	844-481-8821	NA	NA	NA	NA	NA	NA
AS1-3	United Choice Plus Primary	877-835-9861	2640	5150	5430	4020	7920	8340
AS1-3R	United Choice Plus Primary (Retiree Adv.)	844-481-8821	NA	NA	NA	NA	NA	NA
Y81-3	United Choice Primary	877-835-9861	2500	4850	5100	3810	7480	7850
Y81-3R	United Choice Primary (Retiree Adv.)	844-481-8821	NA	NA	NA	NA	NA	NA
LS1-3	United HDHP	877-835-9861	**1990**	**4350**	**4530**	**3280**	**7160**	**7440**
Georgia								
F51-3	Aetna HealthFund CDHP	888-238-6240	3200	7530	6820	5250	12280	11230
2U1-3	Aetna Open Access (Atlanta/Athens)	800-537-9384	10350	23830	23280	15610	35920	35110
F54-6	Aetna Value Plan	888-238-6240	4450	9750	9210	6620	14660	13850
QM1-3	Blue Open Access (Atlanta/Ath)	844-423-9988	2490	5520	6730	3830	8480	10290
AD1-3	Humana CoverageFirst CDHP (Atl)	800-448-6262	5950	12390	12460	9440	19710	19820
S91-3	Humana CoverageFirst CDHP (Col)	800-448-6262	3240	6550	6350	5370	10960	10660
LM1-3	Humana CoverageFirst CDHP (Macon)	800-448-6262	2900	5810	5580	4860	9860	9510
Q71-3	Humana Employers Basic (Atlanta)	800-448-6262	4140	8510	8350	6360	13160	12920
RM1-3	Humana Employers Basic (Columbus)	800-448-6262	3500	7130	6900	5390	11090	10750
RJ1-3	Humana Employers Basic (Macon)	800-448-6262	2820	5630	5770	4370	8830	9040
AR1-3	Humana HDHP (Atlanta)	1-800-4HUMA	2350	4880	5170	3770	7840	8260
B21-3	Humana HDHP (Columbus)	1-800-4HUMA	2370	4930	5220	3800	7900	8340
AZ1-3	Humana HDHP (Macon)	1-800-4HUMA	2340	4860	5150	3760	7800	8230

Lowest costs in bold type. Family costs are lower than self-plus-one in some plans. Medicare Advantage plans have special enrollment procedures.

| Average yearly cost (continued) | | | Medicare wrap-around | Day limit in skilled nursing facility | Pays for... | | | | | |
| Annuitants 65 or older with Medicare Parts A & B | | | | | Routine dental | Chiro-practic | Acupuncture | Hearing aids | Adult vision care | Non network providers |
Self only	Self plus one	Family								
7080	14260	14440	Yes	60	None	Some	Some	None	None	No
6920	13920	14410	Yes	60	None	Some	Some	None	None	No
6970	14010	14430	Yes	60	None	Some	Some	None	None	No
3930	**7530**	**7710**	Yes	100	Yes	Yes	Yes	Yes	Yes	No
3770	**7190**	**7680**	Yes	100	Yes	Yes	Yes	Yes	Yes	No
3780	**7210**	**7380**	Yes	100	Yes	Yes	Yes	Yes	Yes	No
3820	**7280**	**7700**	Yes	100	Yes	Yes	Yes	Yes	Yes	No
6930	13940	14110	Yes	60	None	Some	Some	None	None	No
7500	15150	17430	No	60	Some	Some	Some	None	Exam	No
4820	9930	12200	Yes	100	Yes	Some	Some	Some	Exam	Reduced
8080	17130	25000	No	60	Yes	Yes	Yes	Yes	Exam	No
5430	11240	19110	Yes	100	Yes	Yes	Yes	Yes	Exam	Reduced
6110	12220	12640	No	60	Some	Some	Some	Yes	Exam	Reduced
2970	**5910**	**6330**	Yes	100	Some	Yes	Yes	Yes	Exam	Reduced
5910	11770	12150	No	60	Some	Yes	Yes	Yes	Exam	No
2760	**5460**	**5830**	Yes	100	Some	Yes	Yes	Yes	Exam	Reduced
5570	11770	12050	No	60	Some	Yes	Some	Yes	Exam	Reduced
7480	16760	15710	No	60	Some	Yes	Little	None	Exam	Reduced
17830	40190	39380	No	60	Yes	Yes	Some	None	Yes	No
8830	19000	18190	No	60	None	Yes	Little	None	Exam	Reduced
6180	12990	14800	No	60	None	Yes	None	None	Exam	Reduced
11760	24360	24470	Yes	60	None	Some	Some	None	None	Reduced
7690	15600	15310	Yes	60	None	Some	Some	None	None	Reduced
7180	14500	14160	Yes	60	None	Some	Some	None	None	Reduced
8850	18000	17760	Yes	100	None	Some	Some	None	None	No
7890	15930	15600	Yes	100	None	Some	Some	None	None	No
6860	13680	13890	Yes	100	None	Some	Some	None	None	No
6010	12410	12830	No	60	None	Some	Some	Yes	None	Reduced
6040	12470	12900	No	60	None	Some	Some	Yes	None	Reduced
6000	12370	12800	No	60	None	Some	Some	Yes	None	Reduced

Cost & Special Features of All Plans			Average yearly cost in dollars (premiums and out-of-pocket costs)					
			General Schedule			Annuitants 55 to 64		
Plan code	Plan name (primary service area)	Phone number	Self only	Self plus one	Family	Self only	Self plus one	Family of two
AD4-6R	Humana Value Medicare Adv. (Atlanta)	800-448-6262	NA	NA	NA	NA	NA	NA
S94-6R	Humana Value Medicare Adv. (Columbus)	800-448-6262	NA	NA	NA	NA	NA	NA
LM4-6R	Humana Value Medicare Adv. (Macon)	800-448-6262	NA	NA	NA	NA	NA	NA
AD4-6	Humana Value Plan (Atlanta)	800-448-6262	4300	8780	8580	6440	13340	13050
S94-6	Humana Value Plan (Columbus)	800-448-6262	3250	6500	6620	4870	9920	10120
LM4-6	Humana Value Plan (Macon)	800-448-6262	3620	7340	7070	5440	11180	10780
LA1-3	Kaiser Prosper (Most of St)	888-865-5813	**1730**	3490	3750	**2720**	5470	5870
F81-3	Kaiser-Hi (Most of St)	888-865-5813	2710	6280	5430	4140	9590	8310
F81-3R	Kaiser-Hi (Senior Advantage 1)	888-865-5813	NA	NA	NA	NA	NA	NA
F81-3R	Kaiser-Hi (Senior Advantage 2)	888-865-5813	NA	NA	NA	NA	NA	NA
LA1-3R	Kaiser-Prosper (Senior Advantage 2)	888-865-5813	NA	NA	NA	NA	NA	NA
F84-6	Kaiser-Std (Most of St)	888-865-5813	2120	**4390**	**4390**	3280	**6820**	**6820**
F84-6R	Kaiser-Std (Senior Advantage)	888-865-5813	NA	NA	NA	NA	NA	NA
LV1-3	United Choice Plus Advance	877-835-9861	4030	8570	13810	5940	12770	20640
LV1-3R	United Choice Plus Advanced (Retiree Adv.)	844-481-8821	NA	NA	NA	NA	NA	NA
AS1-3	United Choice Plus Primary	877-835-9861	2640	5150	5430	4020	7920	8340
AS1-3R	United Choice Plus Primary (Retiree Adv.)	844-481-8821	NA	NA	NA	NA	NA	NA
Y81-3	United Choice Primary	877-835-9861	2500	4850	5100	3810	7480	7850
Y81-3R	United Choice Primary (Retiree Adv.)	844-481-8821	NA	NA	NA	NA	NA	NA
Guam								
B41-3	Calvo's Selectcare-Hi	671-477-9808	**1650**	**3320**	**4070**	**2510**	**5080**	**6200**
B44-6	Calvo's Selectcare-Std	671-477-9808	**1690**	**3190**	**3900**	**2640**	**5060**	**6130**
KX1-3	TakeCare HDHP	671-647-3526	**1760**	**3640**	**3700**	**2790**	**5930**	**6030**
JK1-3	TakeCare-Hi	671-647-3526	**1620**	**3070**	**3490**	**2510**	**4740**	**5370**
JK4-6	TakeCare-Std	671-647-3526	**1560**	**2900**	**3600**	**2440**	**4510**	**5560**
Hawaii								
JS1-3	Aetna HealthFund CDHP	888-238-6240	4530	10530	9860	7250	16790	15790
JS4-6	Aetna Value Plan	888-238-6240	6050	13450	12790	9000	20220	19230
871-3	HMSA Plan-Hi	800-776-4672	**1700**	3580	3650	**2610**	5500	5600
874-6	HMSA Plan-Std	800-776-4672	2110	**4230**	**4280**	3190	6530	6610
631-3	Kaiser-Hi	808-432-5955	**1980**	**4280**	**4280**	3030	6630	6630

Lowest costs in bold type. Family costs are lower than self-plus-one in some plans. Medicare Advantage plans have special enrollment procedures.

Average yearly cost (continued)			Medicare wrap-around	Day limit in skilled nursing facility	Pays for...					
Annuitants 65 or older with Medicare Parts A & B					Routine dental	Chiro-practic	Acupunc-ture	Hearing aids	Adult vision care	Non network providers
Self only	Self plus one	Family								
5680	11330	11040	Yes	100	Yes	Yes	Yes	Yes	Yes	No
4110	7910	8110	Yes	100	Yes	Yes	Yes	Yes	Yes	No
4670	9170	8770	Yes	100	Yes	Yes	Yes	Yes	Yes	No
8830	18060	17770	Yes	60	None	Some	Some	None	None	No
7260	14640	14840	Yes	60	None	Some	Some	None	None	No
7820	15900	15500	Yes	60	None	Some	Some	None	None	No
5030	9900	10300	Yes	100	None	Some	None	Child	Exam	No
6330	13850	12560	Yes	100	Yes	Yes	None	Child	Exam	No
5850	12780	11490	Yes	100	Yes	Yes	None	Child	Yes	No
4240	9500	8220	Yes	100	Some	Yes	Yes	Child	Exam	No
4770	9310	9710	Yes	100	None	Some	Yes	Child	Exam	No
5570	11230	11230	Yes	100	Yes	Some	None	Child	Exam	No
5080	10170	10170	Yes	100	Yes	Some	Yes	Child	Exam	No
8080	17130	25000	No	60	Yes	Yes	Yes	Yes	Exam	No
5430	11240	19110	Yes	100	Yes	Yes	Yes	Yes	Exam	Reduced
6110	12220	12640	No	60	Some	Some	Some	Yes	Exam	Reduced
2970	**5910**	**6330**	Yes	100	Some	Yes	Yes	Yes	Exam	Reduced
5910	11770	12150	No	60	Some	Yes	Yes	Yes	Exam	No
2760	**5460**	**5830**	Yes	100	Some	Yes	Yes	Yes	Exam	Reduced
4380	8430	9550	Yes	100	Some	Some	Little	Little	Yes	No
4120	7840	8910	Yes	60	Yes	Little	Little	Little	Yes	No
5080	10590	10690	No	100	Yes	Little	Little	Little	Yes	Reduced
4130	7970	8610	Yes	100	Yes	Little	Little	Little	Yes	No
4090	7780	8830	No	60	Some	Some	Little	Little	Yes	No
9480	21270	20260	No	60	Some	Yes	Little	None	Exam	Reduced
11220	24560	23570	No	60	None	Yes	Little	None	Exam	Reduced
4720	9640	9750	No	100	Yes	Some	None	Yes	Exam	Reduced
5280	10830	10900	No	100	None	Some	None	Yes	Exam	Reduced
5190	10950	10950	Yes	120	Yes	None	None	Yes	Exam	No

Cost & Special Features of All Plans			Average yearly cost in dollars (premiums and out-of-pocket costs)					
			General Schedule			Annuitants 55 to 64		
Plan code	Plan name (primary service area)	Phone number	Self only	Self plus one	Family	Self only	Self plus one	Family of two
631-3R	Kaiser-Hi (Senior Advantage 1)	808-432-5955	NA	NA	NA	NA	NA	NA
634-6	Kaiser-Std	808-432-5955	**1710**	**3710**	**3720**	**2630**	**5770**	**5770**
634-6R	Kaiser-Std (Senior Advantage)	808-432-5955	NA	NA	NA	NA	NA	NA
Idaho								
9K4-6	Aetna Health/Altius HDHP	800-837-0977	2740	4920	4740	4400	7980	7720
9K1-3	Aetna Health/Altius-Hi	800-837-0977	5770	12520	11860	8740	18980	17990
DK4-6	Aetna Health/Altius-Std	800-837-0977	4490	9440	8740	6780	14330	13290
H41-3	Aetna HealthFund CDHP	888-238-6240	2840	6720	6010	4710	11080	10010
H44-6	Aetna Value Plan	888-238-6240	3960	8670	8110	5880	13040	12210
PT4-6	Kaiser Washington- Prosper (WA/N ID)	888-901-4636	**2090**	**4150**	**4450**	**3120**	**6300**	**6740**
541-3	Kaiser Washington-Hi (WA/N ID)	888-901-4636	3620	7920	7060	5420	11930	10640
544-6	Kaiser Washington-Std (WA/N ID)	888-901-4636	2330	4820	4820	3540	7380	**7380**
541-3	Kaiser-Hi ID/WA (Med Choice)	800-446-8882	NA	NA	NA	NA	NA	NA
541-3R	Kaiser-Hi ID/WA (Senior Advantage 1)	888-901-4636	NA	NA	NA	NA	NA	NA
541-3R	Kaiser-Hi ID/WA (Senior Advantage 2)	800-446-8882	NA	NA	NA	NA	NA	NA
544-6R	Kaiser-Std ID/WA (Senior Advantage 1)	888-901-4636	NA	NA	NA	NA	NA	NA
544-6R	Kaiser-Std ID/WA (Senior Advantage 2)	800-446-8882	NA	NA	NA	NA	NA	NA
PT4-6R	Kaiser-WA- Prosper (Senior Advantage)	888-901-4636	NA	NA	NA	NA	NA	NA
Illinois								
H41-3	Aetna HealthFund CDHP	888-238-6240	2840	6720	6010	4710	11080	10010
H44-6	Aetna Value Plan	888-238-6240	3960	8670	8110	5880	13040	12210
9G1-3	Blue Preferred-Hi (St L/Other)	888-811-2092	4120	9020	9230	6300	13850	14170
9G4-6	Blue Preferred-Std (St L/Other)	888-811-2092	2480	6000	6680	3830	9350	10380
GB1-3	Humana CoverageFirst CDHP (Cent'l)	800-448-6262	7180	15030	15220	11280	23670	23960
MW1-3	Humana CoverageFirst CDHP (Chi)	800-448-6262	5080	10500	10490	8120	16880	16860
AW1-3	Humana HDHP(Central Illinois)	1-800-4HUMA	2230	4630	4890	3600	7460	7840
BB1-3	Humana HDHP(Chicago)	1-800-4HUMA	2280	4740	5010	3670	7620	8020
RW1-3	Humana Health Basic (Chicago)	800-448-6262	3880	7950	7760	5960	12320	12040
AB1-3	Humana Health Basic (Rockford/NW)	800-448-6262	3940	8060	7880	6040	12480	12210
751-3	Humana Health-Hi (Chicago)	800-448-6262	8040	16880	17140	12160	25490	25890
9F1-3	Humana Health-Hi (Rockford/NW)	800-448-6262	13750	29150	29990	20720	43890	45150

Lowest costs in bold type. Family costs are lower than self-plus-one in some plans. Medicare Advantage plans have special enrollment procedures.

Average yearly cost (continued)			Medicare wrap-around	Day limit in skilled nursing facility	Pays for...					
Annuitants 65 or older with Medicare Parts A & B					Routine dental	Chiro-practic	Acupunc-ture	Hearing aids	Adult vision care	Non network providers
Self only	Self plus one	Family								
4970	10010	10010	Yes	120	None	None	None	Yes	Yes	No
4800	10190	10190	Yes	120	Yes	None	None	Yes	Exam	No
4960	9630	9630	Yes	100	None	Yes	Yes	Yes	Some	No
6200	11660	11390	Yes	30	None	Yes	None	Yes	Yes	Reduced
10140	21720	20740	Yes	30	Yes	Some	None	Yes	Yes	No
8140	16940	15900	Yes	30	None	Yes	None	Yes	Yes	No
6950	15550	14490	No	60	Some	Yes	Little	None	Exam	Reduced
8090	17380	16550	No	60	None	Yes	Little	None	Exam	Reduced
5450	10790	11230	Yes	100	None	Yes	Yes	None	Exam	No
7590	16270	14980	Yes	100	None	Yes	Some	None	Exam	No
5840	11840	11840	Yes	100	None	Yes	Some	None	Exam	No
7050	14610	13320	Yes	100	None	Some	Some	None	Exam	No
7280	15170	13880	Yes	100	None	Yes	Yes	Some	Some	No
6450	13410	12120	Yes	100	None	Yes	Yes	None	Exam	No
5020	10090	10090	Yes	100	None	Yes	Yes	Some	Some	No
4480	8800	8800	Yes	100	None	Yes	Yes	None	Exam	No
5200	10170	10610	Yes	100	None	Yes	Yes	None	Exam	No
6950	15550	14490	No	60	Some	Yes	Little	None	Exam	Reduced
8090	17380	16550	No	60	None	Yes	Little	None	Exam	Reduced
8690	18510	18830	No	150	None	Some	None	None	Exam	Reduced
6260	14100	15140	Yes	150	None	Yes	None	None	Exam	Reduced
13600	28320	28610	Yes	60	None	Some	Some	None	None	Reduced
10450	21530	21510	Yes	60	None	Some	Some	None	None	Reduced
5840	12030	12410	No	60	None	Some	Some	Yes	None	Reduced
5920	12190	12590	No	60	None	Some	Some	Yes	None	Reduced
8460	17160	16880	Yes	100	None	Some	Some	None	Exam	No
8540	17330	17060	Yes	100	None	Some	Some	None	Exam	No
14490	29960	30350	Yes	100	None	Some	Some	None	Exam	No
23060	48360	49620	Yes	100	None	Some	Some	None	Exam	No

Cost & Special Features of All Plans			Average yearly cost in dollars (premiums and out-of-pocket costs)					
			General Schedule			Annuitants 55 to 64		
Plan code	Plan name (primary service area)	Phone number	Self only	Self plus one	Family	Self only	Self plus one	Family of two
754-6	Humana Health-Std (Chicago)	800-448-6262	5420	11180	11170	8240	17010	16990
AB4-6	Humana Health-Std (Rockford/NW)	800-448-6262	8550	17920	18220	12940	27110	27560
GB4-6R	Humana Value Medicare Adv. (Central)	800-448-6262	NA	NA	NA	NA	NA	NA
MW4-6R	Humana Value Medicare Adv. (Chicago)	800-448-6262	NA	NA	NA	NA	NA	NA
GB4-6	Humana Value Plan (Central)	800-448-6262	4310	8810	8610	6470	13390	13100
MW4-6	Humana Value Plan (Chicago)	800-448-6262	4090	8330	8100	6130	12660	12330
L91-3	United Choice Plus Advanced	877-835-9861	2430	4890	5400	3540	7250	8030
L91-3R	United Choice Plus Advanced (Retiree Adv.)	844-481-8821	NA	NA	NA	NA	NA	NA
AS1-3	United Choice Plus Primary	877-835-9861	2640	5150	5430	4020	7920	8340
AS1-3R	United Choice Plus Primary (Retiree Adv.)	844-481-8821	NA	NA	NA	NA	NA	NA
Y81-3	United Choice Primary	877-835-9861	2500	4850	5100	3810	7480	7850
Y81-3R	United Choice Primary (Retiree Adv.)	844-481-8821	NA	NA	NA	NA	NA	NA
Indiana								
JS1-3	Aetna HealthFund CDHP	888-238-6240	4530	10530	9860	7250	16790	15790
JS4-6	Aetna Value Plan	888-238-6240	6050	13450	12790	9000	20220	19230
K84-6	Health Alliance (So IL/So IN/Cen IA)	800-851-3379	2770	5520	5780	4270	8650	9030
W61-3	Humana Health Basic (Cincinnati)	800-448-6262	2750	5490	5620	4270	8620	8830
A64-6	Humana Health-Std (Cincinnati)	800-448-6262	6950	14480	14620	10540	21990	22190
Iowa								
H41-3	Aetna HealthFund CDHP	888-238-6240	2840	6720	6010	4710	11080	10010
H44-6	Aetna Value Plan	888-238-6240	3960	8670	8110	5880	13040	12210
K84-6	Health Alliance (So IL/So IN/Cen IA)	800-851-3379	2770	5520	5780	4270	8650	9030
V31-3	HealthPartners-Hi (Statewide)	800-883-2177	2290	4530	4920	3530	**7020**	7610
V34-6	HealthPartners-Std (Statewide)	952-883-5000	2510	5000	5250	3710	7540	7920
LJ1-3	United Choice Open Access	877-835-9861	3670	7600	9190	5580	11600	13980
LJ1-3R	United Choice Open Access (Retiree Adv.)	844-481-8821	NA	NA	NA	NA	NA	NA
AS1-3	United Choice Plus Primary	877-835-9861	2640	5150	5430	4020	7920	8340
AS1-3R	United Choice Plus Primary (Retiree Adv.)	844-481-8821	NA	NA	NA	NA	NA	NA
Y81-3	United Choice Primary	877-835-9861	2500	4850	5100	3810	7480	7850
Y81-3R	United Choice Primary (Retiree Adv.)	844-481-8821	NA	NA	NA	NA	NA	NA
N71-3	United HDHP	877-835-9861	2450	5370	5410	3970	8690	8750

Lowest costs in bold type. Family costs are lower than self-plus-one in some plans. Medicare Advantage plans have special enrollment procedures.

| Average yearly cost (continued) | | | Medicare wrap-around | Day limit in skilled nursing facility | Pays for... | | | | | |
| Annuitants 65 or older with Medicare Parts A & B | | | | | Routine dental | Chiro-practic | Acupunc-ture | Hearing aids | Adult vision care | Non network providers |
Self only	Self plus one	Family								
10640	21570	21550	Yes	100	None	Some	Some	None	Exam	No
15340	31680	32130	Yes	100	None	Some	Some	None	Exam	No
5700	11380	11090	Yes	100	Yes	Yes	Yes	Yes	Yes	No
5360	10660	10330	Yes	100	Yes	Yes	Yes	Yes	Yes	No
8850	18110	17820	Yes	60	None	Some	Some	None	None	No
8510	17390	17060	Yes	60	None	Some	Some	None	None	No
5690	11610	12380	No	60	Some	Some	Some	Yes	Exam	Reduced
3010	**5690**	**6470**	Yes	60	Some	Some	Some	Yes	Exam	Reduced
6110	12220	12640	No	60	Some	Some	Some	Yes	Exam	Reduced
2970	**5910**	**6330**	Yes	100	Some	Yes	Yes	Yes	Exam	Reduced
5910	11770	12150	No	60	Some	Yes	Yes	Yes	Exam	No
2760	**5460**	**5830**	Yes	100	Some	Yes	Yes	Yes	Exam	Reduced
9480	21270	20260	No	60	Some	Yes	Little	None	Exam	Reduced
11220	24560	23570	No	60	None	Yes	Little	None	Exam	Reduced
4010	8320	8700	Yes	75	None	Yes	Some	Some	Exam	No
6770	13470	13670	Yes	100	None	Some	Some	None	None	No
12960	26630	26830	Yes	100	None	Some	Some	None	None	No
6950	15550	14490	No	60	Some	Yes	Little	None	Exam	Reduced
8090	17380	16550	No	60	None	Yes	Little	None	Exam	Reduced
4010	8320	8700	Yes	75	None	Yes	Some	Some	Exam	No
3840	**7640**	8230	Yes	120	None	Yes	Yes	Yes	Exam	Reduced
4780	9280	9660	No	120	None	Yes	Yes	Child	Exam	No
7820	15840	18230	No	60	Some	Some	Some	None	Exam	No
5140	10620	13000	Yes	100	Yes	Some	Some	Some	Exam	Reduced
6110	12220	12640	No	60	Some	Some	Some	Yes	Exam	Reduced
2970	**5910**	**6330**	Yes	100	Some	Yes	Yes	Yes	Exam	Reduced
5910	11770	12150	No	60	Some	Yes	Yes	Yes	Exam	No
2760	**5460**	**5830**	Yes	100	Some	Yes	Yes	Yes	Exam	Reduced
6260	13310	13370	No	60	Some	Yes	Some	Yes	Exam	Reduced

Cost & Special Features of All Plans			Average yearly cost in dollars (premiums and out-of-pocket costs)					
Plan code	Plan name (primary service area)	Phone number	General Schedule			Annuitants 55 to 64		
			Self only	Self plus one	Family	Self only	Self plus one	Family of two
Kansas								
G51-3	Aetna HealthFund CDHP	888-238-6240	5320	12310	11660	8420	19460	18480
HA1-3	Aetna Open Access-Hi (Kansas City)	800-537-9384	6820	16370	15730	10210	24660	23700
HA4-6	Aetna Open Access-Std (Kansas City)	800-537-9384	4740	11640	10950	7120	17610	16580
G54-6	Aetna Value Plan	888-238-6240	3960	8650	8090	5880	13020	12180
PH1-3	Humana CoverageFirst CDHP (KS City)	800-448-6262	2680	5360	5110	4540	9170	8800
BK1-3	Humana HDHP(Kansas City)	1-800-4HUMA	2200	4560	4800	3550	7350	7710
MS4-6	Humana Health-Std (Kansas City)	800-448-6262	7330	15300	15480	11110	23210	23480
PH4-6R	Humana Value Medicare Adv. (Kansas City)	800-448-6262	NA	NA	NA	NA	NA	NA
PH4-6	Humana Value Plan (Kansas City)	800-448-6262	3070	6110	6210	4600	9330	9500
Kentucky								
H41-3	Aetna HealthFund CDHP	888-238-6240	2840	6720	6010	4710	11080	10010
H44-6	Aetna Value Plan	888-238-6240	3960	8670	8110	5880	13040	12210
6N1-3	Humana CoverageFirst CDHP (Lex)	800-448-6262	3410	6920	6740	5630	11510	11250
TC1-3	Humana Cov'First CDHP (Louisville)	800-448-6262	2680	5340	5090	4530	9150	8770
W61-3	Humana Health Basic (Cincinnati)	800-448-6262	2750	5490	5620	4270	8620	8830
A64-6	Humana Health-Std (Cincinnati)	800-448-6262	6950	14480	14620	10540	21990	22190
MI4-6	Humana Health-Std (Lex/Central)	800-448-6262	4440	9090	8970	6780	13900	13730
MH4-6	Humana Health-Std (Louisville)	800-448-6262	4940	10170	10110	7540	15530	15440
6N4-6R	Humana Value Medicare Adv. (Lexington)	800-448-6262	NA	NA	NA	NA	NA	NA
TC4-6R	Humana Value Medicare Adv. (Louisville)	800-448-6262	NA	NA	NA	NA	NA	NA
6N4-6	Humana Value Plan (Lexington)	800-448-6262	3200	6390	6510	4800	9760	9950
TC4-6	Humana Value Plan (Louisville)	800-448-6262	3090	6160	6270	4640	9410	9580
LJ1-3	United Choice Open Access	877-835-9861	3670	7600	9190	5580	11600	13980
LJ1-3R	United Choice Open Access (Retiree Adv.)	844-481-8821	NA	NA	NA	NA	NA	NA
AS1-3	United Choice Plus Primary	877-835-9861	2640	5150	5430	4020	7920	8340
AS1-3R	United Choice Plus Primary (Retiree Adv.)	844-481-8821	NA	NA	NA	NA	NA	NA
Y81-3	United Choice Primary	877-835-9861	2500	4850	5100	3810	7480	7850
Y81-3R	United Choice Primary (Retiree Adv.)	844-481-8821	NA	NA	NA	NA	NA	NA
N71-3	United HDHP	877-835-9861	2450	5370	5410	3970	8690	8750

Lowest costs in bold type. Family costs are lower than self-plus-one in some plans. Medicare Advantage plans have special enrollment procedures.

| Average yearly cost (continued) | | | Medicare wrap-around | Day limit in skilled nursing facility | Pays for... | | | | | |
| Annuitants 65 or older with Medicare Parts A & B | | | | | Routine dental | Chiro-practic | Acupunc-ture | Hearing aids | Adult vision care | Non network providers |
Self only	Self plus one	Family								
10660	23940	22960	No	60	Some	Yes	Little	None	Exam	Reduced
12410	29280	28330	No	60	Some	Yes	None	Yes	Yes	No
9330	22570	21530	No	60	Some	Yes	None	Yes	Yes	No
8100	17360	16520	No	60	None	Yes	Little	None	Exam	Reduced
6860	13820	13440	Yes	60	None	Some	Some	None	None	Reduced
5790	11920	12280	No	60	None	Some	Some	Yes	None	Reduced
13530	27850	28110	Yes	100	Yes	Some	Some	None	Exam	No
3830	**7320**	**7490**	Yes	100	Yes	Yes	Yes	Yes	Yes	No
6980	14050	14220	Yes	60	None	Some	Some	None	None	No
6950	15550	14490	No	60	Some	Yes	Little	None	Exam	Reduced
8090	17380	16550	No	60	None	Yes	Little	None	Exam	Reduced
7950	16160	15890	Yes	60	None	Some	Some	None	None	Reduced
6850	13800	13420	Yes	60	None	Some	Some	None	None	Reduced
6770	13470	13670	Yes	100	None	Some	Some	None	None	No
12960	26630	26830	Yes	100	None	Some	Some	None	None	No
9200	18540	18370	Yes	100	Yes	Some	Some	None	Exam	No
9960	20170	20070	Yes	100	Yes	Some	Some	None	Exam	No
4030	7750	7940	Yes	100	Yes	Yes	Yes	Yes	Yes	No
3870	**7400**	**7580**	Yes	100	Yes	Yes	Yes	Yes	Yes	No
7180	14480	14670	Yes	60	None	Some	Some	None	None	No
7020	14130	14310	Yes	60	None	Some	Some	None	None	No
7820	15840	18230	No	60	Some	Some	Some	None	Exam	No
5140	10620	13000	Yes	100	Yes	Some	Some	Some	Exam	Reduced
6110	12220	12640	No	60	Some	Some	Some	Yes	Exam	Reduced
2970	**5910**	**6330**	Yes	100	Some	Yes	Yes	Yes	Exam	Reduced
5910	11770	12150	No	60	Some	Yes	Yes	Yes	Exam	No
2760	**5460**	**5830**	Yes	100	Some	Yes	Yes	Yes	Exam	Reduced
6260	13310	13370	No	60	Some	Yes	Some	Yes	Exam	Reduced

Cost & Special Features of All Plans			Average yearly cost in dollars (premiums and out-of-pocket costs)					
			General Schedule			Annuitants 55 to 64		
Plan code	Plan name (primary service area)	Phone number	Self only	Self plus one	Family	Self only	Self plus one	Family of two
Louisiana								
F51-3	Aetna HealthFund CDHP	888-238-6240	3200	7530	6820	5250	12280	11230
F54-6	Aetna Value Plan	888-238-6240	4450	9750	9210	6620	14660	13850
AE1-3	Humana Health-Hi (Baton Rouge)	800-448-6262	6990	14600	14770	10580	22080	22320
BC1-3	Humana Health-Hi (New Orleans)	800-448-6262	5060	10470	10440	7700	15890	15840
BC4-6	Humana Health-Std (New Orleans)	800-448-6262	3080	6170	5920	4740	9530	9150
AE4-6	Humana Health-Std (New Orleans)	800-448-6262	4520	9260	9160	6900	14160	14000
KK1-3	United Choice Open Access	877-835-9861	3460	7150	8660	5260	10910	13180
KK1-3R	United Choice Open Access (Retiree Adv.)	844-481-8821	NA	NA	NA	NA	NA	NA
AS1-3	United Choice Plus Primary	877-835-9861	2640	5150	5430	4020	7920	8340
AS1-3R	United Choice Plus Primary (Retiree Adv.)	844-481-8821	NA	NA	NA	NA	NA	NA
Y81-3	United Choice Primary	877-835-9861	2500	4850	5100	3810	7480	7850
Y81-3R	United Choice Primary (Retiree Adv.)	844-481-8821	NA	NA	NA	NA	NA	NA
LS1-3	United HDHP	877-835-9861	**1990**	**4350**	**4530**	**3280**	**7160**	**7440**
Maine								
EP1-3	Aetna HealthFund CDHP	888-238-6240	5490	12690	12040	8680	20030	19060
EP4-6	Aetna Value Plan	888-238-6240	4710	10320	9800	7000	15530	14740
Maryland								
F51-3	Aetna HealthFund CDHP	888-238-6240	3200	7530	6820	5250	12280	11230
JN4-6	Aetna Open Access Basic	800-537-9384	2990	5770	6020	4590	8930	9300
JN1-3	Aetna Open Access-Hi	800-537-9384	6400	14310	13670	9690	21620	20670
QQ4-6	Aetna Saver	800-537-9384	3010	6050	6280	4450	9110	9440
F54-6	Aetna Value Plan	888-238-6240	4450	9750	9210	6620	14660	13850
B64-6	CareFirst Blue Value Plus	888-789-9065	2780	5010	5920	4220	7690	9060
B61-3	CareFirst HDHP	888-789-9065	**1950**	**3700**	**4150**	**3280**	**6310**	**6990**
2G4-6	CareFirst-Std	888-789-9065	3910	6870	8730	5960	10510	13310
T71-3	Kaiser Prosper	877-574-3337	**1750**	**3700**	**4060**	**2670**	**5700**	**6260**
T71-3R	Kaiser Prosper (Medicare Advantage)	877-574-3337	NA	NA	NA	NA	NA	NA
E31-3	Kaiser-Hi	877-574-3337	2280	5690	4830	**3460**	8620	**7330**
E31-3R	Kaiser-Hi (Medicare Advantage 1)	877-574-3337	NA	NA	NA	NA	NA	NA
E31-3R	Kaiser-Hi (Medicare Advantage 2)	877-574-3337	NA	NA	NA	NA	NA	NA

Lowest costs in bold type. Family costs are lower than self-plus-one in some plans. Medicare Advantage plans have special enrollment procedures.

Average yearly cost (continued)			Medicare wrap-around	Day limit in skilled nursing facility	Pays for...					
Annuitants 65 or older with Medicare Parts A & B					Routine dental	Chiro-practic	Acupuncture	Hearing aids	Adult vision care	Non network providers
Self only	Self plus one	Family								
7480	16760	15710	No	60	Some	Yes	Little	None	Exam	Reduced
8830	19000	18190	No	60	None	Yes	Little	None	Exam	Reduced
12910	26550	26790	Yes	100	None	Some	Some	None	None	No
10030	20360	20310	Yes	100	None	Some	Some	None	None	No
7170	14160	13790	Yes	100	None	Yes	Yes	None	None	No
9320	18800	18640	Yes	100	None	Yes	Yes	None	None	No
7500	15150	17430	No	60	Some	Some	Some	None	Exam	No
4820	9930	12200	Yes	100	Yes	Some	Some	Some	Exam	Reduced
6110	12220	12640	No	60	Some	Some	Some	Yes	Exam	Reduced
2970	**5910**	**6330**	Yes	100	Some	Yes	Yes	Yes	Exam	Reduced
5910	11770	12150	No	60	Some	Yes	Yes	Yes	Exam	No
2760	**5460**	**5830**	Yes	100	Some	Yes	Yes	Yes	Exam	Reduced
5570	11770	12050	No	60	Some	Yes	Some	Yes	Exam	Reduced
10910	24510	23530	No	60	Some	Yes	Little	None	Exam	Reduced
9220	19870	19080	No	60	None	Yes	Little	None	Exam	Reduced
7480	16760	15710	No	60	Some	Yes	Little	None	Exam	Reduced
6850	13410	13780	No	60	Yes	Some	Little	Some	Yes	No
11850	25810	24860	No	60	Yes	Some	Little	Some	Yes	No
6670	13680	14010	No	60	None	Yes	Little	None	Exam	No
8830	19000	18190	No	60	None	Yes	Little	None	Exam	Reduced
5610	10400	11760	Yes	Unlimited	Yes	Some	Some	Yes	Exam	Reduced
3860	**7280**	7960	Yes	Unlimited	Yes	Yes	Yes	Yes	Exam	Reduced
7450	13550	16350	Yes	Unlimited	Yes	Some	Some	Yes	Exam	Reduced
4920	10190	10750	No	100	None	Some	Some	Child	Some	No
4780	9280	9840	No	100	None	Yes	Yes	Child	Some	No
5540	12730	11440	No	100	Some	Yes	Yes	Child	Yes	No
5140	11920	10630	No	100	Yes	Yes	Yes	Yes	Yes	No
3590	8690	**7410**	No	100	Yes	Yes	Yes	Child	Some	No

Cost & Special Features of All Plans			Average yearly cost in dollars (premiums and out-of-pocket costs)					
			General Schedule			Annuitants 55 to 64		
Plan code	Plan name (primary service area)	Phone number	Self only	Self plus one	Family	Self only	Self plus one	Family of two
E34-6	Kaiser-Std	877-574-3337	**1900**	**4080**	**4070**	**2910**	**6280**	**6280**
E34-6R	Kaiser-Std (Medicare Advantage)	877-574-3337	NA	NA	NA	NA	NA	NA
JP1-3	MD-IPA	877-835-9861	4660	8160	14200	7080	12430	21480
JP1-3R	MD-IPA (Retiree Adv.)	844-481-8821	NA	NA	NA	NA	NA	NA
LR1-3	United Choice Open Access	877-835-9861	3260	6710	7300	4960	10260	11150
LR1-3R	United Choice Open Access (Retiree Adv.)	844-481-8821	NA	NA	NA	NA	NA	NA
L91-3	United Choice Plus Advanced	877-835-9861	2430	4890	5400	3540	7250	8030
L91-3R	United Choice Plus Advanced (Retiree Adv.)	844-481-8821	NA	NA	NA	NA	NA	NA
AS1-3	United Choice Plus Primary	877-835-9861	2640	5150	5430	4020	7920	8340
AS1-3R	United Choice Plus Primary (Retiree Adv.)	844-481-8821	NA	NA	NA	NA	NA	NA
Y81-3	United Choice Primary	877-835-9861	2500	4850	5100	3810	7480	7850
Y81-3R	United Choice Primary (Retiree Adv.)	844-481-8821	NA	NA	NA	NA	NA	NA
V41-3	United HDHP	877-835-9861	**2070**	**4500**	**4690**	**3390**	7390	7670
Massachusetts								
EP1-3	Aetna HealthFund CDHP	888-238-6240	5490	12690	12040	8680	20030	19060
EP4-6	Aetna Value Plan	888-238-6240	4710	10320	9800	7000	15530	14740
Michigan								
G51-3	Aetna HealthFund CDHP	888-238-6240	5320	12310	11660	8420	19460	18480
G54-6	Aetna Value Plan	888-238-6240	3960	8650	8090	5880	13020	12180
LX1-3	Blue Care Network (Detroit)	800-662-6667	2920	6850	6870	4430	10320	10360
K51-3	Blue Care Network (Flint/Sag)	800-662-6667	4940	11480	11790	7450	17270	17730
521-3	Health Alliance-Hi (Det/Flint/Sag)	800-556-9765	3930	9180	9340	5980	13890	14130
GY4-6	Health Alliance-Std (Det/Flint/Sag)	800-556-9765	2430	4760	4910	3630	**7190**	**7410**
Y41-3	Priority Health Value (Lower Peninsula)	800-446-5674	2630	5160	5310	3940	7750	7960
LE1-3	Priority Health-Hi (Lower Peninsula)	800-446-5674	5510	11900	12370	8340	17930	18630
LE4-6	Priority Health-Std (Lower Peninsula)	800-446-5674	2690	5190	5370	4060	7950	8230
Minnesota								
H41-3	Aetna HealthFund CDHP	888-238-6240	2840	6720	6010	4710	11080	10010
H44-6	Aetna Value Plan	888-238-6240	3960	8670	8110	5880	13040	12210
V31-3	HealthPartners-Hi (Statewide)	800-883-2177	2290	4530	4920	3530	**7020**	7610
V34-6	HealthPartners-Std (Statewide)	952-883-5000	2510	5000	5250	3710	7540	7920

Lowest costs in bold type. Family costs are lower than self-plus-one in some plans. Medicare Advantage plans have special enrollment procedures.

Average yearly cost (continued)			Medicare wrap-around	Day limit in skilled nursing facility	Pays for...					
Annuitants 65 or older with Medicare Parts A & B					Routine dental	Chiro-practic	Acupunc-ture	Hearing aids	Adult vision care	Non network providers
Self only	Self plus one	Family								
5080	10560	10560	No	100	Some	Some	Some	Child	Yes	No
4670	9580	9580	No	100	Yes	Yes	Yes	Yes	Some	No
8610	15440	24490	Yes	60	Yes	Some	Some	Child	Exam	No
6790	11710	20750	Yes	100	Yes	Yes	Yes	Some	Exam	Reduced
7200	14510	15390	No	60	Some	Some	Some	None	Exam	No
4520	9280	10170	Yes	100	Yes	Some	Some	Some	Exam	Reduced
5690	11610	12380	No	60	Some	Some	Some	Yes	Exam	Reduced
3010	**5690**	**6470**	Yes	60	Some	Some	Some	Yes	Exam	Reduced
6110	12220	12640	No	60	Some	Some	Some	Yes	Exam	Reduced
2970	**5910**	**6330**	Yes	100	Some	Yes	Yes	Yes	Exam	Reduced
5910	11770	12150	No	60	Some	Yes	Yes	Yes	Exam	No
2760	**5460**	**5830**	Yes	100	Some	Yes	Yes	Yes	Exam	Reduced
5680	12010	12290	No	60	Some	Yes	Some	Yes	Exam	Reduced
10910	24510	23530	No	60	Some	Yes	Little	None	Exam	Reduced
9220	19870	19080	No	60	None	Yes	Little	None	Exam	Reduced
10660	23940	22960	No	60	Some	Yes	Little	None	Exam	Reduced
8100	17360	16520	No	60	None	Yes	Little	None	Exam	Reduced
6620	14540	14580	No	Unlimted	None	Yes	None	Yes	Yes	No
9640	21490	21950	No	Unlimted	None	Yes	None	Yes	Yes	No
7430	16600	16840	No	730	None	None	None	Yes	Exam	No
5020	9880	10100	No	100	None	Some	None	Yes	Exam	No
4740	9210	9420	Yes	45	None	Yes	None	None	None	No
10100	21430	22140	Yes	45	None	Yes	None	None	None	No
5210	10220	10500	Yes	45	None	Yes	None	None	None	No
6950	15550	14490	No	60	Some	Yes	Little	None	Exam	Reduced
8090	17380	16550	No	60	None	Yes	Little	None	Exam	Reduced
3840	**7640**	8230	Yes	120	None	Yes	Yes	Yes	Exam	Reduced
4780	9280	9660	No	120	None	Yes	Yes	Child	Exam	No

Cost & Special Features of All Plans			Average yearly cost in dollars (premiums and out-of-pocket costs)					
Plan code	Plan name (primary service area)	Phone number	General Schedule			Annuitants 55 to 64		
			Self only	Self plus one	Family	Self only	Self plus one	Family of two
Missouri								
G51-3	Aetna HealthFund CDHP	888-238-6240	5320	12310	11660	8420	19460	18480
HA1-3	Aetna Open Access-Hi (Kansas City)	800-537-9384	6820	16370	15730	10210	24660	23700
HA4-6	Aetna Open Access-Std (Kansas City)	800-537-9384	4740	11640	10950	7120	17610	16580
G54-6	Aetna Value Plan	888-238-6240	3960	8650	8090	5880	13020	12180
9G1-3	Blue Preferred-Hi (St L/Other)	888-811-2092	4120	9020	9230	6300	13850	14170
9G4-6	Blue Preferred-Std (St L/Other)	888-811-2092	2480	6000	6680	3830	9350	10380
PH1-3	Humana CoverageFirst CDHP (KS City)	800-448-6262	2680	5360	5110	4540	9170	8800
BK1-3	Humana HDHP(Kansas City)	1-800-4HUMA	2200	4560	4800	3550	7350	7710
MS4-6	Humana Health-Std (Kansas City)	800-448-6262	7330	15300	15480	11110	23210	23480
PH4-6R	Humana Value Medicare Adv. (Kansas City)	800-448-6262	NA	NA	NA	NA	NA	NA
PH4-6	Humana Value Plan (Kansas City)	800-448-6262	3070	6110	6210	4600	9330	9500
AS1-3	United Choice Plus Primary	877-835-9861	2640	5150	5430	4020	7920	8340
AS1-3R	United Choice Plus Primary (Retiree Adv.)	844-481-8821	NA	NA	NA	NA	NA	NA
Y81-3	United Choice Primary	877-835-9861	2500	4850	5100	3810	7480	7850
Y81-3R	United Choice Primary (Retiree Adv.)	844-481-8821	NA	NA	NA	NA	NA	NA
Mississippi								
H41-3	Aetna HealthFund CDHP	888-238-6240	2840	6720	6010	4710	11080	10010
H44-6	Aetna Value Plan	888-238-6240	3960	8670	8110	5880	13040	12210
KK1-3	United Choice Open Access	877-835-9861	3460	7150	8660	5260	10910	13180
KK1-3R	United Choice Open Access (Retiree Adv.)	844-481-8821	NA	NA	NA	NA	NA	NA
AS1-3	United Choice Plus Primary	877-835-9861	2640	5150	5430	4020	7920	8340
AS1-3R	United Choice Plus Primary (Retiree Adv.)	844-481-8821	NA	NA	NA	NA	NA	NA
Y81-3	United Choice Primary	877-835-9861	2500	4850	5100	3810	7480	7850
Y81-3R	United Choice Primary (Retiree Adv.)	844-481-8821	NA	NA	NA	NA	NA	NA
LS1-3	United HDHP	877-835-9861	**1990**	**4350**	**4530**	**3280**	**7160**	**7440**
Montana								
H41-3	Aetna HealthFund CDHP	888-238-6240	2840	6720	6010	4710	11080	10010
H44-6	Aetna Value Plan	888-238-6240	3960	8670	8110	5880	13040	12210

Lowest costs in bold type. Family costs are lower than self-plus-one in some plans. Medicare Advantage plans have special enrollment procedures.

Average yearly cost (continued)			Medicare wrap-around	Day limit in skilled nursing facility	Pays for...					
Annuitants 65 or older with Medicare Parts A & B					Routine dental	Chiro-practic	Acupunc-ture	Hearing aids	Adult vision care	Non network providers
Self only	Self plus one	Family								
10660	23940	22960	No	60	Some	Yes	Little	None	Exam	Reduced
12410	29280	28330	No	60	Some	Yes	None	Yes	Yes	No
9330	22570	21530	No	60	Some	Yes	None	Yes	Yes	No
8100	17360	16520	No	60	None	Yes	Little	None	Exam	Reduced
8690	18510	18830	No	150	None	Some	None	None	Exam	Reduced
6260	14100	15140	Yes	150	None	Yes	None	None	Exam	Reduced
6860	13820	13440	Yes	60	None	Some	Some	None	None	Reduced
5790	11920	12280	No	60	None	Some	Some	Yes	None	Reduced
13530	27850	28110	Yes	100	Yes	Some	Some	None	Exam	No
3830	**7320**	**7490**	Yes	100	Yes	Yes	Yes	Yes	Yes	No
6980	14050	14220	Yes	60	None	Some	Some	None	None	No
6110	12220	12640	No	60	Some	Some	Some	Yes	Exam	Reduced
2970	**5910**	**6330**	Yes	100	Some	Yes	Yes	Yes	Exam	Reduced
5910	11770	12150	No	60	Some	Yes	Yes	Yes	Exam	No
2760	**5460**	**5830**	Yes	100	Some	Yes	Yes	Yes	Exam	Reduced
6950	15550	14490	No	60	Some	Yes	Little	None	Exam	Reduced
8090	17380	16550	No	60	None	Yes	Little	None	Exam	Reduced
7500	15150	17430	No	60	Some	Some	Some	None	Exam	No
4820	9930	12200	Yes	100	Yes	Some	Some	Some	Exam	Reduced
6110	12220	12640	No	60	Some	Some	Some	Yes	Exam	Reduced
2970	**5910**	**6330**	Yes	100	Some	Yes	Yes	Yes	Exam	Reduced
5910	11770	12150	No	60	Some	Yes	Yes	Yes	Exam	No
2760	**5460**	**5830**	Yes	100	Some	Yes	Yes	Yes	Exam	Reduced
5570	11770	12050	No	60	Some	Yes	Some	Yes	Exam	Reduced
6950	15550	14490	No	60	Some	Yes	Little	None	Exam	Reduced
8090	17380	16550	No	60	None	Yes	Little	None	Exam	Reduced

Cost & Special Features of All Plans			Average yearly cost in dollars (premiums and out-of-pocket costs)					
Plan code	Plan name (primary service area)	Phone number	General Schedule			Annuitants 55 to 64		
			Self only	Self plus one	Family	Self only	Self plus one	Family of two
Nebraska								
H41-3	Aetna HealthFund CDHP	888-238-6240	2840	6720	6010	4710	11080	10010
H44-6	Aetna Value Plan	888-238-6240	3960	8670	8110	5880	13040	12210
Nevada								
G51-3	Aetna HealthFund CDHP	888-238-6240	5320	12310	11660	8420	19460	18480
G54-6	Aetna Value Plan	888-238-6240	3960	8650	8090	5880	13020	12180
NM1-3	Health Plan of Nevada (Las Vegas)	877-545-7378	3190	4920	7180	4820	7460	10850
KT1-3	United Choice Open Access	877-835-9861	3600	7450	9010	5470	11360	13710
KT1-3R	United Choice Open Access (Retiree Adv.)	844-481-8821	NA	NA	NA	NA	NA	NA
WF1-3	United Choice Plus Primary	877-835-9861	2670	5230	5510	4070	8040	8470
WF1-3R	United Choice Plus Primary (Retiree Adv)	844-481-8821	NA	NA	NA	NA	NA	NA
VD1-3	United Choice Primary	877-835-9861	2650	5180	5460	4040	7970	8390
VD1-3R	United Choice Primary (Retiree Adv.)	844-481-8821	NA	NA	NA	NA	NA	NA
LU1-3	United HDHP	877-835-9861	**2090**	4550	4750	**3420**	7460	7760
New Hampshire								
EP1-3	Aetna HealthFund CDHP	888-238-6240	5490	12690	12040	8680	20030	19060
EP4-6	Aetna Value Plan	888-238-6240	4710	10320	9800	7000	15530	14740
New Jersey								
EP1-3	Aetna HealthFund CDHP	888-238-6240	5490	12690	12040	8680	20030	19060
JR4-6	Aetna Open Access Basic (Northern)	800-537-9384	8040	18480	17880	12210	27990	27100
P34-6	Aetna Open Access Basic (Phil)	800-537-9384	10390	23910	23370	15730	36140	35330
JR1-3	Aetna Open Access-Hi (Northern)	800-537-9384	9760	22550	21990	14720	34000	33170
P31-3	Aetna Open Access-Hi (Philadelphia)	800-537-9384	10620	26120	25600	16010	39350	38570
EP4-6	Aetna Value Plan	888-238-6240	4710	10320	9800	7000	15530	14740
804-6	GHI Health-Std (NY State/N NJ)	212-501-4444	5400	12620	12600	8220	19240	19200
New Mexico								
G51-3	Aetna HealthFund CDHP	888-238-6240	5320	12310	11660	8420	19460	18480
G54-6	Aetna Value Plan	888-238-6240	3960	8650	8090	5880	13020	12180
PS1-3	Presbyterian Wellness (NM/El Paso)	800-356-2219	3170	6480	6580	4770	9940	10100
P21-3	Presbyterian-Hi (NM/El Paso)	800-356-2219	3750	8490	8190	5700	12870	12420
PS4-6	Presbyterian-Std (NM/El Paso)	800-356-2219	3080	6780	6390	4570	10250	9660

Lowest costs in bold type. Family costs are lower than self-plus-one in some plans. Medicare Advantage plans have special enrollment procedures.

Average yearly cost (continued)			Medicare wrap-around	Day limit in skilled nursing facility	Pays for...					
Annuitants 65 or older with Medicare Parts A & B					Routine dental	Chiro-practic	Acupunc-ture	Hearing aids	Adult vision care	Non network providers
Self only	Self plus one	Family								
6950	15550	14490	No	60	Some	Yes	Little	None	Exam	Reduced
8090	17380	16550	No	60	None	Yes	Little	None	Exam	Reduced
10660	23940	22960	No	60	Some	Yes	Little	None	Exam	Reduced
8100	17360	16520	No	60	None	Yes	Little	None	Exam	Reduced
6610	10820	14220	Yes	100	None	Yes	None	Yes	Yes	No
7710	15610	17950	No	60	Some	Some	Some	None	Exam	No
5030	10380	12730	Yes	100	Yes	Some	Some	Some	Exam	Reduced
6170	12340	12770	No	60	Some	Yes	Some	Yes	Exam	Reduced
3030	**6020**	**6450**	Yes	60	Yes	Yes	Yes	Yes	Exam	Reduced
6130	12270	12690	No	60	Yes	Some	Some	Yes	Exam	No
2990	**5950**	**6380**	Yes	100	Some	Some	Some	Yes	Exam	Reduced
5710	12080	12380	No	60	Some	Yes	Some	Yes	Exam	Reduced
10910	24510	23530	No	60	Some	Yes	Little	None	Exam	Reduced
9220	19870	19080	No	60	None	Yes	Little	None	Exam	Reduced
10910	24510	23530	No	60	Some	Yes	Little	None	Exam	Reduced
14090	31910	31020	No	60	Yes	Some	Little	None	Yes	No
17620	40060	39250	No	60	Yes	Some	Little	None	Yes	No
16950	38290	37460	No	60	Yes	Some	Little	None	Yes	No
18240	43640	42860	No	60	Yes	Some	Little	None	Yes	No
9220	19870	19080	No	60	None	Yes	Little	None	Exam	Reduced
9430	21530	21490	Yes	30	Some	Some	None	Child	Yes	No
10660	23940	22960	No	60	Some	Yes	Little	None	Exam	Reduced
8100	17360	16520	No	60	None	Yes	Little	None	Exam	Reduced
6280	13120	13270	Yes	60	None	Yes	Yes	Child	None	No
7240	15890	15440	Yes	60	None	Some	Some	Child	Exam	No
5860	12660	12070	Yes	60	None	Some	Some	Child	None	No

Cost & Special Features of All Plans			Average yearly cost in dollars (premiums and out-of-pocket costs)					
Plan code	Plan name (primary service area)	Phone number	General Schedule			Annuitants 55 to 64		
			Self only	Self plus one	Family	Self only	Self plus one	Family of two
New York								
EP1-3	Aetna HealthFund CDHP	888-238-6240	5490	12690	12040	8680	20030	19060
JC4-6	Aetna Open Access Basic (NYC/Upst)	800-537-9384	8320	20520	19940	12630	31060	30190
JC1-3	Aetna Open Access-Hi (NYC/Upst)	800-537-9384	10350	26110	25590	15610	39340	38560
EP4-6	Aetna Value Plan	888-238-6240	4710	10320	9800	7000	15530	14740
SG4-6	CDPHP-Std (Alb/Sch)	877-269-2134	3030	6550	6810	4620	10020	10410
804-6	GHI Health-Std (NY State/N NJ)	212-501-4444	5400	12620	12600	8220	19240	19200
511-3	HIP HMO-Hi (NYC/Southeast)	800-447-8255	5400	8340	16570	8130	12600	24940
YL4-6	HIP HMO-Std (NYC/Southeast)	800-447-8255	5510	9360	16940	8300	14330	25690
QA4-6	Independent Health HDHP (Buffalo)	800-501-3439	2170	4820	4970	3710	8200	8420
QA1-3	Independent Health-Hi (Buffalo)	800-501-3439	3300	9190	9300	5050	13980	14130
C54-6	Independent Health-Std (Buff)	800-501-3439	2900	8120	8150	4470	12430	12470
North Carolina								
F51-3	Aetna HealthFund CDHP	888-238-6240	3200	7530	6820	5250	12280	11230
F54-6	Aetna Value Plan	888-238-6240	4450	9750	9210	6620	14660	13850
KK1-3	United Choice Open Access	877-835-9861	3460	7150	8660	5260	10910	13180
KK1-3R	United Choice Open Access (Retiree Adv.)	844-481-8821	NA	NA	NA	NA	NA	NA
AS1-3	United Choice Plus Primary	877-835-9861	2640	5150	5430	4020	7920	8340
AS1-3R	United Choice Plus Primary (Retiree Adv.)	844-481-8821	NA	NA	NA	NA	NA	NA
Y81-3	United Choice Primary	877-835-9861	2500	4850	5100	3810	7480	7850
Y81-3R	United Choice Primary (Retiree Adv.)	844-481-8821	NA	NA	NA	NA	NA	NA
LS1-3	United HDHP	877-835-9861	**1990**	**4350**	**4530**	**3280**	**7160**	**7440**
North Dakota								
H41-3	Aetna HealthFund CDHP	888-238-6240	2840	6720	6010	4710	11080	10010
H44-6	Aetna Value Plan	888-238-6240	3960	8670	8110	5880	13040	12210
V31-3	HealthPartners-Hi (Statewide)	800-883-2177	2290	4530	4920	3530	**7020**	7610
V34-6	HealthPartners-Std (Statewide)	952-883-5000	2510	5000	5250	3710	7540	7920
Ohio								
JS1-3	Aetna HealthFund CDHP	888-238-6240	4530	10530	9860	7250	16790	15790
JS4-6	Aetna Value Plan	888-238-6240	6050	13450	12790	9000	20220	19230
3A4-6	AultCare HDHP (Canton)	330-363-6360	**1580**	**3560**	4720	**2750**	**6060**	7790

Lowest costs in bold type. Family costs are lower than self-plus-one in some plans. Medicare Advantage plans have special enrollment procedures.

Average yearly cost (continued)			Medicare wrap-around	Day limit in skilled nursing facility	Pays for...					
Annuitants 65 or older with Medicare Parts A & B					Routine dental	Chiro-practic	Acupunc-ture	Hearing aids	Adult vision care	Non network providers
Self only	Self plus one	Family								
10910	24510	23530	No	60	Some	Yes	Little	None	Exam	Reduced
14510	34980	34110	No	60	Yes	Some	Little	None	Yes	No
17830	43620	42840	No	60	Yes	Some	Little	None	Yes	No
9220	19870	19080	No	60	None	Yes	Little	None	Exam	Reduced
6160	12980	13360	No	90	None	Yes	Some	Yes	Exam	No
9430	21530	21490	Yes	30	Some	Some	None	Child	Yes	No
10460	17050	29390	Yes	90	Some	Yes	None	Yes	Exam	No
10860	19510	30880	Yes	30	Some	Yes	Alot	Yes	Exam	No
6200	12990	13210	No	45	Some	Yes	None	None	None	Reduced
7390	18430	18590	No	45	None	Yes	None	None	None	Reduced
6870	16980	17020	No	45	None	Yes	None	None	None	Reduced
7480	16760	15710	No	60	Some	Yes	Little	None	Exam	Reduced
8830	19000	18190	No	60	None	Yes	Little	None	Exam	Reduced
7500	15150	17430	No	60	Some	Some	Some	None	Exam	No
4820	9930	12200	Yes	100	Yes	Some	Some	Some	Exam	Reduced
6110	12220	12640	No	60	Some	Some	Some	Yes	Exam	Reduced
2970	**5910**	**6330**	Yes	100	Some	Yes	Yes	Yes	Exam	Reduced
5910	11770	12150	No	60	Some	Yes	Yes	Yes	Exam	No
2760	**5460**	**5830**	Yes	100	Some	Yes	Yes	Yes	Exam	Reduced
5570	11770	12050	No	60	Some	Yes	Some	Yes	Exam	Reduced
6950	15550	14490	No	60	Some	Yes	Little	None	Exam	Reduced
8090	17380	16550	No	60	None	Yes	Little	None	Exam	Reduced
3840	**7640**	8230	Yes	120	None	Yes	Yes	Yes	Exam	Reduced
4780	9280	9660	No	120	None	Yes	Yes	Child	Exam	No
9480	21270	20260	No	60	Some	Yes	Little	None	Exam	Reduced
11220	24560	23570	No	60	None	Yes	Little	None	Exam	Reduced
5050	10550	12280	Yes	unlimited	None	Yes	Yes	Yes	None	Reduced

Cost & Special Features of All Plans			Average yearly cost in dollars (premiums and out-of-pocket costs)					
			General Schedule			Annuitants 55 to 64		
Plan code	Plan name (primary service area)	Phone number	Self only	Self plus one	Family	Self only	Self plus one	Family of two
3A1-3	AultCare-Hi (Canton)	330-363-6360	4020	7950	9860	6120	12110	14950
X31-3	Humana CoverageFirst CDHP (Cin'ati)	800-448-6262	3840	7840	7700	6270	12900	12690
DT1-3	Humana HDHP (Cincy)	1-800-4HUMA	2380	4960	5260	3830	7960	8400
W61-3	Humana Health Basic (Cincinnati)	800-448-6262	2750	5490	5620	4270	8620	8830
A64-6	Humana Health-Std (Cincinnati)	800-448-6262	6950	14480	14620	10540	21990	22190
X34-6R	Humana Value Medicare Advantage (Cincy)	800-448-6262	NA	NA	NA	NA	NA	NA
X34-6	Humana Value Plan (Cincinnati)	800-448-6262	3320	6650	6790	4980	10150	10360
UX1-3	Medical Mutual Basic (Cleve/Akron)	800-315-3144	2490	4900	5060	3700	7460	7710
YF1-3	Medical Mutual Basic (Dayton)	800-315-3144	2500	4920	5090	3710	7490	7740
X61-3	Medical Mutual Basic (Toledo)	800-315-3144	2480	4880	5030	3680	7420	7660
644-6	Medical Mutual-Std (Cleve/Akron)	800-315-3144	5340	11490	12300	8080	17440	18660
YF4-6	Medical Mutual-Std (Dayton)	800-315-3144	6510	14060	15110	9830	21300	22870
X64-6	Medical Mutual-Std (Toledo)	800-315-3144	5840	12580	13500	8830	19080	20450
Oklahoma								
JS1-3	Aetna HealthFund CDHP	888-238-6240	4530	10530	9860	7250	16790	15790
JS4-6	Aetna Value Plan	888-238-6240	6050	13450	12790	9000	20220	19230
Oregon								
H41-3	Aetna HealthFund CDHP	888-238-6240	2840	6720	6010	4710	11080	10010
H44-6	Aetna Value Plan	888-238-6240	3960	8670	8110	5880	13040	12210
571-3	Kaiser Northwest-Hi	800-813-2000	2660	6020	5160	4060	9190	7910
574-6	Kaiser Northwest-Std	800-813-2000	2360	4930	4800	3610	7580	**7390**
571-3R	Kaiser NW-Hi (Senior Advantage 1)	800-813-2000	NA	NA	NA	NA	NA	NA
571-3R	Kaiser NW-Hi (Senior Advantage 2)	877-221-8221	NA	NA	NA	NA	NA	NA
574-6R	Kaiser NW-Std (Senior Advantage 1)	800-813-2000	NA	NA	NA	NA	NA	NA
574-6R	Kaiser NW-Std (Senior Advantage 2)	877-221-8221	NA	NA	NA	NA	NA	NA
AM1-3	Kaiser-Northwest-Prosper	877-221-8221	**1710**	**3290**	**3540**	**2640**	**5060**	**5450**
AM1-3R	Kaiser-NW-Prosper (Senior Advantage)	877-221-8221	NA	NA	NA	NA	NA	NA
KT1-3	United Choice Open Access	877-835-9861	3600	7450	9010	5470	11360	13710
KT1-3R	United Choice Open Access (Retiree Adv.)	844-481-8821	NA	NA	NA	NA	NA	NA
WF1-3	United Choice Plus Primary	877-835-9861	2670	5230	5510	4070	8040	8470
WF1-3R	United Choice Plus Primary (Retiree Adv)	844-481-8821	NA	NA	NA	NA	NA	NA

Lowest costs in bold type. Family costs are lower than self-plus-one in some plans. Medicare Advantage plans have special enrollment procedures.

Average yearly cost (continued)			Medicare wrap-around	Day limit in skilled nursing facility	Pays for...					
Annuitants 65 or older with Medicare Parts A & B					Routine dental	Chiro-practic	Acupunc-ture	Hearing aids	Adult vision care	Non network providers
Self only	Self plus one	Family								
7520	14940	17780	Yes	unlimited	Yes	Yes	Yes	Some	Yes	No
8590	17550	17340	Yes	60	None	Some	Some	None	None	Reduced
6070	12530	12970	No	60	None	Some	Some	Yes	None	Reduced
6770	13470	13670	Yes	100	None	Some	Some	None	None	No
12960	26630	26830	Yes	100	None	Some	Some	None	None	No
4210	8140	8350	Yes	100	Yes	Yes	Yes	Yes	Yes	No
7360	14870	15080	Yes	60	None	Some	Some	None	None	No
5960	11990	12240	No	100	None	Yes	None	Child	Exam	No
5970	12010	12260	No	100	None	Yes	None	Child	Exam	No
5940	11950	12190	No	100	None	Yes	None	Child	Exam	No
9590	20290	21510	No	100	None	Yes	None	Child	Exam	No
11340	24130	25710	No	100	None	Some	None	Child	Exam	No
10340	21930	23300	No	100	None	Yes	None	Child	Exam	No
9480	21270	20260	No	60	Some	Yes	Little	None	Exam	Reduced
11220	24560	23570	No	60	None	Yes	Little	None	Exam	Reduced
6950	15550	14490	No	60	Some	Yes	Little	None	Exam	Reduced
8090	17380	16550	No	60	None	Yes	Little	None	Exam	Reduced
5100	11760	10470	Yes	100	None	Some	Some	Child	Yes	No
5910	12000	11810	Yes	100	None	Some	Some	Child	Exam	No
5670	12230	10940	Yes	100	None	Yes	Yes	None	Yes	No
4230	9240	7950	Yes	100	None	Some	Some	None	Yes	No
5200	10600	10410	Yes	100	None	Yes	Yes	None	Exam	No
3750	**7600**	**7410**	Yes	100	None	Some	Some	None	Exam	No
4590	9310	9700	Yes	100	None	Yes	Yes	Child	Exam	No
4910	9380	9770	Yes	100	None	Yes	Yes	None	Exam	No
7710	15610	17950	No	60	Some	Some	Some	None	Exam	No
5030	10380	12730	Yes	100	Yes	Some	Some	Some	Exam	Reduced
6170	12340	12770	No	60	Some	Yes	Some	Yes	Exam	Reduced
3030	**6020**	**6450**	Yes	60	Yes	Yes	Yes	Yes	Exam	Reduced

Cost & Special Features of All Plans			Average yearly cost in dollars (premiums and out-of-pocket costs)					
			General Schedule			Annuitants 55 to 64		
Plan code	Plan name (primary service area)	Phone number	Self only	Self plus one	Family	Self only	Self plus one	Family of two
VD1-3	United Choice Primary	877-835-9861	2650	5180	5460	4040	7970	8390
VD1-3R	United Choice Primary (Retiree Adv.)	844-481-8821	NA	NA	NA	NA	NA	NA
LU1-3	United HDHP	877-835-9861	**2090**	4550	4750	**3420**	7460	7760
Panama								
431-3	Panama Canal	800-424-8196	**2050**	**3910**	**4050**	**3110**	**5890**	**6080**
Pennsylvania								
H41-3	Aetna HealthFund CDHP	888-238-6240	2840	6720	6010	4710	11080	10010
YE1-3	Aetna Open Access (Western)	800-537-9384	5960	15770	15140	9030	23840	22910
P34-6	Aetna Open Access Basic (Phil)	800-537-9384	10390	23910	23370	15730	36140	35330
P31-3	Aetna Open Access-Hi (Philadelphia)	800-537-9384	10620	26120	25600	16010	39350	38570
H44-6	Aetna Value Plan	888-238-6240	3960	8670	8110	5880	13040	12210
AJ1-3	Geisinger-Basic	844-863-6850	4890	10080	10140	7320	15230	15320
GG4-6	Geisinger-Std (Harr/York/Lanc/N'th)	800-447-4000	5150	10780	10950	7640	16180	16430
LR1-3	United Choice Open Access	877-835-9861	3260	6710	7300	4960	10260	11150
LR1-3R	United Choice Open Access (Retiree Adv.)	844-481-8821	NA	NA	NA	NA	NA	NA
AS1-3	United Choice Plus Primary	877-835-9861	2640	5150	5430	4020	7920	8340
AS1-3R	United Choice Plus Primary (Retiree Adv.)	844-481-8821	NA	NA	NA	NA	NA	NA
Y81-3	United Choice Primary	877-835-9861	2500	4850	5100	3810	7480	7850
Y81-3R	United Choice Primary (Retiree Adv.)	844-481-8821	NA	NA	NA	NA	NA	NA
V41-3	United HDHP	877-835-9861	**2070**	**4500**	**4690**	**3390**	7390	7670
8W4-6	UPMC HDHP (Western)	888-876-2756	2300	4740	4860	3860	7990	8170
UW4-6	UPMC-Std (Western)	877-648-9641	3080	6730	6450	4590	10210	9800
Puerto Rico								
ZJ1-3	Humana Health	800-314-3121	**1340**	**2790**	**2880**	**2000**	**4160**	**4300**
891-3	Triple-S Salud	800-981-3241	**1030**	**2180**	**2220**	**1580**	**3330**	**3380**
Rhode Island								
EP1-3	Aetna HealthFund CDHP	888-238-6240	5490	12690	12040	8680	20030	19060
EP4-6	Aetna Value Plan	888-238-6240	4710	10320	9800	7000	15530	14740
South Carolina								
JS1-3	Aetna HealthFund CDHP	888-238-6240	4530	10530	9860	7250	16790	15790
JS4-6	Aetna Value Plan	888-238-6240	6050	13450	12790	9000	20220	19230

Lowest costs in bold type. Family costs are lower than self-plus-one in some plans. Medicare Advantage plans have special enrollment procedures.

| Average yearly cost (continued) | | | Medicare wrap-around | Day limit in skilled nursing facility | Pays for... | | | | | |
| Annuitants 65 or older with Medicare Parts A & B | | | | | Routine dental | Chiro-practic | Acupuncture | Hearing aids | Adult vision care | Non network providers |
Self only	Self plus one	Family								
6130	12270	12690	No	60	Yes	Some	Some	Yes	Exam	No
2990	**5950**	**6380**	Yes	100	Some	Some	Some	Yes	Exam	Reduced
5710	12080	12380	No	60	Some	Yes	Some	Yes	Exam	Reduced
5220	9980	10180	No	60	Yes	Yes	Yes	Some	None	Reduced
6950	15550	14490	No	60	Some	Yes	Little	None	Exam	Reduced
11260	28110	27170	No	60	Yes	Yes	Some	None	Yes	No
17620	40060	39250	No	60	Yes	Some	Little	None	Yes	No
18240	43640	42860	No	60	Yes	Some	Little	None	Yes	No
8090	17380	16550	No	60	None	Yes	Little	None	Exam	Reduced
9630	19750	19840	No	60	None	Yes	None	None	Exam	No
8800	18140	18390	Yes	60	None	Some	None	Child	Exam	No
7200	14510	15390	No	60	Some	Some	Some	None	Exam	No
4520	9280	10170	Yes	100	Yes	Some	Some	Some	Exam	Reduced
6110	12220	12640	No	60	Some	Some	Some	Yes	Exam	Reduced
2970	**5910**	**6330**	Yes	100	Some	Yes	Yes	Yes	Exam	Reduced
5910	11770	12150	No	60	Some	Yes	Yes	Yes	Exam	No
2760	**5460**	**5830**	Yes	100	Some	Yes	Yes	Yes	Exam	Reduced
5680	12010	12290	No	60	Some	Yes	Some	Yes	Exam	Reduced
6160	12470	12650	No	100	None	Yes	Some	Yes	None	Reduced
5950	12530	12110	No	100	None	Yes	Some	Some	Exam	No
3900	7940	8090	Yes	30	Some	Yes	None	None	Exam	Reduced
3490	**7120**	**7170**	Yes	Unlimited	Yes	Yes	Yes	Yes	Yes	Reduced
10910	24510	23530	No	60	Some	Yes	Little	None	Exam	Reduced
9220	19870	19080	No	60	None	Yes	Little	None	Exam	Reduced
9480	21270	20260	No	60	Some	Yes	Little	None	Exam	Reduced
11220	24560	23570	No	60	None	Yes	Little	None	Exam	Reduced

Cost & Special Features of All Plans			Average yearly cost in dollars (premiums and out-of-pocket costs)					
			General Schedule			Annuitants 55 to 64		
Plan code	Plan name (primary service area)	Phone number	Self only	Self plus one	Family	Self only	Self plus one	Family of two
South Dakota								
G51-3	Aetna HealthFund CDHP	888-238-6240	5320	12310	11660	8420	19460	18480
G54-6	Aetna Value Plan	888-238-6240	3960	8650	8090	5880	13020	12180
V31-3	HealthPartners-Hi (Statewide)	800-883-2177	2290	4530	4920	3530	**7020**	7610
V34-6	HealthPartners-Std (Statewide)	952-883-5000	2510	5000	5250	3710	7540	7920
Tennessee								
F51-3	Aetna HealthFund CDHP	888-238-6240	3200	7530	6820	5250	12280	11230
F54-6	Aetna Value Plan	888-238-6240	4450	9750	9210	6620	14660	13850
TT1-3	Humana CoverageFirst CDHP (Knox)	800-448-6262	3410	6930	6750	5630	11530	11260
ER1-3	Humana HDHP(Knoxville)	1-800-4HUMA	2190	4530	4770	3530	7310	7670
GJ4-6	Humana Health-Std (Knoxville)	800-448-6262	4420	9050	8940	6750	13850	13670
TT4-6R	Humana Value Medicare Adv. (Knoxville)	800-448-6262	NA	NA	NA	NA	NA	NA
TT4-6	Humana Value Plan (Knoxville)	800-448-6262	3620	7340	7070	5440	11170	10780
AS1-3	United Choice Plus Primary	877-835-9861	2640	5150	5430	4020	7920	8340
AS1-3R	United Choice Plus Primary (Retiree Adv.)	844-481-8821	NA	NA	NA	NA	NA	NA
Y81-3	United Choice Primary	877-835-9861	2500	4850	5100	3810	7480	7850
Y81-3R	United Choice Primary (Retiree Adv.)	844-481-8821	NA	NA	NA	NA	NA	NA
LS1-3	United HDHP	877-835-9861	**1990**	**4350**	**4530**	**3280**	**7160**	**7440**
Texas								
JS1-3	Aetna HealthFund CDHP	888-238-6240	4530	10530	9860	7250	16790	15790
JS4-6	Aetna Value Plan	888-238-6240	6050	13450	12790	9000	20220	19230
TV1-3	Humana CoverageFirst CDHP (Austin)	800-448-6262	3900	7960	7830	6350	13080	12880
TP1-3	Humana CoverageFirst CDHP (C Ch)	800-448-6262	2800	5600	5360	4710	9540	9180
T31-3	Humana CoverageFirst CDHP (H'ston)	800-448-6262	3600	7330	7170	5920	12130	11890
TU1-3	Humana CoverageFirst CDHP (S Ant)	800-448-6262	2810	5630	5380	4720	9570	9210
AN1-3	Humana HDHP(Austin)	1-800-4HUMA	2310	4800	5080	3710	7710	8120
DX1-3	Humana HDHP(Corpus Christi)	1-800-4HUMA	2200	4560	4810	3550	7360	7720
CG1-3	Humana HDHP(Houston)	1-800-4HUMA	2420	5040	5350	3880	8070	8530
FD1-3	Humana HDHP(San Antonio)	1-800-4HUMA	2190	4530	4770	3530	7310	7670
QY1-3	Humana Health Basic (Austin)	800-448-6262	3930	8040	7850	6030	12450	12180
Q21-3	Humana Health Basic (Corpus Christi)	800-448-6262	3770	7710	7510	5800	11960	11660

Lowest costs in bold type. Family costs are lower than self-plus-one in some plans. Medicare Advantage plans have special enrollment procedures.

Average yearly cost (continued)			Medicare wrap-around	Day limit in skilled nursing facility	Pays for...					
Annuitants 65 or older with Medicare Parts A & B					Routine dental	Chiro-practic	Acupunc-ture	Hearing aids	Adult vision care	Non network providers
Self only	Self plus one	Family								
10660	23940	22960	No	60	Some	Yes	Little	None	Exam	Reduced
8100	17360	16520	No	60	None	Yes	Little	None	Exam	Reduced
3840	**7640**	8230	Yes	120	None	Yes	Yes	Yes	Exam	Reduced
4780	9280	9660	No	120	None	Yes	Yes	Child	Exam	No
7480	16760	15710	No	60	Some	Yes	Little	None	Exam	Reduced
8830	19000	18190	No	60	None	Yes	Little	None	Exam	Reduced
7960	16180	15910	Yes	60	None	Some	Some	None	None	Reduced
5780	11880	12240	No	60	None	Some	Some	Yes	None	Reduced
9180	18480	18310	Yes	100	Yes	Some	Some	None	Exam	No
4670	9170	8770	Yes	100	Yes	Yes	Yes	Yes	Yes	No
7820	15900	15500	Yes	60	None	Some	Some	None	None	No
6110	12220	12640	No	60	Some	Some	Some	Yes	Exam	Reduced
2970	**5910**	**6330**	Yes	100	Some	Yes	Yes	Yes	Exam	Reduced
5910	11770	12150	No	60	Some	Yes	Yes	Yes	Exam	No
2760	**5460**	**5830**	Yes	100	Some	Yes	Yes	Yes	Exam	Reduced
5570	11770	12050	No	60	Some	Yes	Some	Yes	Exam	Reduced
9480	21270	20260	No	60	Some	Yes	Little	None	Exam	Reduced
11220	24560	23570	No	60	Routine	Yes	Little	Hearing	Exam	Reduced
8680	17730	17530	Yes	60	None	Some	Some	None	None	Reduced
7030	14180	13820	Yes	60	None	Some	Some	None	None	Reduced
8240	16780	16540	Yes	60	None	Some	Some	None	None	Reduced
7050	14220	13860	Yes	60	None	Some	Some	None	None	Reduced
5960	12280	12690	No	60	None	Some	Some	Yes	None	Reduced
5800	11920	12290	No	60	None	Some	Some	Yes	None	Reduced
6120	12640	13100	No	60	None	Some	Some	Yes	None	Reduced
5780	11880	12240	No	60	None	Some	Some	Yes	None	Reduced
8520	17300	17020	Yes	100	None	Some	Some	None	Exam	No
8290	16810	16510	Yes	100	None	Some	Some	None	Exam	No

Cost & Special Features of All Plans			Average yearly cost in dollars (premiums and out-of-pocket costs)					
			General Schedule			Annuitants 55 to 64		
Plan code	Plan name (primary service area)	Phone number	Self only	Self plus one	Family	Self only	Self plus one	Family of two
Q61-3	Humana Health Basic (Houston)	800-448-6262	2900	5840	5830	4490	9150	9130
QX1-3	Humana Health Basic (San Antonio)	800-448-6262	4130	8470	8310	6330	13090	12850
UU4-6	Humana Health-Std (Austin)	800-448-6262	9870	20760	21190	14920	31410	32050
UC4-6	Humana Health-Std (Corpus Christi)	800-448-6262	4190	8550	8420	6410	13100	12890
EW4-6	Humana Health-Std (Houston)	800-448-6262	4600	9440	9350	7030	14430	14280
UR4-6	Humana Health-Std (San Antonio)	800-448-6262	5560	11490	11490	8460	17510	17510
TV4-6R	Humana Value Medicare Advantage (Austin)	800-448-6262	NA	NA	NA	NA	NA	NA
TP4-6R	Humana Value Med. Adv. (Corpus Christi)	800-448-6262	NA	NA	NA	NA	NA	NA
T34-6R	Humana Value Medicare Adv. (Houston)	800-448-6262	NA	NA	NA	NA	NA	NA
TU4-6R	Humana Value Medicare Adv. (San Antonio)	800-448-6262	NA	NA	NA	NA	NA	NA
TV4-6	Humana Value Plan (Austin)	800-448-6262	3440	6940	6900	5160	10590	10530
TP4-6	Humana Value Plan (Corpus Christi)	800-448-6262	2900	5760	6000	4360	8810	9170
T34-6	Humana Value Plan (Houston)	800-448-6262	3120	6220	6510	4680	9500	9940
TU4-6	Humana Value Plan (San Antonio)	800-448-6262	3160	6310	6430	4740	9640	9830
A81-3	Scott & White Basic (Austin/Central)	800-321-7947	2430	4760	4910	3630	**7190**	**7410**
P81-3	Scott & White Basic (Dallas/Ft W)	800-321-7947	2820	5840	5990	4190	8850	9070
A84-6	Scott & White-Std (Austin/Central)	800-321-7947	5180	11190	11380	7750	16820	17110
P84-6	Scott & White-Std (Dallas/Ft W)	800-321-7947	5770	12700	12920	8600	19130	19460
L91-3	United Choice Plus Advanced	877-835-9861	2430	4890	5400	3540	7250	8030
L91-3R	United Choice Plus Advanced (Retiree Adv.)	844-481-8821	NA	NA	NA	NA	NA	NA
AS1-3	United Choice Plus Primary	877-835-9861	2640	5150	5430	4020	7920	8340
AS1-3R	United Choice Plus Primary (Retiree Adv.)	844-481-8821	NA	NA	NA	NA	NA	NA
Y81-3	United Choice Primary	877-835-9861	2500	4850	5100	3810	7480	7850
Y81-3R	United Choice Primary (Retiree Adv.)	844-481-8821	NA	NA	NA	NA	NA	NA
Utah								
9K4-6	Aetna Health/Altius HDHP	800-837-0977	2740	4920	4740	4400	7980	7720
9K1-3	Aetna Health/Altius-Hi	800-837-0977	5770	12520	11860	8740	18980	17990
DK4-6	Aetna Health/Altius-Std	800-837-0977	4490	9440	8740	6780	14330	13290
G51-3	Aetna HealthFund CDHP	888-238-6240	5320	12310	11660	8420	19460	18480
G54-6	Aetna Value Plan	888-238-6240	3960	8650	8090	5880	13020	12180
WX1-3	SelectHealth HDHP	844-345-3342	**1880**	**3790**	**4130**	**3170**	**6410**	**6930**
SF4-6	SelectHealth-Std	844-345-3342	2440	4760	5150	3660	7230	7810

Lowest costs in bold type. Family costs are lower than self-plus-one in some plans. Medicare Advantage plans have special enrollment procedures.

| Average yearly cost (continued) | | | Medicare wrap-around | Day limit in skilled nursing facility | Pays for... | | | | | |
| Annuitants 65 or older with Medicare Parts A & B | | | | | Routine dental | Chiro-practic | Acupuncture | Hearing aids | Adult vision care | Non network providers |
Self only	Self plus one	Family								
6990	13990	13980	Yes	100	None	Some	Some	None	Exam	No
8820	17940	17700	Yes	100	None	Some	Some	None	Exam	No
17340	36040	36690	Yes	100	None	Some	Some	None	Exam	No
8830	17740	17530	Yes	100	None	Some	Some	None	Exam	No
9450	19070	18920	Yes	100	None	Some	Some	None	Exam	No
10880	22150	22140	Yes	100	None	Some	Some	None	Exam	No
4400	8580	8520	Yes	100	Yes	Yes	Yes	Yes	Yes	No
3590	**6800**	**7170**	Yes	100	Yes	Yes	Yes	Yes	Yes	No
3910	**7490**	7940	Yes	100	Yes	Yes	Yes	Yes	Yes	No
3980	**7640**	**7820**	Yes	100	Yes	Yes	Yes	Yes	Yes	No
7550	15310	15250	Yes	60	None	Some	Some	None	None	No
6740	13530	13900	Yes	60	None	Some	Some	None	None	No
7060	14220	14670	Yes	60	None	Some	Some	None	None	No
7130	14370	14550	Yes	60	None	Some	Some	None	None	No
4890	9590	9800	Yes	60	None	Some	None	None	Exam	No
4980	9760	9980	Yes	25	None	Yes	None	None	Exam	No
9020	19220	19510	Yes	60	None	Some	None	None	Exam	No
9400	20040	20370	Yes	25	None	Yes	None	None	Exam	No
5690	11610	12380	No	60	Some	Some	Some	Yes	Exam	Reduced
3010	**5690**	**6470**	Yes	60	Some	Some	Some	Yes	Exam	Reduced
6110	12220	12640	No	60	Some	Some	Some	Yes	Exam	Reduced
2970	**5910**	**6330**	Yes	100	Routine	Yes	Yes	Yes	Exam	Reduced
5910	11770	12150	No	60	Some	Yes	Yes	Yes	Exam	No
2760	**5460**	**5830**	Yes	100	Some	Yes	Yes	Yes	Exam	Reduced
6200	11660	11390	Yes	30	None	Yes	None	Yes	Yes	Reduced
10140	21720	20740	Yes	30	Yes	Some	None	Yes	Yes	No
8140	16940	15900	Yes	30	None	Yes	None	Yes	Yes	No
10660	23940	22960	No	60	Some	Yes	Little	None	Exam	Reduced
8100	17360	16520	No	60	None	Yes	Little	None	Exam	Reduced
5290	10610	11130	No	60	None	Some	None	Yes	Exam	Reduced
5110	10140	10720	No	60	None	Some	Yes	Yes	Exam	No

Cost & Special Features of All Plans			Average yearly cost in dollars (premiums and out-of-pocket costs)					
Plan code	Plan name (primary service area)	Phone number	General Schedule			Annuitants 55 to 64		
			Self only	Self plus one	Family	Self only	Self plus one	Family of two
Vermont								
EP1-3	Aetna HealthFund CDHP	888-238-6240	5490	12690	12040	8680	20030	19060
EP4-6	Aetna Value Plan	888-238-6240	4710	10320	9800	7000	15530	14740
Virgin Islands								
851-3	Triple-S Salud	800-981-3241	**1600**	**3540**	**3540**	**2440**	**5350**	**5360**
Virginia								
F51-3	Aetna HealthFund CDHP	888-238-6240	3200	7530	6820	5250	12280	11230
JN4-6	Aetna Open Access Basic	800-537-9384	2990	5770	6020	4590	8930	9300
JN1-3	Aetna Open Access-Hi	800-537-9384	6400	14310	13670	9690	21620	20670
QQ4-6	Aetna Saver	800-537-9384	3010	6050	6280	4450	9110	9440
F54-6	Aetna Value Plan	888-238-6240	4450	9750	9210	6620	14660	13850
B64-6	CareFirst Blue Value Plus	888-789-9065	2780	5010	5920	4220	7690	9060
B61-3	CareFirst HDHP	888-789-9065	**1950**	**3700**	**4150**	**3280**	**6310**	**6990**
2G4-6	CareFirst-Std	888-789-9065	3910	6870	8730	5960	10510	13310
9V1-3	HealthKeepers HDHP	855-580-1200	**1880**	**3980**	**4150**	**3180**	**6780**	**7040**
T71-3	Kaiser Prosper	877-574-3337	**1750**	**3700**	**4060**	**2670**	**5700**	**6260**
T71-3R	Kaiser Prosper (Medicare Advantage)	877-574-3337	NA	NA	NA	NA	NA	NA
E31-3	Kaiser-Hi	877-574-3337	2280	5690	4830	**3460**	8620	**7330**
E31-3R	Kaiser-Hi (Medicare Advantage 1)	877-574-3337	NA	NA	NA	NA	NA	NA
E31-3R	Kaiser-Hi (Medicare Advantage 2)	877-574-3337	NA	NA	NA	NA	NA	NA
E34-6	Kaiser-Std	877-574-3337	**1900**	**4080**	**4070**	**2910**	**6280**	**6280**
E34-6R	Kaiser-Std (Medicare Advantage)	877-574-3337	NA	NA	NA	NA	NA	NA
JP1-3	MD-IPA	877-835-9861	4660	8160	14200	7080	12430	21480
JP1-3R	MD-IPA (Retiree Adv.)	844-481-8821	NA	NA	NA	NA	NA	NA
PG4-6	Optima Health HDHP (Hampton Roads)	800-206-1060	2160	**4400**	**4450**	3620	7450	7530
PG1-3	Optima Health-Hi (Hampton Roads)	800-206-1060	3120	7640	6780	4660	11580	10300
LR1-3	United Choice Open Access	877-835-9861	3260	6710	7300	4960	10260	11150
LR1-3R	United Choice Open Access (Retiree Adv.)	844-481-8821	NA	NA	NA	NA	NA	NA
L91-3	United Choice Plus Advanced	877-835-9861	2430	4890	5400	3540	7250	8030
L91-3R	United Choice Plus Advanced (Retiree Adv.)	844-481-8821	NA	NA	NA	NA	NA	NA
AS1-3	United Choice Plus Primary	877-835-9861	2640	5150	5430	4020	7920	8340

Lowest costs in bold type. Family costs are lower than self-plus-one in some plans. Medicare Advantage plans have special enrollment procedures.

Average yearly cost (continued)			Medicare wrap-around	Day limit in skilled nursing facility	Pays for...					
Annuitants 65 or older with Medicare Parts A & B					Routine dental	Chiro-practic	Acupunc-ture	Hearing aids	Adult vision care	Non network providers
Self only	Self plus one	Family								
10910	24510	23530	No	60	Some	Yes	Little	None	Exam	Reduced
9220	19870	19080	No	60	None	Yes	Little	None	Exam	Reduced
4360	9150	9160	Yes	Unlimited	Yes	Yes	Yes	Yes	Yes	Reduced
7480	16760	15710	No	60	Some	Yes	Little	None	Exam	Reduced
6850	13410	13780	No	60	Yes	Some	Little	Some	Yes	No
11850	25810	24860	No	60	Yes	Some	Little	Some	Yes	No
6670	13680	14010	No	60	None	Yes	Little	None	Exam	No
8830	19000	18190	No	60	None	Yes	Little	None	Exam	Reduced
5610	10400	11760	Yes	Unlimited	Yes	Some	Some	Yes	Exam	Reduced
3860	**7280**	7960	Yes	Unlimited	Yes	Yes	Yes	Yes	Exam	Reduced
7450	13550	16350	Yes	Unlimited	Yes	Some	Some	Yes	Exam	Reduced
5390	11160	11420	No	150	Yes	Yes	None	None	Yes	Reduced
4920	10190	10750	No	100	None	Some	Some	Child	Some	No
4780	9280	9840	No	100	None	Yes	Yes	Child	Some	No
5540	12730	11440	No	100	Some	Yes	Yes	Child	Yes	No
5140	11920	10630	No	100	Yes	Yes	Yes	Yes	Yes	No
3590	8690	**7410**	No	100	Yes	Yes	Yes	Child	Some	No
5080	10560	10560	No	100	Routine	Some	Some	Child	Yes	No
4670	9580	9580	No	100	Yes	Yes	Yes	Yes	Some	No
8610	15440	24490	Yes	60	Yes	Some	Some	Child	Exam	No
6790	11710	20750	Yes	100	Yes	Yes	Yes	Some	Exam	Reduced
5920	11950	12030	No	100	None	None	None	None	Exam	Reduced
6260	14640	13350	No	100	None	None	None	None	Yes	Reduced
7200	14510	15390	No	60	Some	Some	Some	None	Exam	No
4520	9280	10170	Yes	100	Yes	Some	Some	Some	Exam	Reduced
5690	11610	12380	No	60	Some	Some	Some	Yes	Exam	Reduced
3010	**5690**	**6470**	Yes	60	Some	Some	Some	Yes	Exam	Reduced
6110	12220	12640	No	60	Some	Some	Some	Yes	Exam	Reduced

Cost & Special Features of All Plans			Average yearly cost in dollars (premiums and out-of-pocket costs)					
			General Schedule			Annuitants 55 to 64		
Plan code	Plan name (primary service area)	Phone number	Self only	Self plus one	Family	Self only	Self plus one	Family of two
AS1-3R	United Choice Plus Primary (Retiree Adv.)	844-481-8821	NA	NA	NA	NA	NA	NA
Y81-3	United Choice Primary	877-835-9861	2500	4850	5100	3810	7480	7850
Y81-3R	United Choice Primary (Retiree Adv.)	844-481-8821	NA	NA	NA	NA	NA	NA
V41-3	United HDHP	877-835-9861	**2070**	**4500**	**4690**	**3390**	7390	7670
Washington								
G51-3	Aetna HealthFund CDHP	888-238-6240	5320	12310	11660	8420	19460	18480
G54-6	Aetna Value Plan	888-238-6240	3960	8650	8090	5880	13020	12180
571-3	Kaiser Northwest-Hi	800-813-2000	2660	6020	5160	4060	9190	7910
574-6	Kaiser Northwest-Std	800-813-2000	2360	4930	4800	3610	7580	**7390**
571-3R	Kaiser NW-Hi (Senior Advantage 1)	800-813-2000	NA	NA	NA	NA	NA	NA
571-3R	Kaiser NW-Hi (Senior Advantage 2)	877-221-8221	NA	NA	NA	NA	NA	NA
574-6R	Kaiser NW-Std (Senior Advantage 1)	800-813-2000	NA	NA	NA	NA	NA	NA
574-6R	Kaiser NW-Std (Senior Advantage 2)	877-221-8221	NA	NA	NA	NA	NA	NA
L11-3	Kaiser Washington Options	888-901-4636	3070	6690	5830	4580	10130	8850
L14-6	Kaiser Washington Options HDHP	888-901-4636	2250	4800	4800	3690	7900	7900
PT4-6	Kaiser Washington- Prosper (WA/N ID)	888-901-4636	**2090**	**4150**	**4450**	**3120**	**6300**	**6740**
541-3	Kaiser Washington-Hi (WA/N ID)	888-901-4636	3620	7920	7060	5420	11930	10640
544-6	Kaiser Washington-Std (WA/N ID)	888-901-4636	2330	4820	4820	3540	7380	**7380**
541-3	Kaiser-Hi ID/WA (Med Choice)	800-446-8882	NA	NA	NA	NA	NA	NA
541-3R	Kaiser-Hi ID/WA (Senior Advantage 1)	888-901-4636	NA	NA	NA	NA	NA	NA
541-3R	Kaiser-Hi ID/WA (Senior Advantage 2)	800-446-8882	NA	NA	NA	NA	NA	NA
AM1-3	Kaiser-Northwest-Prosper	877-221-8221	**1710**	**3290**	**3540**	**2640**	**5060**	**5450**
AM1-3R	Kaiser-NW-Prosper (Senior Advantage)	877-221-8221	NA	NA	NA	NA	NA	NA
544-6R	Kaiser-Std ID/WA (Senior Advantage 1)	888-901-4636	NA	NA	NA	NA	NA	NA
544-6R	Kaiser-Std ID/WA (Senior Advantage 2)	800-446-8882	NA	NA	NA	NA	NA	NA
PT4-6R	Kaiser-WA- Prosper (Senior Advantage)	888-901-4636	NA	NA	NA	NA	NA	NA
KT1-3	United Choice Open Access	877-835-9861	3600	7450	9010	5470	11360	13710
KT1-3R	United Choice Open Access (Retiree Adv.)	844-481-8821	NA	NA	NA	NA	NA	NA
WF1-3	United Choice Plus Primary	877-835-9861	2670	5230	5510	4070	8040	8470
WF1-3R	United Choice Plus Primary (Retiree Adv)	844-481-8821	NA	NA	NA	NA	NA	NA
VD1-3	United Choice Primary	877-835-9861	2650	5180	5460	4040	7970	8390

Lowest costs in bold type. Family costs are lower than self-plus-one in some plans. Medicare Advantage plans have special enrollment procedures.

Average yearly cost (continued) Annuitants 65 or older with Medicare Parts A & B			Medicare wrap-around	Day limit in skilled nursing facility	Pays for...					
Self only	Self plus one	Family			Routine dental	Chiro-practic	Acupuncture	Hearing aids	Adult vision care	Non network providers
2970	**5910**	**6330**	Yes	100	Some	Yes	Yes	Yes	Exam	Reduced
5910	11770	12150	No	60	Some	Yes	Yes	Yes	Exam	No
2760	**5460**	**5830**	Yes	100	Some	Yes	Yes	Yes	Exam	Reduced
5680	12010	12290	No	60	Some	Yes	Some	Yes	Exam	Reduced
10660	23940	22960	No	60	Some	Yes	Little	None	Exam	Reduced
8100	17360	16520	No	60	None	Yes	Little	None	Exam	Reduced
5100	11760	10470	Yes	100	None	Some	Some	Child	Yes	No
5910	12000	11810	Yes	100	None	Some	Some	Child	Exam	No
5670	12230	10940	Yes	100	None	Yes	Yes	None	Yes	No
4230	9240	7950	Yes	100	None	Some	Some	None	Yes	No
5200	10600	10410	Yes	100	None	Yes	Yes	None	Exam	No
3750	**7600**	**7410**	Yes	100	None	Some	Some	None	Exam	No
5900	12410	11120	Yes	60	Some	Yes	Some	Some	Exam	Reduced
5900	12310	12310	No	60	Some	Some	Some	Yes	Exam	Reduced
5450	10790	11230	Yes	100	None	Yes	Yes	None	Exam	No
7590	16270	14980	Yes	100	None	Yes	Some	None	Exam	No
5840	11840	11840	Yes	100	None	Yes	Some	None	Exam	No
7050	14610	13320	Yes	100	None	Some	Some	None	Exam	No
7280	15170	13880	Yes	100	None	Yes	Yes	Some	Some	No
6450	13410	12120	Yes	100	None	Yes	Yes	None	Exam	Non
4590	9310	9700	Yes	100	None	Yes	Yes	Child	Exam	No
4910	9380	9770	Yes	100	None	Yes	Yes	None	Exam	No
5020	10090	10090	Yes	100	None	Yes	Yes	Some	Some	No
4480	8800	8800	Yes	100	None	Yes	Yes	None	Exam	No
5200	10170	10610	Yes	100	None	Yes	Yes	None	Exam	No
7710	15610	17950	No	60	Some	Some	Some	None	Exam	No
5030	10380	12730	Yes	100	Yes	Some	Some	Some	Exam	Reduced
6170	12340	12770	No	60	Some	Yes	Some	Yes	Exam	Reduced
3030	**6020**	**6450**	Yes	60	Yes	Yes	Yes	Yes	Exam	Reduced
6130	12270	12690	No	60	Yes	Some	Some	Yes	Exam	No

Cost & Special Features of All Plans			Average yearly cost in dollars (premiums and out-of-pocket costs)					
			General Schedule			Annuitants 55 to 64		
Plan code	Plan name (primary service area)	Phone number	Self only	Self plus one	Family	Self only	Self plus one	Family of two
VD1-3R	United Choice Primary (Retiree Adv.)	844-481-8821	NA	NA	NA	NA	NA	NA
LU1-3	United HDHP	877-835-9861	**2090**	4550	4750	**3420**	7460	7760
West Virginia								
F51-3	Aetna HealthFund CDHP	888-238-6240	3200	7530	6820	5250	12280	11230
F54-6	Aetna Value Plan	888-238-6240	4450	9750	9210	6620	14660	13850
Wisconsin								
JS1-3	Aetna HealthFund CDHP	888-238-6240	4530	10530	9860	7250	16790	15790
JS4-6	Aetna Value Plan	888-238-6240	6050	13450	12790	9000	20220	19230
AG1-3	Dean Health Basic	800-279-1301	2260	4670	4810	**3460**	7340	7540
WD1-3	Dean Health-Hi	800-279-1301	7090	14330	15520	10690	21650	23450
WD4-6	Dean Health-Std	800-279-1301	2830	5890	6180	4150	8790	9220
WJ1-3	Group Health High	608-828-4853	4930	10880	13510	7450	16370	20310
WJ4-6	Group Health Standard	608-828-4853	2650	5230	5700	3980	7950	8660
V31-3	HealthPartners-Hi (Statewide)	800-883-2177	2290	4530	4920	3530	**7020**	7610
V34-6	HealthPartners-Std (Statewide)	952-883-5000	2510	5000	5250	3710	7540	7920
Wyoming								
9K4-6	Aetna Health/Altius HDHP	800-837-0977	2740	4920	4740	4400	7980	7720
9K1-3	Aetna Health/Altius-Hi	800-837-0977	5770	12520	11860	8740	18980	17990
DK4-6	Aetna Health/Altius-Std	800-837-0977	4490	9440	8740	6780	14330	13290
H41-3	Aetna HealthFund CDHP	888-238-6240	2840	6720	6010	4710	11080	10010
H44-6	Aetna Value Plan	888-238-6240	3960	8670	8110	5880	13040	12210

Lowest costs in bold type. Family costs are lower than self-plus-one in some plans. Medicare Advantage plans have special enrollment procedures.

| Average yearly cost (continued) Annuitants 65 or older with Medicare Parts A & B | | | Medicare wrap-around | Day limit in skilled nursing facility | Pays for... | | | | | |
Self only	Self plus one	Family			Routine dental	Chiro-practic	Acupunc-ture	Hearing aids	Adult vision care	Non network providers
2990	**5950**	**6380**	Yes	100	Some	Some	Some	Yes	Exam	Reduced
5710	12080	12380	No	60	Some	Yes	Some	Yes	Exam	Reduced
7480	16760	15710	No	60	Some	Yes	Little	None	Exam	Reduced
8830	19000	18190	No	60	None	Yes	Little	None	Exam	Reduced
9480	21270	20260	No	60	Some	Yes	Little	None	Exam	Reduced
11220	24560	23570	No	60	None	Yes	Little	None	Exam	Reduced
4610	8770	8980	No	30	None	Some	Some	Yes	Exam	No
12300	24670	26470	No	120	None	Yes	Some	Yes	Exam	No
5430	11110	11530	No	120	None	Yes	Some	Yes	Exam	No
9420	20240	24190	No	30	Yes	Yes	Some	Yes	Exam	No
4550	9140	9850	No	30	Yes	Yes	Yes	Yes	Exam	No
3840	**7640**	8230	Yes	120	None	Yes	Yes	Yes	Exam	Reduced
4780	9280	9660	No	120	None	Yes	Yes	Child	Exam	No
6200	11660	11390	Yes	30	None	Yes	None	Yes	Yes	Reduced
10140	21720	20740	Yes	30	Yes	Some	None	Yes	Yes	No
8140	16940	15900	Yes	30	None	Yes	None	Yes	Yes	No
6950	15550	14490	No	60	Some	Yes	Little	None	Exam	Reduced
8090	17380	16550	No	60	None	Yes	Little	None	Exam	Reduced

Appendix

Our Methods and Data Sources

We compare plans in terms of their likely dollar cost to you, including both the "for sure" expense of the premium and the out-of-pocket (OOP) expenses you face for costs the plan does not pay. We estimate OOP expenses using actuarial methods to evaluate the cost-sharing details of each plan for various categories of costs. All FEHB plans cover 80 percent or more of most types of expenses whenever your costs are high and provide a reasonably solid catastrophic limit guarantee. The premium covers not only true insurance for rare, high-cost situations, but also pre-payment of routine expenses. When your medical costs are zero the premium is the only expense, but when your medical costs run into the tens of thousands the catastrophic limit (which in most plans is between $6,000 and $12,000 a year) comes into play. Most of the analysis underlying the *Guide* is aimed at quantifying, and expressing in terms of annual costs, the various risks you face, and the reimbursement provided by each plan at each level of risk. We calculate costs assuming that you use only preferred providers, or providers who will agree to network fees, both because sensible consumers will avoid leaving the network if they can, and also because there is no realistic way to estimate the many unknown rates that individual providers may charge.

We calculate likely out-of-pocket costs, taking into account the probabilities of families of various sizes and ages incurring relatively low, medium, or high levels of expense (we actually use eight different expense levels, but do not present detailed results for all of these). The low-cost situations are most common but, when weighted for dollar amounts, accounts for a relatively small portion of likely spending. In statistical terms, health care expenses are a highly "skewed" distribution, and the average (or "mean") is far higher than the typical (or "median") spending level.

Although most persons do not know whether they will incur large expenses or not—heart attacks, serious accidents, and most other costly scenarios are relatively unpredictable—some persons do have a pretty good idea of some future costs. For example, they may be planning major surgery for a congenital problem. We present data for both groups: persons with and without good information on next year's expenses and, for those with good prior information, estimated out-of-pocket expenses at several expense levels for each plan. We caution users, however, to beware of attempting to estimate the costs of "known usage" expenses for anything much beyond maintenance drugs. The problem is few are likely to know, and few to have access to, information on such simple questions as the number of visits involved in dealing with a pinched nerve, or with the mix among hospital, surgical, and rehabilitation costs for a condition such as a knee or hip replacement. No one is likely to know if he or she will have a heart attack, a stroke, or a case of Lyme disease next year. Our methods do not force you to make guesses over such matters, or to pretend that the worst will not happen.

Most of the data used in the *Guide* come from the plan brochures themselves. Plans have several different benefit levels: one for most enrollees when using preferred providers, one for enrollees with Medicare, and one for enrollees when using out-of-plan providers (for most HMOs, reimbursement is zero in this last case, except in emergencies). When analyzed carefully, taking into account the exact wording of benefit descriptions, the brochures tell a clear story. The premiums tell another clear story. However, more is needed to compare the plans usefully and completely.

The estimates of annual expenses we use in the cost tables are based on information taken from a number of sources. The most important of these is the Medical Expenditure Panel Survey (MEPS) of the Agency for Healthcare Research and Quality. This valuable survey produces information for researchers, health plans, and consumer advisors like us on what proportions of the population incur expenses of what kinds and at what dollar levels. We adjust MEPS data slightly to "smooth" the estimates and to cover persons most likely to approximate current FEHB plans' spending levels. Our cost tables also use rounded estimates to make them easier to read, and the cost headings represent ranges. For example, the entries for expenses of $3,000 represent a range from about $2,000 to $4,500.

Because some plans impose different deductibles and coinsurance for different services, the distribution of costs between hospital and other expenses can significantly affect the amount that a plan will require you to pay for a particular expense total. We model our comparisons closely to average experience. Though few persons or families will have exactly the same cost profile as used in our tables, most situations will be at least close. Our profile, when weighted for probability, corresponds closely to projected expenses of the employed and retired American population as a whole, both in total and in category of expense. Some of the details are shown in the table "Profile of Expenses Used for Cost Tables."

Our cost comparisons make several other simplifications. First, in analyzing most plans we have to make assumptions about the number of doctor visits and prescriptions to calculate the patient's share of expenses.

Second, we assume that all bills are for amounts negotiated between plans and preferred providers. Many doctors who are not in the plan network charge more than the plan allows, and all plans do not have the same "profiles" for calculating their maximums. Absent any basis for adjustment, we simply assume what is generally true: all preferred doctors have agreed to limit their charges to plan allowances, and some others will agree to meet that level (or will do so if you tell them what plan you have and explain your cost concerns). There are instances in which some plans' schedules for some procedures are well below those used by other plans. Unfortunately, there is no way to adjust for this in our tables, though you can protect yourself in the real world by using preferred providers or by getting your provider to promise to stay within your plan's payment level before getting any expensive service.

Profile of Expenses Used for Cost Tables (Approximate)

Level of expense	$0	$1,000	$3,000	$6,000	$12,000	$30,000	$60,000	$130,000
Components of Total Expense:								
Hospital	$0	$0	$0	$0	$5,000	$10,000	$29,000	$86,000
Surgical & Outpatient Facility	0	0	0	0	0	3,000	8,000	8,000
Primary & Specialist Physician	0	500	1,500	3,000	3,000	8,000	10,000	20,000
Prescription Drugs & Other	0	500	1,000	2,500	3,000	7,000	11,000	14,000
Dental	0	0	500	500	1,000	2,000	2,000	2,000
Risk of expense at each level:								
Self under age 55	12.0%	49%	15%	11%	8%	5%	1%	0.30%
Family of two under age 55	1.0%	35%	18%	16%	16%	12%	1%	1.00%
Self age 55 to 64	5.0%	33%	20%	19%	12%	9%	1%	1.00%
Family of two age 55 to 64	0.3%	12%	14%	17%	27%	24%	3%	3.00%
Self age 65 and older	4.0%	24%	20%	21%	16%	13%	2%	1.00%
Family of two age 65 and older	0.1%	6%	9%	14%	28%	34%	5%	3.00%

Third, we assume that you take advantage of the best cost-sharing rate in each plan. Specifically, we assume that you get network rates by using network providers rather than providers who are not preferred with that plan. For drugs, we assume you use those in the plan formulary.

Fourth, we make assumptions about how many family members incur expenses at each total cost level in a year to calculate deductibles. For example, we assume that in a year with $1,000 in expenses, a family of five will have expenses for three members, and in a year with $130,000 in expenses, for all family members. In the real world, no one's actual set of yearly expenses will exactly match our assumptions. For plans whose coinsurance rates and deductibles are low or the same for most services, a different mix of expenses would have little or no effect on the cost estimates we present. For other plans, such as those with 100 percent coverage of hospitalization and limited coverage of prescription drugs, a different mix of expenses could change the estimates considerably. However, a different mix would not likely change any cost entry at $3,000 by more than two or three hundred dollars, or any entry for the $30,000 column by more than one or two thousand dollars. (Highly expensive specialty prescription drugs, such as some AIDS, hemophilia, growth hormone, chemotherapy, and osteo-arthritis drugs are the most important potential exceptions.)

We apply our methodology consistently across plans, so that any estimating problem is likely to be small in its effects on the comparative information in the tables.

Acknowledgements

The Guide is dedicated to the memory of David F. Lawton, a dedicated civil servant who worked hard and well at creating and improving the Federal Employees Health Benefits Program during its formative years. Special thanks to many OPM and plan staff who graciously provided information, assistance, and answers at short notice.

About the Authors

Walton Francis is a self-employed economist and policy analyst, expert in the analysis and evaluation of public programs. He has written on a wide range of subjects including program evaluation, statistical analysis, managed health care, and retirement benefits. His education includes Master's degrees from Yale and Harvard universities. He is a member of the National Academy of Social Insurance. He developed regulatory, budgetary, and legislative reforms for many policies and programs while working at the Office of Management and Budget and in the Office of the Secretary at the Department of Health and Human Services. He pioneered the systematic comparison of health insurance plans from a consumer perspective, starting with the 1979 edition of this guide. He has published articles and testified several times before Congress on the Federal Employees Health Benefits and Medicare programs. He evaluated both programs' performance in *Putting Medicare Consumers in Charge: Lessons from the FEHBP*.

Checkbook is a magazine and website produced by the nonprofit Center for the Study of Services. Checkbook rates the quality and prices of consumer services, ranging from auto repair shops to home improvement services to health-care providers in seven metropolitan areas: Washington, Boston, Chicago, Philadelphia, San Francisco, Seattle, and Minneapolis-St. Paul. In the health care field, Checkbook rates doctors, hospitals, dentists, and health insurance plans. The Center has a health care survey research arm that, in addition to conducting surveys for the Center's own publications and website, routinely conducts surveys under contract for government agencies, employer coalitions, and health plans, including many of the health plans evaluated in this book. The Center also produces national guides that evaluate surgeons and hospitals and provides comparison tools for several states' marketplace exchanges that help consumers choose health plans.